MY DAD'S A
POLICEMAN

MY DAD'S A POLICEMAN

An Essex childhood

Robert Druce

Matador
9 Priory Business Park,
Wistow Road, Kibworth Beauchamp,
Leicestershire. LE8 0RX
Tel: 0116 279 2299
Email: books@troubador.co.uk
Web: www.troubador.co.uk/matador
Twitter: @matadorbooks

ISBN 978 1788036 030

British Library Cataloguing in Publication Data.
A catalogue record for this book is available from the British Library.

Printed and bound by CPI Group (UK) Ltd, Croydon, CR0 4YY
Typeset in 11pt Minion Pro by Troubador Publishing Ltd, Leicester, UK

Matador is an imprint of Troubador Publishing Ltd

© 2016 Edited by Graham Frankel

My Dad's a Policeman!...

And that was your last resort, your final proud and menacing appeal for mercy when a gang of enemies had you up against the playground wire.
A child would be wiser nowadays, no doubt, to keep quiet about such a relationship for fear of worse aggression.

But in those far-off times your attackers, with luck, would stay their hands...

MY DAD'S A POLICEMAN

My past self is arrived at only by a process of inference... We are so accustomed each to consider his past self as his own, that it is worthwhile to reflect how very largely it may be foreign. My own past is, in the first place, incompatible with my own present, quite as much as my present can be with another man's... I may regard it even with a feeling of hostility and hatred. It may be mine merely in the sense of a poisoning incumbrance, a compulsory appendage, joined in continuity and fastened by an inference...

F.H. Bradley: *Appearance and Reality.*

Every occupation of man requires of him the wearing of a mask symbolizing his peculiar trade. These masks are in no way assumed, they grow out of people as they live, the way skin grows, the way fur develops over skin. There are masks for the merchants as well as for the professors, there are masks that fit thieves and there are masks that look natural only on saints. The greatest of all the masks is nakedness. If I believed in God, this would be the mask I would conceive him in.

F.W. Nietzsche: *My Sister and I.*

Et si m'atorne en itel guise,
En tel manière me devise,
Ja ne soit beste qui me voie
Qui sache a dire que je soie.
Anon: *Le Roman de Renart*

1

LONDON

Swiftly the world that opened into warmth and milk and light and shadow and sleep began to widen its horizons.

Beyond the first hovering faces of his mother and father.

Beyond the planes of the room and the brightness streaming from the windows. Beyond the blind masks of strangers.

And that was when he learned to say 'nanna' and 'grandad' and could discover them at the end of his words.

London nanny and London grandad in the queer-smelling house at the end of a ride on a tram like an old red coffin full of bones that went grinding through the dark and the mists of the Thames embankment.

And Cambridge nanny and Cambridge grandad at Rectory Farm across the cobbles and moss in the path past the privy at the back of the Red Lion, after an hour of over-excited sleep on the Varsity coach.

But if you were a good boy it wouldn't be long before you could see London nanny and London grandad and that was his daddy's mummy and daddy.

The tram made his ears sing and the house in Clapham was full of uncles and their wives who loomed out of corners unlit by the gas, wheezing over to pull up his socks and pluck the pocket flaps out of his pockets. And there was a parrot who screamed to make him jump so they could all laugh. Then his father would show around to everyone the scar below his fingernail that poor Polly had given him five years before he himself was born.

The house spilled over with a froth of laughter and talk, Clapham cockney and Westminster School and the Irish of County Cork. And all the while he sat like a good boy on the hard edge of a chair and sipped milk and soda-water, tracking the patterns on the lino and the wallpaper by winding his head and eyes from side to side.

Until they noticed him, and someone prodded him out into the smiling silence in the centre of the room. Or, when she was ill, propped him upstairs on the bed rail of his granny's bed to recite.

GEN—till JEE—zuss MEE—can MILD
LOOK—a PON—a LIT—tull CHILD
PIT— e MICE—im PLISS—it TEA
SUFF—a MEE—ta CUM—ta THEE

And, O! Erm—erm—

RIPP—a RAPP—a!
RIPP—a RAPP—a!

Holy Mary, there was no halting him once he was launched!

CON—diddle LOR—um
NO—va SCO—sha TIPPY—eye O—ka
THAT'S the WAY that CHI—na MEN TALK!

'Bravo, me gossoon!' his granny cried. And off and away he galloped into half-a-dozen rhymes that his mother had taught to her charges, a minor Colonial Governor and a banker and a soldier and a bishop in their days in the nursery when she'd been in service as a children's nanny.

And now when he'd gabbled and gasped it all through to the end, 'Bravo!' his Irish grandmother would cry, and kiss him and catch him up to her loving, cancer-eaten body.

A world away, Rectory Farm was a babble of aunts and aunts' husbands, and cousins hiding and seeking all over the house and picnicking in the plantation and running wild in the barns and fields. He was the oldest cousin, and he carried a candle upstairs to bed. There were no water taps to turn on. Only jugs and bowls in the bedrooms, and big pails in the scullery. There weren't any doors between the bedrooms, just a step and a stile like from the garden into the orchard. Nanny brought him tea and arrowroot biscuits in the morning. Then she emptied the wash-bowl and the chamberpot into an enamel slop-pail and carried the pail away, clanking, down the stairs.

London grandad had a big torch and stood outside the privet hedge one night, and shone it bloody through the bones in his fingers.

London grandad had a beard and little eyes and he was a Buffalo, with a drawerful of insignia that he pinned onto his chest, and he made bicycles in the basement, and he smelt of D—R—I—N—K.

Cambridge grandad had a moustache and he carried a shotgun and kept a handful of cartridges loose in his coat pocket. He had two wooden privies standing among the roses. Nanny threw the washing-up water across the flower-beds, but she emptied out the slop-pail into a cesspit and nobody was to play near it and that means YOU.

*

First he lived in an upstairs flat in Camden Town and then he lived in Clarence Buildings in Kentish Town, and his daddy was a policeman. Every morning only sometimes it was still nighttime his daddy used to put on his uniform and count, 'One Two Three Four': touching his shiny black belt with the silver snake, and his pocket with the book in it, and the pocket with the whistle in it, and the pocket under the back of his tunic with the truncheon in it.

The truncheon was made of hickory wood but although it was wood you couldn't make it float in the sink, see? And it was for trunching anyone who cut up nasty.

He used to join in with his daddy, counting 'ONE two three four, one TWO three four, one two THREE four'. And then his daddy would call out louder, counting, to drown his voice, and 'Dorothy? Dorothy! Will you take the child away,' he'd shout, 'I'm counting my appointments.'

Sometimes he could go to the Zoo with his mummy if they liked, and throw bread at the ducks in the Park, and walk on the grass in Parliament Hill Fields and talk to the squirrels in Ken Wood. He sipped the red water from the fountain that his daddy said was good for him because it was full of iron. And anyone could tell that by the colour, and it tasted as if it had been kept for years in the forks of old bicycles. It was just like, well go on then, take a deep breath: 'ipe—cacu—anha—wine' — good boy! did you hear that, Dorothy? — that the crippled man poured out in the market. That was good for you too, even though it tasted like sucking a penny and made his face go sour.

The market was a nice place to be, but then it always went on too long, and his daddy had to hoist him up round his neck and it ached his back, but he could look at the stripy roofs. Or mummy squeaked his pushchair along through the legs, and you mustn't pick up squashy oranges and bits of lovely blue paper that got caught in the wheels because it was naughty, and well it just was and that was an END of it.

In the market there was a man with a table full of just pieces of clock. Mummy wheeled him away to look at them when his daddy showed her up, leaning against a shelf in front of everyone to suck the meat off eels and spit the bones out. And then his daddy went along and scratched with a penknife at the underneaths of bronze statues to see if they really were: 'Look, now. D'you see the difference?' What the neighbours saw, and what might lie hidden under surfaces, O, those were concerns a child could never be confronted with too soon.

At dusk they squeaked his pushchair all the way home, and 'all right, all right, I'll oil the bloody thing tomorrow without fail,' his daddy said while his mother pursed her lips. The waning moon tilted over in the smoky sky above the chimney pots just like the pale brown label on a bottle of G, and one night 'G is for Guinness, Guinness!' he shouted. 'Now shush!' she said, bending over him to shake him. 'Don't you let people hear you say that word.'

Once it was Christmas and there was a circus with clowns and tigers and sea-lions. The best of all was when they came up and down the gangways and sprayed him with Jeyes Fluid to kill the germs. At Collins Music Hall there were fishtail flames of gas to light the passages and a fat lady with yellow hair sang, 'Come an' drink port wine wiv me down at the ol' Bull an' Bush — Bush, Bush,' with black stockings and her dress off. Then a lot of other ladies pranced on in a line and waggled their legs up and showed what they had on underneath and that was being naughty. Then his daddy and mummy took him home on the top of a bus in the dark.

*

It was very easy to be naughty. Saying you hadn't if you had was naughty, and riding his tricycle backwards and forwards on the table was very naughty even when he'd been doing it for hours and hours without falling off. And he only fell off that time because they opened the door behind his back and made him jump. Putting your chamberpot on your head was naughty, too, and especially in front of important visitors.

But there were two kinds of naughty, and sometimes they laughed and sometimes they didn't. Sheer defiance was the worst of all, and then you were every bit as bad as the wicked men his daddy caught and might have to trunch. If he'd been much older, my lad, he could have been put in the cells for that.

But you didn't always need to be caught. One day his daddy knocked over a vase that his mummy treasured and broke it into three pieces. If he'd done that they'd have called it sheer defiance. But his daddy looked at him and said, 'Now you didn't see a thing, d'you hear me?' and balanced the pieces together so it wouldn't notice.

You see, his mummy would be bound to knock it over again sooner or later, and when that happened of course daddy would only pretend to be upset, but he wouldn't be really, because inside he'd know he was the guilty party. And that was a useful thing to understand if you wanted a quiet life.

There was a mangle in the scullery with white rubber rollers like raw pastry that he liked to stroke, but his mummy said, 'Keep your fingers away from the rollers.' But aha! she forgot to say, 'Don't put your finger in the cogwheels,' so that's where he put it and they chopped the top off.

Then it was away to hospital again on the tram where he'd been only the month before for drinking carbolic acid out of a bottle she'd put on top of the dresser in the kitchen. That time he'd had to stand on a chair and climb up two rungs of the back as well, to defy her when she was out of the room. Not that he swallowed a lick of it, but the rim of the bottle blistered his mouth.

At the hospital it took a doctor and a nurse and his mummy to hold him down and try to get his jaws apart for the mustard water and they gave up trying after about five minutes, so he'd won. But after the carbolic bottle he didn't defy them so brazenly, at least not as a policy; and he concentrated on looking for loopholes in the law.

But you see that was what God was like, too.

Like the bottled demons in the Arabian Nights, God only gave you exactly what you asked for. So if you said: 'Please God let me find my canary' that had flown out of his cage, you might find him with his head off and the cat chewing him up if you forgot to say, 'And please God he must be alive and not hurt when I find him.'

God was never far away if your daddy was a policeman. And God could pop round the corner and open you up like those wooden dolls his aunty had in her bedroom at Cambridge where each one lived inside another one. And bit by bit God would find you skulking in the middle. And He could come and watch you sitting on the lavatory and it wasn't fair.

But Gentle Jesus was different. He was meek and mild and He had a pet lamb with a fleece as white as snow, and if you were naughty you made Jesus cry, so you just had to hope He wouldn't notice.

*

Quick as a wink and as long as he lived, depending on which way round you were holding the telescope, the world in those green years grew wider and taller and deeper.

Leaves turned yellow and ponds froze and the sun made the tar in the street too hot to sit on. You could look through a piece of blue glass at cold pale faces, and stroke your mummy's fox collar, and sniff your fir-cone. Salt melted in vinegar but pepper didn't, and his daddy's soldering iron turned the gas flames green. He could feel things fizzing and prickling and glowing and collapsing, he listened to shapes and he tasted noises, and some days it was like living inside a hot firework.

But at the foot of the stairs in Kentish Town there were other worlds waiting. The water in the drains was bluey slime, the door might bang shut on your back, and then it took all of his hands to turn the knob. And there were other children there, brothered and sistered, whose categorical imperatives were different from his. That was easy too, if your dad was a policeman.

As London stretched out its perspectives around him, he found himself hating it more and more. It was bricks and mortar and soot and shiny granite and tramrails and tar. It groaned and clattered and gasped all night. Once he ran away from home at Rectory Farm, scudding off through a field high with wheat to crouch among the sawn-off bones up by the old slaughterhouse. He waited until the coach had swum safely away past the Red Lion and over the hillside. Then he strolled back, smug with success, and only remembered to howl as he came into earshot, never never to go back to dirty smelly smoky old London.

And they forgave him, poor mite; they knew how he felt. But the next morning they pounced on him, pounce! and sat him in the coach. After that he never knew when a holiday was going to end. They told him lies to stop that little game.

If people wanted to grow things in London, they had to dig out a big hole in the bricks and the tar and fill it up with earth from Cambridge and put seeds in it. The belief took root in his head. Twenty years later he was digging a trench in a Stepney street in a gang of Irishmen, when under the concrete and rubble his shovel scooped up earth, black pasty stuff that stank like a gasworks. But it was earth all right, and how soon will we get back down to the bricks and tar again? he asked himself.

In that far-off time he learned to hate it all day long, and cried to go to Cambridge, while his mother, translated to slates and stones from the green countryside of her childhood, wept too, grew ill and threw all the medicines the doctor gave her down the lavatory, and made herself worse.

*

When he was four and a half he went to school for three weeks in Camden Town to catch diphtheria. The Police Surgeon, elderly and cantankerous, didn't hold with immunization and insisted that what PC Druce's boy had got was tonsillitis. For a fortnight the cocci multiplied until the white membrane in his throat grew thick and almost choked him. At last the old man poked swabs down, tufts of cotton wool on bits of stick, and sent them away to somebody.

Then suddenly there was an ambulance at the kerb and he was swaying across the pavement on a stretcher, ashamed to be ill in front of everyone, with a swerving ring of faces peering down. And then the bell was banging and he cried all the way to Hampstead Fever Hospital. There they dragged his pyjamas off and stuck a needle into him and a nurse thrust him into a scorching bath and scratched him all over with a flannel and said, 'Ah, for Christ's sake give over snivelling.'

In seven weeks he learned a new way of speech and wrote letters of scrapes and scribbles begging his mummy and daddy to take him home.

But the nurses never posted them, and he didn't know how to write yet anyway, and visitors were not allowed past the lodge gates because of the epidemic.

During that time his London grandmother died, asking after him until the last, and gently shaking her head when they told her that he was at home with a cold and a neighbour looking after him. After her funeral his grandfather sat in the empty, grimy house, scarcely eating, emptying a pint bottle of whisky a day, while the room full of bicycles gathered dust. When he moved about the house he carried with him a photograph of his lost wife, setting it down wherever he was so that he could gaze at it, and all day long the tears dribbled down his cheeks.

For eight months he outlived her, and then he died. They opened the grave in Streatham Cemetery to lay his coffin on hers, and that evening Police Constable Druce 498C came home to Camden Town and sobbed all night for the smell that welled out of the earth. Margaret Druce, George Buer Druce: there is no stone to mark where they lie, but their passing is recorded in a fat black register.

And in Hampstead Fever Hospital while his grandmother died, they had Jimmy to mourn and be glad for, 'cause they gives ya fish there every day, n' orangiz n' sweets, don' they sister? n' fings…'

You see, Jimmy had been taken away in the middle of the night while they were all asleep, and so nobody had said 'goodbye, Jimmy.' But it was all right though, because he'd gone to another hospital where you could eat all this lovely food, and he'd left his comics and his two tin cars and five pennies for them to share out, because he hadn't wanted to wake them up to say goodbye.

But *he* didn't believe what the sister told them, and he whispered the truth to his mate in the next bed when she was out of earshot. 'Naow, 'e's gorn to a nastier 'ospital, that's what 'e's done, but sister won't let on, n' they don' even let ya keep yer comics n' fings *there*.'

But the night before you left for 'ome, if you didn't have to go to the other 'ospital, you could sit by the stove wrapped up in a dressing gown and eat an orange, and the others would lie and look over their blankets at the lucky one with the firelight flickering on his face. And weeks later, he too could stagger along to the foot of his bed and back and be sent to do weewees on his own. And suddenly one night he sat up by the fire watching sister peeling an orange for *him*, and in the bottom of the dressing gown pocket his fingers found a row of dry little pips.

The next morning the sister stood him outside the door and he started walking out to the gate where his mother and father were waiting. The gravel was squeaky and the leaves were all slithery with rain and it made his legs ache. His parents didn't recognize him at first, and then they caught him up and clung to him desperately. So they'd turned up after all, had they? Well, awright. And the one who was his father said, 'Would you like an ice cream?' and he said, 'Naow, I wanna go 'ome,' and *she* said, 'Wouldn't you like to visit the Zoo and say hallo to the animals again?' and he said, 'Naow, I wanna go 'ome.'

There was a clockwork train on the tablecloth with a big round track, and look! this is the key, and this is where you wind it up, but you couldn't turn the key round, it was too stiff if you'd just come 'ome from 'ospital. 'I wanna see Nanny. But I wanna see 'er naow,' he said. 'But why carn I see 'er?' And they said, 'Oh darling, she's gone to live in heaven with gentle Jesus; do you like your train?' and he said, 'When is she coming back again?' and they said, 'She's happy now in heaven,' and the train clattered round and round, and he hated it and he hated gentle Jesus, and he hated his granny staying in heaven.

*

It was not a contented household, though it seemed so for a while as they sat in the warm kitchen. His mother standing at the stove and him with his toys and PC Druce committing his Constable's Pocket Guide to memory, or setting out chess pieces to play through a famous game. But too often there were nights when Bobby lay awake pleading with God to stop the voices quarrelling.

His father was quick-tempered, flaring up into a fury — 'Just hear what I've got to say for a moment now: there's nothing like plain-speaking to clear the air' — and as quickly contrite, asking to be forgiven. Then his mother would bite her lip and bide her time. And when his father had begun to make jokes again and everything was easy, she would return to the cause of the quarrel, and it all flared up again. 'Not in front of the child', one or the other would say when they saw his eyes watching them, and then their voices sank to a bitter whisper.

With the passing years things did not change.

One evening, while they still lived in Kentish Town, his mother bundled him into a coat and took him to walk the streets until his father was safely away on night duty. They came to a toyshop and loitered by the window.

Amid the bright clutter behind the glass, a single object lured him. A gas-stove, four or five inches high, stamped and folded out of painted tin. With proper cabriole legs, like the stove in his mother's kitchen, and an oven-door ajar to reveal a tiny Sunday roast, and tin saucepans and a frying pan no bigger than a sixpence clustering on top.

Desperately, he craved for it. Beyond all reason, knowing it was beyond all reason.

'You don't want that,' she said. 'It's not a toy for a boy. It's for girls. It's meant for a doll's house.'

Yet she rummaged through her purse as he pleaded and wept, but there wasn't money enough for so expensive a thing. Her voice shook and there were tears on her cheeks too, as they trailed home through the dusk.

*

But soon it was Christmas and then it was Spring. They were going down a hill on the front seats of a bus and all along there were trees and at the bottom there was a pond covered with grass-green duckweed, and his father was saying, 'Well, do you like it, Dorothy?' and his mother was crying because she was happy. She made silky orange curtains and hanged them up in 99 Sparrowfields Lane, because that was where they were going to live for ever and ever, and things would be different now.

At the end of the garden he started to dig a hole for a paddling pool where perhaps some ducks might want to come and live too. But it took a long time and made a mess so his father bought a shed made of raw white wood and helped him to paint it pink instead. And then you painted it grey, and then his father painted it green and that was the topcoat and that's why his father had to do it green on his own. But pink was best.

They lived in a narrow row of clay-yellow boxes and at 97 there was Alfie and Bob and their dad was a policeman, and at 101 there was Nancy and her dad was a policeman, but at 103 Betty's dad was a milkman, and Mr Ramper at 105 was a butcher at the Co-op and he had a bald head and a wife and no children. His own bedroom window looked out onto the houses opposite, and his father screwed bars across it, so that he wouldn't perch on the sill and overbalance and fall out.

But out of the back bedroom window you could see cows and the hilly fields and the stream and his own garden. And they all lived there happily ever after until 1940 when a German parachute-mine blew the roof to pieces.

Robert Druce age 5

2

SPARROWFIELD LANE

The meadows at the back of Sparrowfield Lane have long since given way to brick and mortar, an invasion that began with a trickle of jerry-building in the thirties, stopped with the second World War, and came back again in a flood-tide five years after Hiroshima. Only the bit in the middle, the hilly fields with its row of hawthorns and oaks that defined the skyline, has been left to stand now, a preserved amenity. But they filled up the pond and uprooted the hedges, while the waist-high hay the children romped through every summer, helping to pile it up into castles to dry, is shaved to its green bone once a month in summer by the Council. Rusting chain-link fences and tarred roads blossom where children scooped frog spawn from the stream, and over old Bottle Atkins' dung heap where Bobby Druce catapulted his glider one long summer's week of evenings. Three-bedroom semis fill the Cesspit Field and Mrs Slade's nursery, where Roy Shotley and he played cowboys and Indians and stalked one another among Mrs Slade's chrysants.

In those early days Sparrowfield Lane was as changeable as his father's moods. It began at the foot of Silver Hill with a handful of shops, and wandered along, with its cramped terraces and fine houses set well back behind laurels. Then came Mrs Slade's fenceful of notices. Then a slab of Victorian farm-labourers' cottages sideways on with their gravel yard that dribbled all winter.

On past Bottle Atkins' farm-gate, and a thirty-yard stretch of creosoted fence, and then his own row of boxes, 97 to 105, in the middle.

Then the cottages where Billy Saxon lived, the White House made of wood that creaked when the wind blew or the sun shone hard, a brief row of council houses behind their tennis-court-high wire, a hundred yards of hedgerow, a curve and a scatter of elms, the end of Ruby Lane, blackberry bushes, Clay Hill, the wilderness, conker-trees, the toadstool ditch, the rim of the forest — and that was as far as he dared to ride his bicycle alone in those early days.

*

The Village between the wars was a long, straggling capital E, with puddles of people clustered on each of its fat little arms. Sparrowfield Lane at the top of the E was only the Village itself in microcosm. The High Road — it was always a Road, or a Lane, or a Way, or a Drive: there are still no streets in the Village — was the backbone, two miles long. It ran down the flank of Arabins, and half a mile later swooped up and down St Anne's Hill and then went clambering along the edge of Silver Hill, and finally disappeared through the forest towards London. At the Warrens lived the bishops and bankers and Cabinet Ministers. In the middle was his father's Police station, All Saints church, the Regal, Woolworth's, the two schools and the seven pubs. Away at the Silver Hill end, Sparrowfield Lane was nearer to Woodlands Green than it was to the centre of the Village.

The forest hugged the Village at each end and all along one side. In those days you could stand in front of Woolworth's, lean over the fence, and tell how things were going in the forest by looking down into the Brook. In spring and autumn it spun along cold and clear in a swirl of leaves or blossom. But after a winter's week of rain, when the forest trunks were black with wet and you could squeeze a lump of moss out like a flannel, the water boiled noisily, clay-dark and deeper than a man. In summer, when distances were blurred by haze, and a shimmer of insects hung in the trees, and tiny caterpillars dropped gossamer into your face from the branches overhead, the Brook sank to a trickle that fumbled its way through old buckets and rusting wheels, too frail to float even a paper boat.

When World War II came to an end, they caught the Brook and stuffed it into a concrete pipe and nailed it down with a shop. But the waters still run, emptying out of the forest slopes, wandering a little way in daylight, truanting past the backs of gardens in Water Lane, before they swallow down into another pipe and flow to join the river.

The river defined the remaining side of the Village, winding through willows four or five broad fields away to the east. In summer children jumped it or walked dry shod across its pebbles as the river oozed round and under them. But at thaw, like its tributary the Brook, the river would break out and run amuck, clawing down its banks yards deep, and sucking the earth away from the concrete footings of bridges. It flooded the water meadows for a quarter of a mile on either side and lapped over roads and licked at gardens.

Today it is tame, flowing in a narrow bed, and housing estates have flooded across the fields to meet it. But in those days it mesmerized the water in every ditch. Even their tiny hilly-fields stream meandered off due east by his dad's prismatic compass, and you could find it still wandering eastward past the stile a field away from Ruby Lane, seeking the river. But it wasn't until he was nine that he walked with it and found their meeting in a knot of water among green-powdered trees.

*

His six and seven year old horizons ended at Atkins' farm and the Cesspit Field and the White House fence and the ridge of the hilly-fields trees: and even those friendly boundaries were too far to be from home when twilight fell and Atkins' cows came mooching along the edge of the stream. Here he played with the others in the echoing spaces: princes and princesses who made pacts for life and betrayed them within the hour, picked buttercups in armfuls, dammed the stream and chased the cows, unravelled jerseys and barbwired their frocks, struck matches and grew round-eyed at the talk of the fires they would light tomorrow. Day by day among them, he learned to fit his fingers round tools, his tongue round words and meanings, and his conscience round adult rules, and the rules of their shifting friendships. Words, above all, possessed him. The longer, and the more intricate their meanings, the better. He couldn't get enough of them into his head.

As an only child, what do you learn? That privacy pays off. To hug your secrets close. To tell those under whose surveillance you must survive, what they would like to hear. And only that and nothing more.

For a member of a close-knit group of siblings, privacy is not likely to be what an only child would define it as. Among other competing souls it's a simple right to be oneself, a unique part of a shared pattern. To the only child things seem otherwise.

Left to his own resources to discover where his parents' truths and irrealities might lie down together, left to pick a path through the fears and hopes of others, the taste he developed for solitude went hand in hand with terror.

Terror that, while he was clenching his eyes tight and counting up to a hundred, the other hiders-and-seekers would creep away to play without him somewhere else. That at any time and in any game you would look around to find the meadow or beach or woodland glade or house quite empty.

In later days he pays the price of those years when he was Prince and Heir Apparent and Court Fool of a rainy kingdom older than himself. It is levied in sudden imperative needs to be alone.

In sudden giddying descents, when he *is* alone, into a biting loneliness.

PC Druce's only son learned too, with Bob and Alf from next door, that you weren't always wanted for yourself alone if your dad was a policeman. You were fortune's hostage, an insurance policy against trouble with the law. If there was trouble, your dad would get you off, and your mates along with you.

In Sparrowfield Lane and Ruby Lane and nearby Silver Hill — girl and boy, friend and Judas, policeman, butcher, teacher, salesgirl, beggarman, thief — all unaware that their green world was sweeping to an end, they raced together towards manhood and womanhood through the threadbare days of the thirties.

His closest friend was Roy Shotley, like him an only child, who lived down Sparrowfield Lane opposite the shops. Roy's dad was a policeman, too. He kept a shed full of canaries and coloured their coats by feeding them turmeric and red pepper, so Roy said. PC Shotley had a wife who cringed when he spoke. But Roy was often moody like his dad, 'poor little sod,' said Mr Ramper. And then his best friend wasn't Roy, but Billy Saxon was. Billy didn't have a father.

*

One afternoon Mrs Saxon had installed them in her wash-house with a zinc bath full of water for them to sail Billy's motorboat. It was tiny and Japanese and made of painted tin, with a little boiler in the roof and a pipe that curved under and out at the back. And when they'd blown and shaken the boiler full of water, Billy pushed a bit of birthday-cake candle inside and lit it, and before long steam was poppling through the pipe and the boat set off on a tinkling circuit of the bath.

By the time they'd had enough of it and had sunk it and wetted the candle, Mrs Saxon had gone off to the shops in the Village. So then the pair of them crept down through Billy's garden and into the wastelands of the Cesspit Field.

In the middle of the Cesspit Field a great clump of man-high nettles flourished all the year round. Around them was unmown grass and ragwort and the thistles which every year exploded into a bloom of fluff that soppy girls like the Puddicks collected and stuffed pillows for their dollies with. They were all forbidden to play in the Cesspit Field, it wasn't healthy.

That afternoon, Billy and he chased through the grass and wrenched up spears of ragwort, and hurled them at each other and fell down dead. But however close they ventured to the middle of the field, the nettles stood there tall and rank, guardians of a mystery. They went and fetched a paling from the White House fence, and took it in turns to bash the nettles flat.

At the centre of the charmed space, they came upon a rusty lid in the ground, half-hidden by weeds, with rings at either end. He stood a moment and gazed over at the roof of number 99 a world away, where he had left his mother making pastry. Then down at the rust-brown rings that cried to their fingers to grasp them. There were bound to be steps, at least — eh? — and a secret tunnel.

And treasure. If the treasure had been stolen already, well never mind, they could always use the place for their underground den.

Suddenly, except for the narrow corridor they had entered by — and as they turned to look, their enemies were not trampled and slain but twitched against each other, lurching back to duty — they were alone in a ring of guards with a sharp green flame in every sinew.

Billy and he crouched down and scrabbled the earth away from the rings with greedy fingernails. Then with the fencepost and a bottomless bucket to lever against, they shut their eyes, prayed — 'Open Sesame!' — and heaved downwards. At a fourth or fifth attempt they got the lid free, levering it up into daylight with a festoon of dewy cobwebs on its underside, and they gazed down at their treasure.

A couple of feet below them lay a lake of thick, unbroken sewage, leather-brown. And that was that. Nothing else. No pieces of eight, no gold moidores, no secret staircase. And they sighed with rage and loss.

Billy dropped the bucket in, but it only cut a gash in the leathery skin, and he had to prod it down with the stick before it gulped and disappeared. Then after that everywhere started to stink, but they were too unhappy to care. They searched around and found a pram wheel and some lumps of concrete and sent them to join the bucket. And then Billy found a chipped bottle they couldn't take back and get the deposit off, and some big flints and dropped *them* in.

When there was nothing else left to drown, they got the lid standing up diagonally and, sweating and grunting, they posted it like a letter and watched it slide away into the welling sludge.

He was going to post the fence-stick as a final tribute, but Billy grabbed his arm in time, and they turned and hacked their way out through the nettles. Once free, they scampered back to the friendly roofs and the little tin boat, and refloated it, and got the candle going again. They were still sailing the seas when Mrs Saxon came in with her shopping and was amazed to discover how well-behaved they'd been. And then he went home for tea.

That night he dreamed of living in an underground den with brick walls and an iron lid, not guessing that five years later his wishes would be granted the way God and the bottled demons always granted wishes when you weren't careful what you said.

And a little later that night he sat up in his sheets in sudden horror, seeing a figure walking across the Cesspit Field who tripped and pitched forward and was swallowed up in gulping sewage, and he called out to stop it.

But when his father came in with a wedge of lamplight through the door, he remembered in time he couldn't say they'd been playing in the Cesspit Field. So he answered, O, he'd had a nasty dream, and his father fetched him a glass of water and went away. And after a bit he told himself that nobody would go walking through nettles, would they? and fell asleep again.

*

There was other magic in the Cesspit Field: enchantment of deadly nightshade and bryony berries, lords and ladies along the hedge, and puffballs and elderflowers and hemlock; and later on, now that he was going to be a famous scientist when he grew up and he had a microscope, he began to explore in earnest. He covered his bedside table with piles of mildewing vegetation, and once he made an important collection of snails and left it under the bed for safety's sake. The next morning to his astonishment and rage, his mother tipped them over into Atkins' meadow while he was at school, just because she'd found trails across the lino; and if she'd *looked* where she was going, she didn't *have* to tread on one.

Before that summer was out, he had laid the mantle of the scientist aside for a month or two to become a mass poisoner, which was a rich and gloating thing to be. And you did it in the shed where your mother couldn't interfere and throw your valuable specimens away. With a candle in a flowerpot for fire, and Billy Saxon for apothecary's apprentice, he pounded and stewed together everything venomous he could lay hands on: nightshade berries and buckthorn and a good shake of slug powder and a handful of ants' nest and stinging nettles, and geranium leaves for their smell. They poured the fluid into a curly glass bottle they'd found in the Cesspit Field, and hid it away behind the compost heap. And he and Billy waggled their heads knowingly whenever they met, thinking of all the people who were going to get it. Old Moggy Jenkins at school for a start-off, and Alfie Charlock, and Bobby Chalk, and them yellow-haired Gibbses, and old Hitler — yeah, him all right! — and Mussolini, and their mums and dads if they didn't watch their step. And that was their poison.

If you boiled up red rose petals or better still red cabbage from out of old Ramper's cabbages when his back was turned, you got a juice that went greeny-blue when you dropped a lump of soda in it; and then if the soda wasn't too big you fizzed it red again with vinegar. And coloured magic was where you got everything that was red — nasturtiums and wallflower petals and beetroot and red lead from his dad's tin on the shelf and a bit of lipstick and red pencil wax and blood from the meat — and you boiled it up and that was red magic. And blue magic was washing-blue and ink and delphinium flowers and a bit of sugar-bag and that was blue magic.

They decanted each brew into its special bottle, and blue magic had a real blue bottle, and he kept them by him just in case. Then a feather or two out of the eiderdown, and thistle fluff and dandelion parachutes and some flies and a dead moth all boiled up into flying magic, and if you'd ever dared to drink it you would have flown.

Nobody ever clutched his belly like a bully in a comic and groaned, Aaargh! from sampling their potions, but that was only because they chose to be merciful. Neither Billy nor he ever drank deep and sailed over the haystacks. But they *did* stumble unwittingly across one of the truths of magic. And that's that it's nothing like a recipe: 4 tbsp this and 1¼ oz that and bake at gasmark 5 for 15 mins; but it's *some* this and a sprinkle of those, and a handful or three of that, and what alone counts is not exactitude but the intention. Peering into their seething treacle-tin cauldron, they flew in their mind's eyes out across old Bottle Atkins' stackyard and over the trees of the hilly fields and halfway round the Village and back again.

*

Advancing into the landscape like mercenaries of a marauding army, Roy and Billy and he established bases, from where they could carry out each fresh reconnaissance. Bottle's stackyard. The hollow oak in Ruby Lane. Saint Saviour's church standing in a graveyard in a meadow and locked all the year round. The pump in Pump Way. The willows at the foot of Silver Hill. Slowly their worlds widened like ripples on a pond. Interlocking like pond rings too, so that you suddenly knew that if you walked down to the corner of *that* lane, it was the same place as when you came along from *this* row of houses — only facing the opposite way round, of course.

Official journeys with his parents took him further, but not deeper: in their company he walked on the pavement and hadn't to slummock along, and you couldn't go jumping splat! into puddles or fill your pockets with decaying treasures or loiter at a workman's elbow for a quarter of an hour, or go into the baker's and ask for broken biscuits. Left to themselves, he and his mates sniffed along the lane-ends like dogs, and foraged through other people's hedges, pulling off a handful of lavender heads, plucking laurel leaves to write their initials on and put in their armpits to turn the writing brown. They tiptoed up overgrown paths to peer through boarded-up windows remembering ghosts, and crawled under roads through watery pipes, and hopscotched the paving stones.

Along the lanes, *sstt!* they came upon sudden adults — *quick Bill, shove the matchiz up yer jersey* — always ogres in his eyes at first so that he took to his heels in a flash. Or worse, they turned out to be acquaintances of PC

Druce, and then you had to be smilingly polite and hold any incriminating evidence behind your back. But then after a few moments they usually shrank again into mere adults no more treacherous or laughable than any other.

Some people Billy Saxon could hardly wait to turn the corner from before he riotously mocked them. Then off he'd go, old Bottle Atkins, straddling up the middle of the lane. 'Cor dammit!' he'd shout in a whisper, 'Cor dammit mind the bloody way!' and stagger from hedge to gutter. Or he'd blow out his cheeks and roll up his eyes and be Mrs Slade, who echoed every sentence-end you uttered.

'Heard the wireless?'

'… wireless, yerss.'

'Terrible, them poor Abyssinians…'

'… sinians, yerss.'

And they'd thump one another, collapsing in laughter.

Others they learned to steer clear of. Like old And-the-next, who kept the general stores at the end of Sparrowfield Lane. Shirt-sleeved and waistcoated and aproned, Old And-the-next would ingratiate himself to your mother's whim — 'and the next, Mrs Erm?' — for ten minutes by the clock, but he always begrudged the time to discuss the most rewarding way of laying out twopence on sweets. Worse still, he carried tales. So they let him stew in the midst of his clutter — *Never mind 'im, 'is rotten sweets alwiz did taste of soap* — and they trudged — *Yeah! or lamp-oil* — halfway up St Anne's Hill to the fat lady who indulged their weathercock tongues. They soon learned to keep away from Alfie Charlock's dad, a bow-legged weaselly runt of a man, who came home singing every Saturday night from the Plume of Feathers, and knocked his wife about and broke her glasses. And for more than a twelvemonth, he and Roy ran off whenever they saw old Clark who lived in the White House, coming over to his fence to speak to them.

He caught the pair of them unawares one day, engrossed as they were in watching the sixteen-year-old grown-ups playing tennis in his garden. Roy and Bob were sitting that afternoon under a clump of elders at the edge of the Cesspit Field, poking the pith out of elder stems to make blowpipes, and they didn't hear him until he came up close.

'They want someone to fetch the ball when they knock it over,' he said. 'Why don't you both climb in and do it for them?'

And so they did; and were rewarded with a couple of mossy tennis-balls and friendship all too soon cut short.

Mr Clark was lonely, a recent widower, and he wanted children to talk to. Even the teenagers he invited to come and play on his tennis court whenever they liked and whose behaviour seemed so unachievably glamorous didn't satisfy his need for companionship. They were too wrapped up in themselves and one another, and although they made free of his garden and his lemonade, they held the old man aloof from their giggling conversations.

But *his* and Roy's childish secrets were safe with Mr Clark, and he didn't split on you chasing Atkins' cows or lighting brief bonfires at the bottom of the Cesspit Field, although he'd watched you do it. He even lent them the matches once or twice, and they always knew that for two pins he'd have come and climbed trees along with them, if his grown-up daughter hadn't been lurking somewhere in the rhododendrons, waiting to pounce. But Mr Clark escaped her when he could, and she couldn't stop him playing cops and robbers, and he always shouted Aaargh! and fell down dead, even if you hadn't shot him yet.

'Well, what d'ye say to that?' said Mr Clark one day, and gave him a huge wooden shield, wired with plunder from the Indian Raj: ivory horns and a tiger's tooth and two yellowing bracelets, sawn off in rings from an elephant's tusk. He broke the wires and took the bracelets off to give to his mother, and she said, 'Thank you, dear,' and tried them on for the evening, but she didn't ever wear them.

That winter Mr Clark threw snowballs at him and Roy, and borrowed their handwarmers and didn't say they stank and were dangerous, but 'thank you'. And in summer he fetched three table knives from under his daughter's nose and helped them peel ash sticks to make bows. But they'd left it almost too late with their early distrust, and before long Mr Clark had moved away, because the White House, d'ye see, was much too big for Maggie to cope with on her own.

He sold off half his things at lunatic prices, as though they were kittens or puppies, as long as he knew they were going to a good home, and then he went away out of their lives to a little house at the seaside. Ever after, the gilt clock with the angel's head, condemned to silence when PC Druce decided to mend the spring, and the art-nouveau biscuit-barrel, and the mahogany coal-vase into whose patina you could gaze inches deep, that had all been presents to Mr Clark when he married, stood in the quiet of the Druce family's front room. Touching them with gentle fingers, he would remember Mr Clark and his friendship in their first, and the old man's second, childhood.

*

But there was always a new face or place or mystery to become a nine days' wonder in Sparrowfield Lane. One day Alfie and Bob at 97 came round to say that two men were nailing little silver ovals to the trees at the corner of Almshouse Green, and he went along to watch. Only some of the trees were getting them, and these were the ones, the workmen finally told them for the sake of peace and quiet, that would be left standing when all the rest were cut down to make way for houses.

Together they searched their favourite climbing-trees — lowish stunted growths and every one of them without a disk — and went away to join a council of war. Alfie and Bob sneaked a hammer from their dad's shed, and so did the Chalks. 'Right!' they said, and by the end of the week they'd prised all the disks away. Some they nailed back onto the climbing-trees so that *they* wouldn't be cut down, and the rest they kept for their collections.

But then the Gibbses stole the disks off the climbing-trees, just like them rotten Gibbses, and then there were none. Not that you could blame the Gibbses for wanting one or two: it said '£5 PENALTY' stamped into them, and you could have them as badges. The builder applied to the police, as PC Druce was quick to seize upon; 'Now you've been nowhere near there, have you? Tell me the truth. Have you? *Have* you?' The surveyors arrived to see a new set of disks nailed on with longer nails, and watched them vanish almost as fast as the first. After that their workmen tagged the condemned trees with paint, and Sparrowfield Lane was forced to capitulate.

He went along with the others and watched the trees coming down, great falling fans that burst on the ground in a cloud of broken twigs. He found a sitting pigeon, whipped to death by the branches, lying in a nest of maggots and spilt yokes, and he felt sorry for her and wondered if he could boil her up to get her skeleton. For months on end now he and his mates shared a new playground that was utterly forbidden, and if the police had laid their hands on anyone in there, let me tell you, they'd have been for the high jump!

The building site at Almshouse Green was an endless adventure that changed from week to week. Before the new roadway was concreted, the earth was flooded with blast-furnace slag. Billy Saxon and he spent all one Sunday morning sifting through it, finding wonders of iridescent glass; but long before he'd got his treasure to school for the nature table the bubbles, razor-sharp, had slit his fingers and the rainbows were dulled with blood. Every evening after tea, when it wasn't wet, he ran out into the hilly fields to play, and then carefully edged off and away with the others to riot on the building site.

They spent the twilight roofing the end of a newly dug trench with turf and branches for a camp, lugging off scaffold boards to make tree houses of their own, filling the water tanks with bricks, racing in and out of the jerry-built shells, bombing them through the windows with fistfuls of clay, and trying in vain to swing on the electric ceiling-flex, for it could be depended on never to bear your weight.

Primeval inhabitants of Sparrowfield Lane, they hated the houses coming, despoiling their territory, fencing away their private places behind wire; and they declared an unspoken war of hatred on the invaders who came to live in the houses. They swaggered along the pavements and sneered into newly-seeded gardens, and grew furious when treacherous shopkeepers smiled at strangers and took their orders. Let them get to the back of the shop and wait! But as the days passed, they grew accustomed to the changed skylines, and discovered that the children who came to live there were all right after all and being there wasn't their fault. So they rode their bikes and walked to school with them and showed them their secrets and let them climb their trees, those that were left.

And their hooligan instincts were right, however wrong their reasons, that led them to hate the men who built the houses. They flung up their shoddy semis — 3 bds, 2 recep, ktchn, cmpct gdn — uncaring for anything but profit. If the war and post-war planning hadn't stopped them, they would have flooded the hilly fields with pebble-dash and sent it ribboning all the way to Woodlands Green.

3

CHILD'S PLAY

Season by season, their occupations changed in a flash. Suddenly the pavements would rattle and clang with hoops: proper wooden hoops for those whose parents could afford them, and barrel hoops and bike rims for everybody else. You ran alongside them, prodding them up and down the kerbs, or trailed them at heel, if you were an expert, like gun-dogs.

For a week or two his barrel hoop went galloping along the roads and then one morning the sun came out and dried the pavements and he raced off with the others to scour the shops: 'Got any fivestones, missis? No?' And she was still answering the air as they pounded up the hill towards the Village.

By teatime there were clusters of children squatting on doorsteps with hands full of chinking pebbles, remembering with fingers grown stiff the rituals of Big Jingles and Creepsy and Cracksy and — 'O come *on*, it ain't dangerous!' — the Devil's Game, where you had to toss them up and catch them overhand — 'well awright then, but jist you mind our scullery window, Billy Saxon, that's all I got to say!'

Then there was frog spawn in the stream and he needed a net, now! before everybody else had collected it all. But before a fortnight was out he had tipped the tadpoles down the drain or into old Miss Lambourne's water butt, and night and morning was counting his marbles aloud. Fashions raced on, changing, and the bag of marbles gathered dust while he cut a bow and arrows from the hedge.

A week would arrive when you couldn't meet a girl under twelve who wasn't cat's-cradled to another with a skein of coloured wool, while he would be ransacking his father's tool drawer for an old key and a nail that would file down to fit inside it. For days the alleyway would echo, as a gang of them stuffed the keys with red match-heads and hurled them to explode, blap! against the wall. Then suddenly it was cricket or paper airplanes or conkers.

For every pastime there was a ritual and a lore. They tried hardening the conkers by stewing them, and Billy said vinegar and Roy said salt and soda. And some they dried in the airing-cupboard, and others they experimented with by soaking them in paraffin and methylated spirit. And all of that was fair and well within the rules of war. But when somebody noticed that Roger Tomlins had twisted the string of his three-hundreder in a great fat knot that hid the steel nut tied in with it, he lined up with the other losers after school to send Roger Tomlins home with a nose-bleed.

There were other childish crafts whose secrets lingered with his elders. His Sergeant Major Uncle Leonard took leave of his senses one afternoon, and taught him how to fold water-bombs and lob them like grenades so that they burst on the target and didn't drench the thrower with a misfire. His mother had ways of weaving rushes and making tiny baskets out of them. His father would come across a suggestive bit of firewood or a ball-bearing, and remember matchstick guns or jumping beans, and would lay aside his chess books or *The Constable's Pocket Guide* for the evening, and help him to make them.

The guns were an L-shaped piece of wood with an assembly of rubber bands and bent hairpins underneath, and when they were completed, you could fire a match stick, sending it looping to fall ten feet away, and 'Is that *it*, then?' his mother would say: 'I've got my hair falling round my ears for *that*?' But his dad developed a double-barrelled version. His dad made jumping beans by wrapping silver paper round a pencil, and when his dad had made a tube, he closed one end and dropped a big ball-bearing from his tin inside, and closed the other end. Then it would walk, lobbing itself over and over down a sloping board, and then Bobby would get bored with it and squash it, and make another one all by himself.

*

There were street games, too, where they passed on other skills among themselves: prisoners' base and skipping and jump-rope and making slides along the pavement when it snowed, and knocking on people's doors and doing a bolt. Knock Down Ginger was what his dad called that one, although of course, as he said, he'd never done it himself when he was a boy — what, *never?* — certainly not.

For a time Roy Shotley and Billy Saxon and he used to go and chalk 'BUM' on Fatty Pemberton's front path to pay his family out for getting free tickets to the Regal every week, just by having an advertisement on their fence. Police officers were not permitted to display advertising matter on their premises. What, *never?* Why don't you listen, son? I've told you once, haven't I?

Growing older and more daring, he water-pistolled and pea-shot his way along the street with the others, although he always kept an eye lifting for a blue uniform. The Chalks had a trick for after dark, where they rigged up a coat-button with a rubber band and cotton and a safety pin across a window, and drove people out of their wits with a ghostly fingernail tapping at the pane. Roy and he crouched down and watched when they did it to old Miss Lambourne, and she suddenly threw the front door wide and squealed, 'Leave me alone, Mum. Why can't you leave me alone?' into the twilight. Roy and he crept off in silence from the giggling Chalks, because she seemed so upset.

They loitered at the lane end to argue about it. Old Miss Lambourne hadn't got a mum not as far as they knew, but she must've, and they'd alwiz thought she lived on 'er own.

As soon as there were frosts to remind him, he thought up an excuse and begged a tin can. He punched it all over with nail holes, and filled it with oily rag and set it smouldering and swung it round his head on a wire to keep it going, and that was a hand-warmer. Sooner or later you always singed your woolly gloves with it, and 'cor, you are narf goin' ta get it,' friends would sympathize, 'when they get you indoors.'

There were traditional words to learn, handed down along with the archetypal lore. They weren't above altering them for a topical jibe, so that Sparrowfield Lane knew 'The farmer's in the dell' for years on end as 'Ole Bottle's down the pub' in tribute to Farmer Atkins. But it was the original versions that they passed on as accurately as they could.

'Here comes the Bride,
All fat and wide!'

he sang, back home for tea after marrying Doris Puddick in the Cesspit Field one afternoon, and 'don't you *EVER* let me hear you singing *that* again,' his mother said. He couldn't see why she was so alarmed by the words, interpreting them as a reference to pre-marital pregnancy, although years afterwards it dawned on him. She taught him to sing instead:

'Here comes the Bride,

The Belle of Zanzibar;

Bangled and spangled

From the Om Pom Pom Bazaar,'

another gem from the prize collection she'd sung as a children's nanny to the banker and the governor and the soldier and the bishop. But Sparrowfield Lane wouldn't have it at any price, and he didn't blame them.

So innocent Doris, skinny as a ferret, went on being fat and wide, and he plumply remained the groom, thin as a broom.

There was big trouble over 'God bless our ole tom cat, Feed 'im on bread an' fat,' which he roared out one day to the tune of God Save the King. His dad gave him a dirty great clip over the ear'ole for that: but then policemen were royalists by definition. As for:

Rule Britannyer!

Two tanners make a bob;

King George never, never, never

Shaves 'is knob,

it sent him and Billy into near-hysterics for the space of a whole afternoon. But it didn't bear thinking about, much less singing, nearer home than the bottom of Atkins' meadow.

He used to sit in Sunday-school sometimes, while the Rector boomed halfway up the aisle, and pray not to remember rhymes like that. 'DER — der, DER — der, DER — der, DUM!' he muttered inside his head, and counted, 'ONE, two, three HALOES in the windows, — keep going! — ONE, two three, four, five, — don't stop! — SIX, seven CANDLES, six elevens are SIXTY-SIX, six twelves are SEVENTY-TWO...' Anything to drown the wicked whisperings out, to keep him from exploding into maniacal laughter, Gadarene mirth. So that the Rector wouldn't drag him again by the earlobe out into the churchyard, to come to his senses amidst the sneering dead.

They all acquired their playground lore by a kind of social osmosis, remembering a ritual rhyme word-perfect in a single hearing, but struggling for months through the morning multiplication tables like a fly in glue.

'Twelf twelfs are a 'undridden fawtyFAW!' a hallful of children ended in weary triumph every weekday assembly, as Moggy Jenkins drew himself up: '*Left* turn lead *on!*' — and glowered them away to their classrooms.

But there were yawns and quicksands in the middle. He never *did* get to remember what nine TIMES seven was. Only that nine TIMES seven IS seven TIMES nine — IS — sixty-*THREE*.

*

There were occasions when for the older ones the ritual of protocol — the exact sequence, the precise pattern of words — was more important than the game itself. With twenty minutes to play in, Bobby Chalk and Freddy Wade and the Garlicks would devote the first eight to picking up sides and arguing about the rules. 'Yeah, but we gotta decide what 'appens if the ball busts and it gets stuck in the gatepost; is that a goal or innit, then?'

While they wrangled, Billy and he slummocked about kicking their heels, hoping for an invitation to join in. 'O, all right then, you two. You'd better go pudden n' beef.' And he and Billy would whisper together; 'Bags I be pudden, awright Bob? You was pudden last time.' The lordly captains made their blind choice, 'C'mon then, I'll have beef...' and he would scamper to his appointed side and hope not to see the captain curl his lip.

The best pursuits were those you could improvise with what was handy, like stoning bottles in the Cesspit Field, or giving Betty's cat a haircut when Betty wasn't looking. Or cowboys and Indians, where you could gallop off anywhere you liked.

Or cops and robbers, and English and Germans, where robbers — if your dad was a policeman — and Germans, invariably, had to lose. He nearly killed a policeman in the days when he was himself an English sentry, and the other was a Jerry soldier.

'You guard this tree, right?' Big Alfie from next door told him. 'If any Jerries come, give us a shout.' He looked around and found a smooth round flint that weighed three or four pounds, lovely, and carried it up into the branches with him. When Ronnie Puddick, younger than him by a twelvemonth, came spying out the English front line, it was the obvious thing to do to drop his stone bomb square on top of Ronnie's head.

He poised it by his eye, lining it up, and then watched it grow smaller at thirty-two feet per second per second. The effect was gratifying. Ronnie didn't even look up, but staggered about like Alfie Charlock's dad on Saturday nights, saying, 'Oooh, Oooh,' before he fell down dead. He gave a good performance, and when he crawled to his feet after a minute or two and ran away howling, to fetch his sisters, it was inexplicable.

'We're tellin' your dad on you, Bobby Druce. You jist wait till you get indoors! You are narf goin' ta get it.' The Puddicks screamed themselves red in the face, and he stayed up the tree out of their reach, while the remainder of the English soldiery lurked about muttering amongst themselves. The game fell flat after the Puddicks had taken themselves off.

'Well, see, you shouldn've dropped a brick on 'im, we never said drop a brick on 'im,' said his English mates, while he attempted something between outraged innocence and guilty nonchalance: both emotions genuine.

It was after nightfall when he crept in. 'You're home, then. I see,' was all a tight-lipped mother said. And 'Dorothy! Dorothy? Is that him? Keep me away from the boy. Keep me away from him, that's all I ask. I'll do him a mischief otherwise,' called his father from upstairs, where he was putting on his uniform.

The flint, entered in evidence hours earlier by Elsie Puddick, squatted malignantly in the polished centre of the dining table. His mother had put a lace doily under it.

She pushed him out into the scullery. 'Hurry up and wash your hands and eat your tea,' she said. 'Your father wants a word with you,' and 'Dorothy? Keep him out of my sight, do you hear?' called his father antiphonally. The stage was set for trouble all right, and the only thing that saved him was the enemy themselves.

Not that they pleaded for mercy on his behalf. Mr Puddick and his harpy daughters — not Doris, he noted, not Doris — and Ronnie, snivelling and avoiding his eye, with his cap perched on an egg-sized lump, and Mrs Puddick bringing up the rear, all trooped across from opposite, demanding to see him thrashed. And that was their cardinal mistake. Nobody told a police officer how to bring up his son.

'I assume, then, that you are ready to come down to the station with me now, and enter a formal complaint in writing? There are witnesses prepared to swear to the evidence, I take it…? — Aha, just one moment, Mister Puddick, just one moment. I think you misunderstand me. I am not speaking about children playing games, Mister Puddick. I am enquiring whether you wish to enter a formal charge.'

He out-Dogberried Dogberry, browbeat the Puddicks into silence in half a dozen sentences, and escorted them to the door. His duty boots clumped back down the hall, and his hand fell onto his son's shoulder. 'Let that remain a warning to you,' he said. 'And now it's long past your bedtime. Kiss your mother. Off you go.'

After such a display of parental solidarity, Bobby could only dissolve into sobs and give his solemn promise to stay right away from those Puddicks: Doris as well? Yes, *yes*, all of them.

Then both parents kissed him goodnight and he took himself to bed, wondering as he said his prayers if he could keep the flint as a souvenir, and trying to puzzle out the psychology of the whole affair.

No more dropping stones out of trees from now on, you could be sure about that. Yet he could almost believe that his dad was pleased with him in some way for dealing with a Puddick. For the Puddicks, that was crystal clear, were family enemies from this evening forth.

But it wasn't long before he and the Puddicks were all back together playing mothers and fathers: they never could remember to maintain a feud the way the grown-ups did. Nor did the incident damage Ronnie's attitude towards the law, any more than his brainpan. Rather the reverse, perhaps — for years later Sergeant Puddick became, in his turn, an ornament of the Force.

*

For the children of Sparrowfield Lane learning the ways of the world, the Cesspit Field was headquarters, consecrated ground. When the lure of other places weakened, or it was prudent to leave elsewhere unvisited until the trouble had blown over from last time, they always came back to it.

There were no secrets lying under the cast iron lids, only sewage; but the field itself was a mine of priceless things. People nipped down the alleyway at night and dumped all kinds of rubbish there. Old broken slabs of ceiling plaster for throwing at trees and making explosions. Bottles to line up on the White House fence and pelt with pebbles out of the stream. A couple of rainwater butts to plunder for hoops. Old paint cans that if you were lucky you might find wet paint in under the crust and write words on walls with. Bits of rope for tying to trees and swinging on. A galvanized water tank for sitting in out of the rain. It was incomprehensible what treasures were tossed away by feckless adults.

There were mattresses. 'Don't you dare go near that thing, it's probably alive,' his mother would say when she sighted a new arrival down the alleyway. But as long as you only poked it with bits of stick you weren't going very near, were you? Then as it rotted in the rains you could rip off the canvas and jangle the springs out. Because the springs were what you wanted and they were useful in hundreds of ways.

O and once a man caught his dad scrumping apples when his dad was a boy and didn't know any better, and held him down and tanned his arse with a bedspring. That's what he'd heard his dad telling uncle Charlie, and he heard the same story himself from his dad often enough, to let that be a warning! Only *then* his dad said 'bottom' and not that other word.

Alive or not when they came, soon the mattresses would be convincingly dead, bulging grey fur through every wound. And then the grass crept over them and sweetened their decay.

But best of all was the ever-replenished supply of bicycle wheels and frames thrown over into the Cesspit Field. Older brothers collected them up and assembled them with their dads' spanners, and made them into bikes again. They bowled up and down Sparrowfield Lane on them, and down the fierce gradient of Clay Hill if they hadn't got a chain, and sometimes they let him have a go on them too, only a good long way from number 99 just in case.

With only the pedal-spikes for pedals and no mudguards and no saddle and no brakes or tyres, they stood up in a jockey's crouch and went clanging over the potholes on naked wheel-rims, and could only stop by falling off. He wondered if his grandad had made any of them, searching in vain for George Buer Druce's maker's stamp on the rusted and peeling frames. If you rode under the hollow oak, you could stand up and grab the branch above your head and watch your steed go clanking on and into the stream, while you dangled there like bold Robin Hood, ha ha! and escaped your foes.

Then it was that the lack of a saddle proved a boon, and not the curse it was if you forgot yourself and sat on the end of the tube.

After hours spent fathoms deep in play down by the Cesspit Field, when all his senses were foaming like Eno's Fruit Salts, excitement would take him by the throat and choke him. And then he trailed home late, if PC Druce was safely out of the way on duty, and forgot himself and cheeked his mother and, 'Honour Thy Father and Thy Mother,' she would solemnly recite, 'That Thy Days May Be Long Upon the Land the Lord Thy God Hath Given Thee.'

4

MIXED INFANTS

Cowlicked and curry-combed each weekday morning, ears and knees still scarlet from his mother's second scrubbing, he joined the others by Farmer Atkins' yard, dutifully linking hands: 'O, come *on*, Moll.' And off they went, the four of them and Moll, sprawling across the pavement.

A quarter of a mile. The off-licence and old And-the-Next's, and he'd drop Eileen's hand and race on ahead for Roy, who was waiting with his nose pressed against the shop window. Unless Roy had succumbed already, and was standing there smirking over a liquorice bootlace or a lucky sherbet bag: 'No, get off, it's mine!' And they'd all forget their dislike of old And-the-Next and shove and pummel into his shop, while Moll clicked her tongue in the doorway, and pulled at them and threatened to tell their mothers.

Another two hundred yards and the Gutteridges, Pat and Peggy, Moll's remaining charges, would be waiting outside the Patent Steam Laundry. Then they all set off up St Anne's Hill, with impatient hare-lipped Moll spluttering about in the middle like a mother hen, 'Come *on*, you lot, hold hands, I tell ya.' Half of them galloped on ahead and away out of sight behind the trees, while the rest dawdled to stamp in every puddle, 'No! I ain't done this un yet,' and gaze into every garden.

'Wotcha got for playtime? Phyllis's mum give 'er an apple n' a bit a pudden.'

'Come on, Roy, race ya to the garridge. I found a nut n' bolt there yes'dy.'

'I got a velvit hair ribbin, look! n' I can waggle me toof.'

'My uncle Leonard's comin' round our house tomorrer.'

'I brought me cap gun. 'ere, don't you let on, will ya?'

'I don' like rotten ole pudden.'

'My uncle Leonard's goin' ta take me to the Zoo on Sat'dy, if I ask 'im.'

'Ooh Eileen, look! I gotta gold ring in me sherbet bag!'

And on past the houses and the beer stinks from the Plume of Feathers and up the curve of the hill to the sweetshop, 'Come on *in*; in't ya comin' *in*?' And minutes later out again in a swirl and a flurry and over the crest of the hill, with Moll still stumping somewhere before or behind them.

Down the other side and more children, none of Moll's responsibilities, were joining them, running up alleyways or dodging through gates. They tagged alongside, linking arms, or pulling hair and dashing away: 'Ooh, I'm tellin' on you, Roger Tomlins. Jist you wait!' And Moll grew more and more flustered minute by minute and threatened to walk off and leave them then and there, but they knew she never would, worst luck.

Down to the foot of the hill and the terrace of shops, and already they were nearly half a mile from home. Past the *Clarion & Weekly Advertizer* with its thumping presses. Past the cold-sour carcasses hanging in the doorway of Thos. Good the Family Butchers. Round past the Royal Arms, more beery stinks. Then up in a sudden fifty-yard dash to the last, the best-of-all sweetshop at the corner of Consort Road.

'Thass done it, then,' Moll would wail, as she plodded up the steps after them. 'Thass tore it. Thass put the tin lid on it.'

But she made her moan to the ambient air, and minutes later they were pelting into the playground riot, forgetting Moll. She'd turn and clump away, a quarter of her daily sixpence for each child delivered without mishap to the Infants bitterly earned. At twelve o'clock she'd be waiting outside to escort them home for their dinners. And at half-past three she'd be back again, and they all climbed up St Anne's Hill and down again for the fourth time of the day.

Daily they bullied Moll, and cajoled her and tried to twist her round their fingers: 'You lot'll 'ave me in Claybury Asylum afore me time,' she'd growl. She was ageless and timeless, plodding along on wrung-over heels, nineteen and soured and older than the Sibyl. And it wasn't until he was older by nineteen of his own years that he heard she'd been a favourite with the lads from Havering, who had journeyed six miles or more by bus, in twos and threes, to lie and moan with her on the straw in the stable-loft up by St Anne's.

*

34

Bean bags were queer things to catch, all slithery and rattling. And rubber quoits scrunched your fingers and squidged them round. There were wooden beads to thread on bootlaces — square and oval and round and all the seven colours of a rainbow — and the nicest were violet colour and next came the green. Those two were almost as beautiful as the glass balls on the Christmas tree every year that you could stroke if you were very careful of the wires and nobody was looking.

'Sleepy time,' said Miss Thomas every afternoon, and they heaved their oval raffia mats from by the window and curled themselves up on the floor. Some of them even went to sleep, like Jimmy Fish did. But Jimmy used to fall asleep in story time. That boy would snore on a clothes line, Doggy said; and every afternoon Jimmy's lids were closing before his shoulders even touched the floor. You'd think he never caught a wink of sleep at home.

But it was stupid to lie down when you weren't even a bit sleepy, and pretending to sleep just gave you the giggles. 'I shall think about being *cross* in a minute,' Miss Thomas said, but she never was.

The raffia had a cakey sort of smell like the bast that Mrs Slade tied up her chrysants with, and she always had a great horse's tail of it out of the pocket of her mac. But the raffia mats were harder than bast and shinier and they had violet and red patterns into them, too. If you peeped, you could see the brick wall of the boys' school and over into the forest, and p'raps he would pretend to sleep a bit.

He loved Miss Thomas, and not altogether innocently. She had the faintest hint of a moustache and she showed them the diamond in her engagement ring, and he gazed adoringly at all the beautiful black hairs on her silk-stockinged legs, and felt his blood stir for her. Perhaps in the afternoon they'd be sticking patterns, and he could eat some of the paste if Miss Thomas wasn't looking: it tasted just like under the icing on a Christmas cake. His uncle Leonard would be coming in the morning; and Doris had a hole in her knickers; and there were a whole lot of new toadstools in the forest; and the leaves were scratching the window panes; and 'Wake up now,' Miss Thomas said.

And then you could remember to make a dash for the car you'd had your eye on since milk time — if Roger Tomlins didn't bags it first — and trundle it round.

Or it might be plasticine. Though *that* wasn't much good, they didn't look after it properly. People mixed the colours up and it all went to a dirty brown and you never got enough and you had to bang it to warm it up. Every time it was plasticine, they had to take the best models to show Miss O'Flynn and she was the Headmistress of the Infants. He invariably made engines and radio sets and machinery with his plasticine, as though it were a kind of molten meccano, but Miss O'Flynn always asked, 'Tell me how it works,' and listened patiently to his convoluted explanations.

Doggy took them for Reading, though her proper name was Mrs Herbert and nobody could tell you why everybody called her Doggy. Perhaps to make a pair with Moggy, the Headmaster of the Junior Boys': for Moggy and Doggy were two of a kind.

Doggy was fat and short-tempered, her corsets creaked when she drew breath, and she smelt all dusty of face-powder. She stood them in a ring, ten or so at a time, to read from a primer with queer little coloured pictures, and they took it in turns to read round the ring.

'The D the D the D—O—G the DOG W—A—S woz the dog woz V woz V V V V woz V—E—R ver the dog woz ver the dog woz VER woz VERY B—A—D bad.'

'Next!' snapped Doggy. 'Wake up Jimmy Fish, and pay attention. Next!'

You could count round the circle, eeny meeny miny mo, to see which your sentence was going to be.

'Next!'

And out they came at half-past three clutching their day's plunder, a crayoning or a pattern or strips of coloured paper woven into a mat, and Moll floundered among them and marshalled them into pairs.

'Bet you don' know wot I got.'

'Wot? O, gis a look then.'

'I gotta put it under me pilla tonight.' A milk-tooth, grimy with blood, rocked on a cupped hand. 'I got it waggled out.'

'Ow much'll they give ya fer it?'

'Frippence.'

'Cor, my mum gives us a tanner, but she alwiz sez it's the fairies take it.'

'*Tis* the fairies!'

'Tain't! *Course* tain't. Ooh, Eileen, you are narf soppy. It's ya mum, *innit* Phyll?'

But you were lucky if your tooth waggled loose: one less for the school dentist to get her claws on.

Doctor, dentist, nurse: three hard-lipped women. The door would fly open and one of them would spring into the school like a judy-in-a-box, take over Miss O'Flynn's room, and work her way through the Infants.

'Mouth open. Wider than that. Hold your hands out. Ever hear of soap and water? Turn them over. Clean your nails. Let's see your head, then.'

And Nitty Norah was knuckling her way through his hair, and her fingers felt like being stabbed with blunted bones, and already she had sent Daphne to sit with all her books and things in a separate desk to weep.

'Mundy she'll be back wiv 'er 'air all short, wontcha Daph? n' they'll wash 'er 'ead wiv sulpha,' Doreen was whispering to the world at large, as he thankfully and self-righteously shut the classroom door, and slid into his place.

The lady doctor dropped in from time to time to see if anyone was deaf or colour blind. Bespectacled and hard of hearing herself, her tests were of the crudest kind. 'What colour is this?' she grunted one day, holding up her pocket book, and, 'Maroon, please Miss,' he answered, trying to be as accurate as possible. 'It's red, child, red!' she roared back again.

He knew she couldn't be a proper doctor after that.

But the dentist was the worst of the trio. He dreaded her coming, and the trips to her surgery a bus ride away that followed. A raw-faced woman, expert in inflicting needless pain, she gritted away with her drill in unanesthetized nerves, got angry if you yelped, and clouted your head when the fancy took her. When she tipped him over in her chairful of smells time stopped, and the clock brimmed over with waiting minutes, although she clattered and banged away as fast as if the Council was paying her on piecework.

Holes in your teeth, nits in your hair, ringworm: turn by turn the plagues passed among them. The nastiest of all while it lasted was impetigo, and impetigo came back year after year and few escaped the scourge. Sit in a desk after a sufferer and within a week *your* knees, too, broke out in rashes that wept and ran together in yellow scabs. You itched and scratched and carried the sores to your neck, your ears, your eyelids. Three times over he loitered by his front gate, patched and clotted with calamine, staring with a leprous envy at the friends he was forbidden to approach, until the uncleanness was purged, and he was fit for human intercourse again. A schooltime later, he watched King Hamlet weep over the tetters that had fouled his flesh, and did not need to grope far back in memory to share that loathing.

In 1938 diphtheria swept back, and carried off gentle Eileen, who when they were infants together, had shyly whispered to him every morning what colour her knickers were. He could not understand her death: if *he* had choked and stayed alive four years before, then why not her?

More than a year after Eileen's death, as he passed her house one afternoon her mother was at the window. She drew him in and took him up to Eileen's room. It was as it had always been: Eileen's dolls waiting in a row, fresh-cut chocolate cake on a plate, the bed made, the sheet turned down for her. Mr and Mrs King could not accept that their only child was dead. That afternoon as he hurried away he knew that her mother, who once had always smiled at him in such welcome, would never forgive him for being alive.

*

Two winters of gaslit classrooms, with forest twigs glistening out of the mist in a haze of frost, and snow stained yellow in the boys' outdoor lavatories. Two springs of sticky buds and beans and tadpoles sprouting in jam-jars on the window-sills. Two summers of dust and birdsong. And the door of the Infants closed behind them. Now he could scamper the mile and a half to school all by himself; and he racketted back and forth through Moll's convoyed cissies: 'Gor, look at 'em 'oldin' 'ands!' up St Anne's Hill and down again. And innocence was falling from him like a garment.

A month or so before he was translated from the Infants, he was mooching about in the empty hall one rainy playtime, when Barbara came through the door.

'What you got there, then?'

Barbara did not deign to answer. She was holding a trayful of newly-sharpened stubs of pencils and sticking her tummy out with pride, like the ice-cream lady at the Regal with the bicycle lamp to shine in your eyes. In that instant it flooded upon him that if he kicked up under the tray, all the pencils would fly up in a fountain, whee! and that would be a good thing to watch. Barbara shrank back against the door as he raced at her, 'Mind *out!*'

And then they stood together in a marvellous crimson rain up, and a marvellous crimson rain down. Barbara threw down the tray and burst into tears. But he was already on his knees, scrabbling over the floorboards. 'Come on. Help me pick 'em up, n' then you can 'ave a kick.'

Barbara sobbed bitterly. 'I'm jist *tellin'* on you.'

She clutched at the door handle, 'Leave me *go!*' while he snatched her arm and tried to explain. But she wrenched free and fled to Miss O'Flynn's bosom.

He wanted to tell her that the erupting pencils were a marvellous, a breathless thing, like putting a match to a catherine wheel or zonking a bottle in the pond with your very first stone: he could have taken turns all playtime to pick the pencils up and kick them away. But he hadn't the words.

He was hooking out stubs from under the radiator when Miss O'Flynn's skirts rustled in.

'I'm glad to see that at least you're picking them up.'

He looked up to see her contemplating him, while Barbara hung at her side, grinding out her last tears with her knuckles.

'And now you can say you're sorry to Barbara.'

'Sorry,' he mumbled. But he couldn't see what *she*'d got to be upset about.

He waylaid Barbara once or twice that week to try to explain that what mattered was not them rotten old pencils, but the beauty of a moment's vision. But he couldn't command the right words, although he knew they were there somewhere in his head, and she wouldn't listen. After the summer holidays they were Infants no more. She was mincing among the girls a playground away, and he was back to square one in Moggy's kingdom, learning a new kind of toughness in a world of boys who understood the rules. That pencils were for kicking out of people's hands, and scarves for knotting and chopping the unwary with, that anyone's new cap was for slinging into the brook, and that might was right.

Half a world away, in Fascist Italy, Benito Mussolini's son-in-law strutted through the streets, and remembered in his memoirs the beauty of a vision of human flesh flowering open like a rose, where his bomb had fallen among Abyssinian tribesmen. 'God Almighty!' said PC Druce, reading the words aloud from a newspaper. 'Is this what the human race is coming to?'

Suddenly he felt a shudder of guilt faintly shared, and could only see in his mind's eye a fountain and a rain of crimson.

*

Now, Infants no longer, Roy Shotley and he began to find other routes between school and Sparrowfield Lane: short cuts that were twice as far on the map and three times as long by the clock. At first they clipped off a corner here and took a footpath there. Then they cut away at an angle from the top of St Anne's Hill and came down Victoria Road with its yellow brick and its slates that on a rainy day ran bluer than all the blues in your paintbox, spilling down the slopes of the hill. And there at the bottom in Consort Road they fell up the steps and into the bright gloom of the best sweetshop of all.

Before long, growing heedless at eight-thirty of Moggy and the cane he fetched out every day at milk break, they ventured further still, past the iron pump in Pump Way, and past the houses and out onto the flanks of Maze Hill.

Or was it Maid's Hill? People argued about the answer.

And then they'd come racing the last hundred yards through the trees to the back of the school playground and the clanking bell in its roof.

It wasn't long before their journey home at night and their journey to school in the morning wound through the forest all the way, from Consort Road to Almshouse Green and the foot of Silver Hill. Longer by a mile at least, it took them romping through drifts of leaves, slithering along clay paths at the edge of the forest brook, and leaping its channels back and forth from each high bank into the steely crunch of pebbles below.

For the pupils of Consort Road, the forest was the setting and the backdrop for their lives in the Village. Fungus sprouting overnight, a branch broken, a fallen tree, ice in the brook, birds' nests, crab apples, blackberries, tramps: there was always a fresh wonder to deny the school bell and trap you like a moth in a spider's web.

They clambered into the puddle-crowned pollard hornbeams in Abbot's Wood to squat in ambush there, and played hide and seek among the thorny shadows of the witches' forest and through the bracken in Sandpit Plain, whose sinews manacled and shackled you. They squelched about in the rust-red swamps by Rushey Lane hunting for adders, and kicked off the tops of anthills to watch the owners seethe out and grab their eggs and run. They king-of-the-castled the stumps that thrust up out of seas of moss in Dead Man's Slade, they ducked-and-draked the gravel ponds and the reservoir, and rampaged through the fox earths of Roman Camp in the last-ditch struggles of their own wars.

The forest was a wilderness haunted by jays, by forest keepers who shouted you down from the trees and out of the ponds, by cattle that ambled through the distant mist of their breaths, by lovers and peeping Toms, and botanists, and rapists, and picnickers, and out-of-works, and suicides. There he crept and ferreted, eight years old, for tadpoles and fungi and lovers, through grass where he would lie himself at twenty-one, a lover.

Like every primal place, the forest was for him the prototypical forest: from such fragments dreams are woven.

In his mind's eye, biblical Adam walked barefoot through the rose briars and hollyhocks, and wiped his bottom on squares of newspaper in the privy in his grandfather's garden at Rectory Farm, while Eve climbed over a tarred stile and trod through chicken cack to bring an apple out of the orchard. Because that was the first garden and the garden of gardens, Paradise and Avalon and Gethsemane and the Bower of Bliss. And is still.

And so, too, the forest at the back of Consort Road School was Sherwood and Arden and a wood near Athens and a wood above Camelot and every other wood. Peter Quince called his roll among the thorn brakes of Fairmead, and a Red Cross Knight rode forever jingling down Clay Ride towards Hangboy Slade and Long Ridings. In after-years in dreams of his own making, he still heard the wind roaring through branches, as nightly he threaded the mazes of Maze Hill, hooting like an owl in his cupped hands, feeling the grass blades wet against his legs.

5

MOGGY JENKINS

Although the tide of trees lapped against the walls, and every autumn leaves came whirling into the roofless lavatories and choked the drain, the Boys' School in Consort Road ignored the forest, at least in Moggy's time. With a grassy plain a wall away, in all but high summer the juniors drilled in the asphalt yard. With living things to draw and paint, they made patterns. O, there was an iron gate from the playground to the forest, but the tongue of the lock was stilled with scabs of rust and paint.

One day he was sent to clear out a cupboard in the school hall. Right at the back of a shelf, as he wobbled on a chair, he found wonders. In a cardboard box, a wasps' nest like a dried brain, with husks of larvae still embedded in its miraculous maze. An adder, coiled up as tight as a spring, in a jar of brownish fluid, the label faded: 'Common Viper, Lord's Path, Augu—', the rest indecipherable.

'Sir, sir, *look*!' he said, tapping on Moggy's door, clutching the bottle with the viper slowly revolving in the moving liquid.

'Ah,' said Moggy, emerging in a haze of smoke, and taking the bottle for a moment in nicotine-stained fingers. 'Dustbin's the place for that.'

Someone must once have been aware of the forest, and looked at things in it and tried to possess them, even if only in so mortuary a way. But not Moggy Jenkins. He trotted along asphalt pavements, and scarcely ever set a foot among leaves except to snarl a cluster of boys down out of the pollard hornbeams.

*

To and from Consort Road now, in morning light and dusk, he and Roy Shotley took the forest paths. Again and again, he drifted into the classroom, minutes and tens of minutes late, lured by some deadly green magic upon the way, while Roy raced towards the clanking bell and left him to it: 'Well, *be* late then. I ain't gettin' caned!'

Again and again, Mr Evans folded his arms on the register and heard his explanations to the bitter end: tales of breakfasts burnt and cooked a second time, damp shirts to be ironed before his mother would let him out the door, of neighbour's dogs that followed him and had to be dragged home again, of alarm-clocks never wound or overwound or stopped by the hand of God. 'Remarkable, Druce, remarkable. Worthy of Ananias. Sit down, boy, and see Mr Jenkins after milk. He'll be overjoyed to renew the acquaintance, I'm sure.'

And at ten o'clock he'd line up by the table with the stinking grey milkrag on it, with the taste of milk in his mouth, till Moggy came out of his room. 'Right hand out!' — slash! — and anguish slashed and seared into his fingers. 'Left. Come on, boy. Higher. Get it up higher.'

And then he was walking across the hall to his classroom, looking desperately straight ahead, writhing his fingers in his armpits to quench the pain, forcing his lips up into a quivering smile, swaggering back, — 'Didn't 'urt *me*,' — to his desk. You could try to rub the pain away with soap, or orange peel. But it didn't help.

*

Once a week they went to Mr Parrot for Craft. They sat at long tables with a pudding basin each from home, and lined it with fragments of tissue paper. 'I don't want to see any pieces bigger than a fingernail. Got that?' said Mr Parrot. They had to stick the bits in, overlapping, with vaseline. It took nearly a whole lesson to get the inside of the basin covered. Mr Parrot prowled up and down between the tables, and knuckled your nut if you spoke. Then you had to go over it round and round inside the basin with flour-paste and scraps of newspaper.

He thought he'd get on faster and slapped in a four-inch square, crumpling it down well with a pasty brush. Mr Parrot leaned across his shoulder — 'What did I tell you? No bigger than your fingernail,' — and clawed out a handful of sodden newsprint, right down to the china. 'Start all over again. And this time do as you are told.' His spirits sank utterly.

But then he decided that if you got your big piece of newspaper ready under the table and stuck it all over with little bits, then you *could* slap the whole lot in at one go, and Polly Parrot wouldn't notice. And so it proved.

When the basins had been set out to dry on top of the art cupboard for a week, they could give them back to their mums, and everyone had made a vaseliny paper basin.

Mr Parrot it was who held Standard I spellbound one day, telling them how you cured tapeworm. You had to put a dish of smelly spicy food on the sufferer's pillow and the worm would scent it and crawl up out of his mouth as he slept, and you could catch the worm and kill it. He taught them that NEWS was called N-E-W-S because it came from North East West and South. And that it was a deadly sin to begin a sentence with and. Or but. And that you could tell how old a horse was, by counting the rings in its teeth. But *sir!* 'Put your hand down, boy.' But *sir!* 'I'm not going to tell you a second time.'

No, there was no questioning him. And there was always a clout across the ear for the knave and the promise of Claybury Asylum for the fool to look forward to as *a fortiori* arguments. Truths there must have been somewhere in Mr Parrot's learning — or how could he have held his place? — but so were there approximations, guesses, nonsense. They all stuck like scabs, and one day each one would have to be picked off.

When Moggy retired as headmaster the following summer, and the new headmistress put the boys' and the girls' schools together, Polly Parrot took himself off to the Boys' Senior School a mile distant. The war came, he put on a blue uniform, and went to his death in a burning aircraft: and so Consort Road remembered him.

*

Mr Evans never clouted your ear. He had a round ebony ruler instead. Catch his eye just once too often, and he had you out in front. 'Which hand is it you write with? Other hand flat on my desk, then.' And crunch, the ruler came down on spread-eagled knuckles. The agony was an agony of bone, perfect in its concentration.

Mr Evans wrote a play for them to do in History, and recited the parts. 'Eggs and bacon for to maken,' quoth Mr Evans, 'and green cheese to grease your cheeks.' Standard I dutifully split their sides, but they never took to his play. It was just this Piers Ploughman mooching around a market and telling everybody, 'I have no penny,' and there wasn't any fighting. Mr Evans abandoned the attempt to brighten up History, and went back to lecturing them on mediaeval strip-farming and the rotation of crops with chalk diagrams on the blackboard.

They had him for Geography, too, and they did England and France, and once Mr Evans spent two whole lessons talking about a boat called the Cross Channel Packet. But Druce had toothache and missed the first lesson, and spent the next wondering why Taffy Evans was going on about some sort of parcel.

One day Mr Evans got down the globe from the top of the cupboard in the hall, and fetched it into History and everything that was pink was THE BRITISH EMPIRE and that was something to be proud of, wasn't it? — that was something to think about — 'but, please sir, Ireland's green, isn't it?' — and, 'None of your business, Druce,' said Mr Evans.

In English lessons Mr Evans stuck to Nouns Common Proper Abstract And Collective, because every Sentence had got to have a Subject and a Predicate, and it was Standard I's job to find them and get them down on paper. And a Verb. And then there were Plurals to do. And laundry-lists of Similes. They scrawled them down out of the exercises, while Mr Evans sat at his desk and dreamed about getting his Headship.

'Seraph — SERAPHIM. Charabanc: cor that's a good job I learned this lot last night, CHARSABANC. Ssstt, Pike! Wot's a charsabanc, eh? A somefink of trumpets, wossat then? Band, I reckon. O yeah, Band. Tisn't. It's a Fanfare of trumpets. Wot? Fanfare. N' oo arst *you*, Perfessor Martin? As sober as a. Hey Charlock, wot's as sober as a? As dead as — A DORMOUSE! Shut up. You'll cop it if Evansy 'ears you. It's a doornail. Wot is? As dead as. O, yeah. As black as — YER 'AT! I know that un. Well, *tis* yer 'at, then, *see*. My dad's forever sayin' that, it's as black as your bloody 'AT outside. Well, 'e does. Woss old Evans know about English, anyway? 'E's jist a daft Taffy.'

A pride of geese and a gaggle of lions, Standard I missed no chance to peck the tamer and snarl at the gooseboy.

*

45

For a brief season he walked home with Mr Evans, who lived in Silver Hill, trotting along at the side of the man, both of them adrift on a babble of talk. Mr Evans talked about his dream: 'Now, when I get my Headship…'

It became a catchphrase with PC Druce at number 99. 'When I get my Headship, indeed to goodness. And what had our Welsh pedagogue to say for himself today, eh? What pearls of wisdom did he see fit to cast before you?'

O, Mr Evans had been telling him how he'd been an amateur boxer in the valleys.

'Ha! That creature a boxer? Don't make me laugh. Did you hear that, Dorothy? Our Mr Evans is a boxer, indeed to goodness. Well, you'd better tell him to step round to the Police Station any time, and we'll have the gloves on. A boxer? He couldn't box the skin off a rice pudding. Anytime, tell him. O, and I was forgetting — is there any news of his Headship, did he say?'

Enemies each morning, sworn soldiers of opposing armies, they ambled peaceably homeward at the end of the day, and took their ease in one another's company, before the turn of the sun brought another day of conflict. But their friendship came to an abrupt end, and it was Mr Evans' fault.

'Listen now, why don't you behave yourself properly, eh?' Mr Evans suddenly asked. 'You're a brainy kiddy. Walking here now you're as different as chalk and cheese. Well? Well? You don't answer me.'

What *could* he answer? It was an unfair, an impossible question. He did what he did because it was to be done. Taffy Evans knew that as well as he did. 'Didn't you play about in school, sir?'

'What has that got to do with it? Hoh! We'd have been knocked into the middle of next week if we'd tried that game, I can tell you. I'm far too soft, that's my trouble. I shall start tightening up. Look here, how many times did you get the ruler today, eh? What possesses you to keep letting off gunpowder caps, if you only get caught?'

What was the right answer to that? He'd come across half a dozen caps in his pocket and had spatted them on the desk in Geography, scratching them one by one with a pen-nib until they exploded. Three times over he'd been caught and sent back to his desk with a paralysed hand, until Evansy had thought of making him turn his pockets out. The last few caps Evans had confiscated, locking them up in his drawer. Yes. *Yes*. 'Sir, when can I have my caps back?'

'Duw, is that all you're thinking of? Talking to you sometimes is like running at a brick wall. Now, pull your socks up. Try to behave decently, boy. Now *try*. Promise me that.'

O yes, he'd *try*. Nothing to be lost by making promises. And tomorrow he'd walk home on his own.

The next day he was throwing chalk the instant Mr Evans turned to the blackboard, and Mr Evans caught him and paralysed his knuckles, and he went back to his place and threw another piece a moment later, and that time he didn't get caught. Why discuss it? It was the rule of the game in Moggy's school, cut and dried. You played them up: they clonked you.

Only much later did he look back and question it. And then he felt only resentment at the system itself, not at the hapless individuals, children and teachers alike, caught up in it. Except for Moggy: perpetrator, patriarch, cock of the walk. A self-designated little god in a cupboardful of cigarette smoke.

For two years they lived under the shadow and then, suddenly, Moggy had shuffled off into retirement, and Mrs Baldwin was throwing all the windows open to the sunlight. But a month before he left, Moggy Jenkins made his final, appalling gesture.

*

There was a knot of boys over by the lavatories at playtime. But nobody was chanting, 'Fight! Fight!' so that couldn't be the case.

'Woss up?'

'Smudger n' Bennett. Got caught thievin'.'

'Down Woolworth's.'

'Knockin' off toy cars. Manager of Woollie's copped 'em.'

'What, are they at the Police Station? My dad—'

'*Naow*. Moggy's got 'em in 'is room. 'E's goin' ta give 'em a frashin'.'

''E can't.'

''Oo can't?'

'Moggy. Moggy can't. Not if it was Woolworth's. Woolworth's is nothing to do with 'im, is it? Their dads should give them a hiding. Not '*im*.' Shame flooded through him at the thought.

'Don't be *daft*. 'E's the bloody headmaster, ain't 'e? Jist cos your dad's a copper you fink you know it all.'

'Yeah. Awright fer you. You can get caught thievin', and your dad'll get you off. We all know that.'

'I don't thieve. I ain't a thief. It's just not Moggy's business, that's all.'

'Aw, shut ya gob. Course it's 'is business. Stands to reason. 'E's the soddin' headmaster, ain't 'e? It's 'is job!'

A boy walked out of the school, ringing the handbell.

He crossed the yard, his cheeks still burning with shame. To be caned by Moggy for what you did outside school. It wasn't fair.

And he *did* thieve. It wasn't true, what he'd said.

He'd been helping himself out of the larder, half-handfuls of sultanas, swigs of condensed milk from the tin, glacé cherries, for months. Creeping in when his mother was out shopping or upstairs. Only a little at a time, so she'd never notice the level going down. Only one or two scarlet-dyed cherries a day, sucking their syrupy sweetness across his tongue. Only one or two a day. Well, three sometimes.

But that added up to twenty in less than a fortnight. 'That's queer,' his mother said. 'I could have sworn I had more glacé cherries than this. You haven't been helping yourself, have you?' He shook his head. But his throat choked on acidity, remembered sweetness cloying. 'O well,' she sighed, 'I must have been mistaken.'

But it wasn't *thieving*, was it? No. It was just cherries. And sultanas, and. He wasn't stealing from anybody else. *That* was thieving — taking something that didn't belong to you. Because the cherries were already his in a sort of way, weren't they? If.

Well, if they'd been in a piece of cake his mother made and he'd eaten it. That was the difference. See? He tried to explain it to his imagined mother, to God, to Moggy Jenkins, as he walked across the playground. See? They didn't look convinced.

Mr Evans and Mr Parrot were standing on the platform, glowering down at them all, as they sat themselves cross-legged on the floorboards. Moggy came in, prodding Smudger Smith and Bennett out of Standard IV in front of him; up the steps and onto the stage.

'I have a shocking thing to tell you all. There are thieves in this school, my friends. Did you know that? Thieves.' Moggy's voice boomed and fell like an actor's.

Smudger was already snivelling, and Bennett stood beside him, smirking in terror at the sudden limelight. 'O, I shall soon wipe that smile off your face, boy,' said Moggy, himself smiling.

He couldn't bear to look up at them or listen. Mr Jenkins had no right, no right. '*Led on by an older boy…*' Words broke into his brain, forcing the locks of his ears. He gazed at the floorboards, counting spent matches trapped in the cracks: one, two — anything to take his mind off what was going on.

'*Bend over the table.*'

Three dead matches, four; another one just by Robbins's shoe. Five.

'*One!*' cried Moggy, and he looked up to see the cane whirl down, smash! and flames jolted along his own nerves at what he saw.

'*Two!*' cried Moggy.

He had no right! Nobody should hit you like that. Not even your own father.

But if you were a thief?

'*Three!*'

Stealing from shops? Answer me that: you can't.

'*Four!*'

Smudger was blubbered with tears and wailing aloud. Eating glacé cherries was stealing, too. Admit. Admit.

'*Five!*'

The whirling swish of the cane and the shock of Smudger's body jarring against the table deafened him, and flamed up in his own flesh and racing heart.

'*Six!*'

Moggy had finished with Smudger. Mr Evans led him away, down the steps and out to the cloakrooms. He could not bear to look.

'Come here, Bennett,' said Moggy. 'As for you, thief—'

The words, '*Yes, thief!*' came and went in his ears '*before the assembled school*' like tides in a hollow shell.

'*To make an example of you,*' and he shuddered, half-swooning, '*the ringleader,*' sitting cross-legged on the floorboards, waiting for. How many?

Gazing at the floor and listening for.

'*Six strokes of the cane.*'

No! No!

The first whirr of the cane and the jolt of Bennett's body against the table burst again into his heart and flared up in his flesh. 'Bastard! You fuckin' ole bastard!'

He looked up in terror, shame filling his soul. Bennett was screaming, 'Leave *go* of me, you fuckin' ole bastard!' white-faced in panic, clutching the table, fighting to drag himself out of Moggy's arms.

'Silence,' shouted Mr Parrot, striding to the edge of the platform with eyes wide-glaring. He and Mr Evans each held Bennett down by an elbow and a wrist across the table.

'*You foul-mouthed, cowardly, little, thief,*' said Moggy, and the table jolted again and again with each word.

Bennett's cries blurred into a roar of sobbing.

When it was at an end, Mr Jenkins addressed the school.

'As for the despicable conduct you have just witnessed: well, you may thank God, at least, that one member of this school had the guts to take his medicine like a man. Now, when I give the order, dismiss in silence, and get off home. I want to see none of you loitering about outside. Stand...

'Good afternoon, school...

'What, the cat has got your tongues, has she? I said, Good after*noon*, school.'

'Good afternoon, *Sir*.'

*

He lay alone in the grass, looking down at the golden-glowing pebbles in the forest brook, at green nets of leaves reflected, trying to forget the noises in his head, seeking to drown the shouting voices in the ripple of the stream.

He stretched a hand into the icy water, plunging it deep and clawing out a smooth pebble. The chill bit into his muscles, and he dragged his jersey down over still-wet flesh. He caressed the pebble in his fingers for a long while.

He stood up at last, and moved homeward, fingering the pebble as it lay, smooth and dry now, in his pocket. Along the foot of Maze Hill, kicking through leaves. Up Long Ridings, and over Gregories, kicking through leaves.

He came to a halt by the pond at Almshouse Green. Cupping the pebble in his hand for a moment, he suddenly drove it with all his force into the black water.

Then he scrambled up through the willows, and walked home along Sparrowfield Lane.

6

RECTORY FARM

Rectory Farm lay snug among trees at the foot of a slow swoop of chalky countryside. You ducked out of the front door, through the briar roses and the geranium pots, to the low gate of the horseyard, and a world cut off on three sides by the black walls of barns.

Beyond the barns lay the road and the duckpond and the Red Lion, with its whitewashed walls and its cool brown parlour standing open to the midday sunshine, or spilling a fan of lamplight into the dark. Eastward, past gipsy caravans, the road ran towards Haslingfield and Frog End. Westward it wound the length of the village. Past Dolly Bolton's General Stores, past the cottages and the green, past the Three Horseshoes, the school and the Rectory.

At the triangle beside St Mary's church it split in two. One half swung north in a great curve towards Cambridge seven miles distant. The other turned south, passing through a spatter of cottages and council houses, past old Towett's place, where old Towett's wife made him sleep in the woodshed when the fit took her — 'Goo,' said Grandad, 'I'd *dust* her britches for her, do she was a wife of mine' — and away between the pale ploughlands to London.

Grandad. A champion of ploughing matches. A brown-faced man who walked the earth behind his team, swallowing cold tea at midday from a bottle in the fields, hacking bread and cheese across, and munching them with a raw onion or an apple off the flat of his knife. Watching all night long with a sick horse in a lamplit stable. Splicing a rosebud into a hedgerow briar and waiting for the graft to flesh together and grow green. There he stands now, brown fading into yellow, in a photograph, shotgun under his arm.

He was racked with asthma and talked in his sleep. Nanny told how one night Grandad dreamed he was carting hay with that saucy stable-lad who worked for a while at Rectory Farm. 'Mind your tongue,' he called out into the darkness; 'Do you cheek me just once more, my boy, and I'll hev you out of this cart.'

'Shan't, then!' said Nanny, and found herself on the floorboards.

*

Born Alice Jobson, in a farmworker's tied cottage in a Suffolk village, Nanny's whole life was one of childbirth and domestic labour. She was the firstborn, and within a handful of years was toiling alongside her mother to bring up the fourteen children — two sisters and twelve brothers — who followed her. At twenty-five, and now in service as a children's nanny, she married Charlie Wright, the horseman at the nearby Hall, famous in the nearby villages for his singing and his love of dressing up; and she set about making a home and brewing beer and making bread and bearing children of her own.

First she bore Charlie seven daughters in a row. Eva, Dorothy, Lily, Elsie, Mary, Gwen and Kath. See here now, under my hand, Nanny poses for the camera in a sunlit meadow, a mother.

It is 1911, and she is erect and handsome in a starched white smock. Her dark blonde hair is somehow both piled up high and coiling down her back, and her shirt-sleeved and waist-coated husband leans on his scythe at her side. In laced boots and Sunday frocks, Eva, Dorothy, Lily, and Elsie are perched in attitudes around them. Baby Mary is peering out of the perambulator, and her mother's smock is already bellying out with Gwen.

Charlie wasn't content with womenfolk but craved for sons to carry on his name, and at last came John and William. By then the girls were already leaving home one by one to go into service and, all but Eva, to marry. The boys stayed at home as of right to work on the land. They shared a bedroom until 1945, when Bill married a wartime landgirl and moved into a cottage not a quarter of a mile away.

As the 1920s came to an end, Eva left for a while to be cook-housekeeper to a Colonel. But it wasn't long before she came home again, and bicycled into Cambridge every day to serve in a department store, until Nanny was too frail to be left alone. Eva never married. That was the fate of so many eldest daughters, whose lot it was to remain at home; or at the last to return with no encumbrances of their own, and cosset their parents decently into old age and the grave. But it wasn't long before Dorothy, wheeling out other people's babies in Beckenham, met and married her policeman.

And so Bobby became Eva Wright's first godson and Alice Wright's first grandchild.

As long as she lived, he loved and was in awe of his Cambridgeshire grandmother, her trim and tiny figure, her energy. One day when he was sixteen and she was sixty and needed apples for a pie, she raced him to the orchard and had swarmed up into the branches and down again while he was still fumbling with the ladder. 'You might have slipped and hurt yourself,' she said. 'And *then* what would Dorothy have had to say?'

When she was old and white-haired and forgetful he marvelled at her saintliness, and her humbleness in the care of an ageing daughter who often grew impatient and sour of voice. But in earlier years and in his childish eyes, Nanny with her starched apron and her granny glasses and her lovingly sharp tongue and her country lore and her magics was more than half a witch.

She showed him how to butter slices of toast with yeast and float them on a brew of pump water and sugar and flower petals in a five-gallon crock. Within a day or two the earthenware shuddered under your fingertips and you could listen to the liquid alive and simmering. Before long it would have transformed itself into wine. Cleared with eggshells and bottled and kept for a year or two, it would slide across your tongue like oil. Rose-petal, Dandelion, Beetroot, Wheat, Parsley: there were labels tied round the necks of a dozen stoneware jars lined up along Nanny's pantry shelves.

The jars had little metal taps.

When he was seven or so, he found his fingers strong enough to turn the taps and he took a cup and sipped the liquors in three or four of the jars. They twisted his eyes in his head and left him snoring on the flagstones of the pantry while his frantic parents searched the garden and the nearby fields.

He liked to look on as Nanny twirled a fork among eggs and flour and whirled them up into a batter pudding as light as a soufflé. He could never make the foam stand stiff, try as he might, and neither could his mother though he ordered her to stand and *watch* how Nanny did it.

Without surprise or fuss, Nanny drew miracles of food — twice-weekly bread, and roasts and pies and puddings — out of a blackleaded iron cooking-range. Or, in summer, when the weather was too close to keep a fire in all day, from out of a tin-plate stove whose only source of heat was an oil lamp at either end.

Nanny never sat still for a second, except in church on Sunday, and bustled her married daughters out of her path. 'Go you out of my kitchen,' she'd say. 'You're supposed to be here on holiday.' When there were no sheets left to iron, or clothes to stitch, or socks to darn; or morning hot water or slops to carry; or candlesticks to scrape clean, or wicks to level, or lamps to fill with paraffin; or vegetables to fetch in from the garden, or chickens to pluck, or rabbits to skin, or dough to knead, or pastry to trim for the lid of a pie; she stitched rag-rugs and embroidered texts for the bedroom and parlour walls, walls whose bulging surfaces she had papered with roses herself.

'Lo, I am with you alway. Even unto the end of the world.' Half a century later, it is Alice Wright whose voice I hear saying the words in my head. She would have discountenanced the blasphemy, but for me it is *her* presence they speak of.

On Sunday after-dinner walks, she showed her grandchildren the toadstools and berries and roots that were good to eat and those which were deadly poison. She taught them the names of trees and wild flowers and herbs and explained what each was good for. Words, words for his word-hoard.

She had queerer skills that looked back across centuries to ancient lores and magics. When Bobby grazed his knee, she washed the weeping wound and coated it with a dust-laden cobweb from the barn. It healed within a day or two. When his father gashed his forehead on a nail, first she washed and cobwebbed the wound, and then went searching for the nail and greased it with a candle-end. 'Do the nail that made it had started to rust, that cut on your head would've turned septic,' she said.

*

At the back of the farmhouse at Rectory Farm there was a garden smothered in roses, and a chicken-run, and a tiny triangular orchard at the edge of a meadow. For Bobby that orchard was the first orchard in the world. Its paradisal trees bore warty apples no bigger than an eight-year-old's fist, and their flesh broke like sweet green rain in his mouth.

Beyond the apples, fields of wheat and barley strode up the hillside to a bright edge of sky. The soil was thick with flints, as knuckled and gnarled as old men's hands, thrown up to the surface by the ploughshare. When he chimed two of them together, they cracked apart like black ice.

In a field nearby there was a pylon, and electric power went booming along the wires. On wet days it hissed and crackled. There was barbed wire high up round the legs, to stop you climbing. Grandad told him that some daft character did climb it once, showing off for the gals. And he got hisself frazzled.

There were haystacks by the corner of the garden. Bobby scaled them, making his hands into spears and stabbing them deep into the sides of the stack. Then, in beyond the elbows, he turned the spears into grappling hooks and clutched great handfuls of hay, deep inside the mass. Relentlessly, kicking his sandals in as far as they would go, he worked his way up and over the slope of the eaves and on to the crest. 'Grandad! Nanny! Look at me.' He launched himself, and came racing down again, to a sweet dust exploding all around him.

Beyond the haystacks was the field gate and the path to the clunch pits. Long ago worked out now, and overgrown with crab apple and blackthorn and sweet chestnut, the pits had yielded clunch: the limestone from which, like other nearby churches, St Mary the Virgin had been built.

He knew a cave there, a narrow ledge below an overhang, where the roots of trees flowed down past the mouth as dense as a waterfall. He squatted there in ambush. He thrust his way through thorns into weedy nooks that brimmed over wet and rank even in summer. In the high wood above the hollow, he stared over sudden precipices where death grinned up from the boulders of chalk below. By day a place where his aunties lit fires of twigs to boil a picnic kettle, and cousins romped with him through hide-and-seek and plundered the purple-pink orchids, at nightfall the chalky hollows became a secret world, part of a dream where he was master of the landscapes. When the bedroom in Rectory Farm was a flicker of candlelight, and birds that crept in under the thatch had quietened their gabble for the night, the clunch pits lay awake and listened, as they do still, to the murmuring of lovers and the cry of owls.

But snug he slept on goosefeathers, in a room papered with pink and black roses. Under the bed there were clanging white chamberpots to use last thing, and 'Now I Lay me Down to Sleep,' he said, reading Nanny's embroidery aloud, 'I Pray the Lord my Soul to Keep.'

*

They all walked to church together on Sunday mornings when he stayed at Grandad's, for as long as he could remember; and Bill was the choirboy who carried the Cross. Bill was his uncle, but he refused to concede him the title. Bill was fourteen and that was too young to be called Uncle, anyone could tell you that.

Bobby had been christened in St Mary's. Fetched in a shawl from the grime of Camden Town to have cool water trickled across his skull, cupped by the Rector's hand, from out of the font.

The font was made of limestone clunch, lined with dark lead. The whole church was fashioned of limestone. And there was a smell as you swung the weight of the door inward, like the smell if you picked up a lump of chalk in the clunch pits, and snuffed up a deep breath of it. A cool and gravelly smell. Or like a handful of clay out of the river.

The Rector kissed him.

Babies are supposed to cry when they are christened, they told him, because that's the devil coming out. But he had just laughed, looking up into the Rector's face, and the devil stayed in. And that explains all about master Robert, his mother used to say.

The Rector always leaned over as the procession came up out of the vestry, boots squeaking on the tiles, and patted his head. 'Good morning to you, my dears.' A white sleeve swished across the polished wood.

There was an old man and a woman who knelt beyond an iron screen in a side aisle. He couldn't help turning round to stare at them, they were so old and dirty. Then his mother's hand fell on his shoulder, prising him round to face forward, and they all had to slump down off the seats and onto the hassocks with their knees.

Hassocks had little floppy ears that you tugged them along by, and he pretended that they were flat dog's faces. You could feel them nibbling at your bare knees as you were kneeling, and when you sat back up you had to rub your skin to stop it itching from their teeth. There were ant hills in the forest at home, sticking up out of the marsh by Jack's Hill, like big green hassocks, and they were full of sharp little red ants. If you liked, you could pretend there were red ants in the hassocks at church.

Hassocks was a rhyming word. It rhymed with cassocks, and cassocks were those black gowns that the choirboys wore. He couldn't think of any other words to rhyme with hassocks. Hassocks and cassocks both had to do with church.

The man and the woman behind the iron screen had hassocks to themselves like big fat bolsters. The man's name was Henry Fryer and he had died ye 5 of Iune 1631, and there was a rhyme about him underneath the iron screen.

He always felt frightened of God in this church to which he had been assigned, where the water from the cross on his forehead had dripped back into the font, and his name was in a book. He was frightened of the nightmare songs, and frightened of the miracle. 'Hymn Four Hundred and Seven Ah,' called the Rector. 'Immortal Invisible God Only Wise. Four O Seven.' The organ keys pattered, and off they went with aunties shrilling out all round him.

In the British Museum they had Gods in boxes, who had been Kings in Egypt. There was box after box of wood and painted patterns. And in the middle there was just something wound up in dirty bandages. You couldn't see a King.

His mother handed him down a hymnbook in a waft of mothbally air, her gloved fingernail pressing against the place.

'Great Father of Glory, Pure Father of Light,
While Angels Adore Thee, All Veiling their Sight...'

If you went to the British Museum you could look at Ginger. 'Come to see ol' Ginger, have you?' said the man in the uniform, and walked along with them to hear what he would say. There was a big glass case and inside there was a man curled up like a side of bacon. His father told him that the man had been caught in a sand storm two thousand years ago, and had fallen asleep without any pain. His hair was made of gingery wool and he was naked, and his skin had burst open a bit here and there. The man walked round the case and muttered something to his father, and his father laughed.

His mother gave him a sudden nudge with her hip. It made him cross. He hadn't been daydreaming, he was thinking about being dead. Old Ginger was dead, and wasn't that what the hymn was all about?

'We Blossom and Flourish, Like Leaves on the Tree,
And Wither, and Perish…'

But he wouldn't sing those words, he didn't like what they meant. Withered is what apples did, and potatoes did when they grew long whiskers and went soft and puffy. And 'perish' was a word about rubber hot-water bottles. But not about stone ones. 'Perish' meant when the rubber went all gluey and the water leaked into the bedclothes.

Nanny's face was a bit withered.

He didn't want to think about people who withered and perished and burst and leaked out. So he wouldn't sing those words out loud. And then, *Amen*, at the end of the hymn they sat down with a clump on the varnished pitchpine, but none of them burst because they weren't perished enough yet.

While the Rector said his sermon, he listened to some of it and sometimes he looked at Henry Fryer and tried to puzzle out the poem about him that said, 'The Poor Man's Bowells Were his Chest.' And sometimes he gazed out of the white pieces in the coloured window to see if it would still be sunshiny when they got home. And then he could shoot arrows over the house and perhaps he'd find where they'd hidden the hatchet and he could chop up some sticks after dinner before they came out and stopped him. Or he'd do the jigsaws if it was raining.

It wouldn't be long now.

Then Bill was leading the way out of the choirboys' seats into the aisle, lifting up the Cross until the black knobs of his boots were sticking out under his cassock. Now it was going to happen. He looked up from his childish height at the glittering brass as it seemed to sway among the roofbeams, and he knew that in half a second it would go clanging into the stone screen if God didn't make the miracle. His stomach ached with tightness as Bill drew near the steps. At the last instant, just before Bill lowered his arms, he clenched his eyes and listened for the terrifying curse of a crash.

But it never came. When he opened his eyelids again he knew that the brass had passed through stone like a ghost through a wall, and God had made His miracle again.

His mother shoved him down for a last bob onto the hassocks, and then it was time to smile at the Rector and shake hands and crunch away along the path between the graves.

*

The scullery floor at Rectory Farm was made of huge paving stones, and the chimney was so wide that he could stand inside on the hearth and see the rain falling and falling all the way down. But it was the cupboard that stretched along the whole length of the wall that drew him back to peer and pry.

'Observe. Note things, my son. Count them. Fix them in your head,' his father admonished him; and for as long as he could remember he had been a ferret and a magpie, nosing out and snatching away bright baubles of knowledge. Sent to wash his hands in a strange house, he worked his way through the bathroom medicine-cupboard, uncapping pill boxes, spelling out the legends on ointments and linctus. He sniffed under sinks, and hauled out soap packets to read the tiniest print; he ransacked garden sheds, raking through tins of screws and nails, trying the edges of tools, denting his thumb with a saw's teeth, trying its bite. He sniffed up the savours of louse powder, weedkiller, creosote.

Whenever he creaked open the doors of the kitchen cupboard at Rectory Farm, its secret smells poured out and caught him by the throat. Lamp oil, floor polish, acetylene, soap: even the newspaper that lined the shelves was rank with it. He shut his eyes and played a solitary game of remembering, crouching on the stone flags, trying to recall all he had seen in a single glance. On the top shelf? Candles, yes, bootbrushes, Cherry Blossom boot polish, dubbin, and a wodge of white packets in a rubber band. 'All the Year Round', 'Fillbasket', 'Early Gem': lettuce, cabbage, carrots. Seeds rattled and scratched, a different shape in every packet. Witch Hazel, crystals of Condy's Fluid, the Horse Oils that had the lovely smell of ammonia, Flowers of Sulphur. He rolled the names on his tongue, tasting them. He held the bottles up to the light and looked through them; he shook the tins to hear if they'd rattle or splash.

Sooner or later he always had to take out the china man, although he hated him, and he had to stroke him and feel the rough part of his skull. The china man was no more than a lifesized head made out of white pottery, a bit like that head his father had shown him in the Museum, with all its bumps and knobs labelled. *Memory, Reason, Dex* — that's right, go on! — *Dexterity?* — Good boy! But Shockheaded Peter hadn't any names written on his head, and Grandad had brought him home from the fair. 'Shockheaded Peter,' Grandad said. 'That's what he was christened. And that's a rum 'un, that is. How can he hev a name like that when his head is as bald as a baby's bum?'

It was a joke, you see. You had to soak him in water, and sprinkle mustard and cress seeds on the rough part at the top and then the man would grow a great shock of grassy green hair and you could cut it off and eat it in a sandwich. He always pulled Shockheaded Peter out into the daylight and glared at him hard. That was because he hated coming across him in the cupboard by surprise, with his white unsleeping eyeballs gleaming like the eyes of God. Perhaps he would have liked Shockheaded Peter, if his grandfather would have given him to him as a present.

At night they all sat round the oil lamp in the parlour and Grandad rocked and sang, beating time with his hands, singing stories of Black-eyed Susan and O! It's my Delight on a Shiny Night in the Season of the Year. Then suddenly, 'Hark!' Grandad would say. 'Is that a ghoost I can hear?' There would be a soft slither in the bedroom overhead and on the parlour stair. Then the latch crashed and the door swung open, and he always jumped out of his skin though it was only the old tomcat who came in that way every night. 'Don't put such ideas into the child's head!' said Nanny, but Grandad went on laughing and coughing in delight. Grandad's asthma wouldn't clear up, and sometimes when he was bad he had to lie in bed and breathe blue smoke out of a little burner. But he always tried not to have to go to bed when they were there on holiday.

*

And then one day he had to spend the afternoon traipsing round the yard while the others were at church. And whatever he did, they told him, he had to keep clean. Understand? But water lured him, beckoning him to the pond and the horse trough and the rainwater butts alive and tickling with mosquito larvae.

Summer heat hung stilly over the cobbled yard, haze of dust and pollen, and the meadows were hissing with grasshoppers.

The Red Lion pond was coated with weed at the edge. The ducks came paddling across to him hopefully, and edged away again when he didn't throw them any bread. But he dabbled his fingers in, because.

Well, because this was the water they'd all walked across last winter, slipping and sliding, and bouncing pebbles down onto it, sending them chirruping over the ice to rap against the barn. 'You're not to attempt to go on there, Bobby. D'you hear me?' his mother called. But Grandad, O Grandad, said, 'Goo on Dot, let him hev a try. You could drive a horse and cart across that pond. He 'ont fall through.' But now it was summer, and now it was summer, and.

The flowers were beautiful, weren't they? So many.

The water was slimy, mouthed by cattle, and now he'd have to wash his hands. He rattled his fingers along the boards of the barn, clattering over dry tar and tiny cobwebs, caressing them; cracking a grey bubble under his nails right through to its shiny black inside; focusing the sensation in his fingertips. There were tar bubbles on the orchard gate, too; and in a minute he'd better go up and swing on it, before they all came back. He wouldn't get another chance.

His clean-polished shoes went squelch in the straw of the horseyard, though he did his best to dodge the wettest bits, walking over to the stone trough. He caught the knob of the pump handle, hot as a stove knob in his hand, and threw it upwards, clanking, once or twice. Dust fell from the cast-iron mouth. 'Us'll hev to prime her, bor.' Clamber up and tip water in at the top to wet the leather, so that it swelled up and kept the suction in.

But supposing the only water anywhere was still down under, there in the well. You couldn't prime the pump until you got the water, and you couldn't get the water, until. So what did you do? That was a puzzle. But he always forgot to ask. You just had to see that the pails in the scullery never ran empty.

They did, though. They did that day when. O, that day when Grandad watched him put the horseradish on his plate. 'Goo on then, bor, get a good forkful in. You'll never taste that little mite you're a-holding there.' And then he'd put it on his tongue, and tears had come screaming into his eyes and his mouth was alight, and he raced out to the water pails in the scullery, and they were all of them empty. Then he'd fled back past the laughter, fumbling the door latch open, still clenching the agony between his teeth, until he could spit it down onto the cobbles. And then he was flinging the pump handle up and biting at the stream of water as it tailed away after each clanking downfall of the handle, looking through a screen of tears at the faces framed among the geraniums in the doorway. That day, that day the pump had flowed first go. But today in powdery heat it wheezed only air from its open mouth.

There was a scoop lying on the lid of the water butt by the barn. He reached up to it, and creaked the lid open on its hinges. Sunlight fell into the water, and a score of tiny creatures flicked away, down towards the gloom. He waited, his chin touching the rim of the tank, watching until they came twitching back upwards to hang at the surface, gulping atoms of air. He smacked the water with the flat of his hand and sent them racing down again.

Now he could see hundreds all clinging to the rusty inner surface, and he boomed the outside of the metal with his fist and watched them fling themselves away in panic. Gnats. That's what they'd turn into one day. Gnats dancing between the hedgerows like flecks of stinging smoke.

How did they know always to choose the same place to haunt, always the same spots along the path up to the clunch pits? Perhaps Grandad knew the. No. He hammered with his fist on the side of the tank and the tiny specks flickered away again out of the swathe of sunlit water. He scooped up a scoopful and let the lid fall, bang.

He could hear a dog barking somewhere away in the distance, towards Haslingfield. The hens were clucking.

He nursed the bowlful of water, his wrist aching, across the yard and set it down in the dry trough. Then he got a knee up to the edge and clambered so that he could tip the water in through the slot, past the pump-rod. Still crouched there, he worked the handle and water came grinding-gushing out, clashing down to brim in puddles on the stone. He sprang down and dabbled his hands in the water, gritting away the dust of tar and slime. Much more to do yet.

He set Grandad's water scoop back on the lid of the tank as he went past. Its handle was wormed away into a honeycomb. He'd not noticed that before. But today was a day for seeing and touching and asking your fingers to remember. He plucked a geranium petal, crushing it into a smear of juice, and sniffing the lovely stink in. That was the same smell as Herb Robert, and that was *his* name for a flower.

The flowers! O, There were so many!

He tiptoed into the barn, dreading a rat. Grandad went after the rats, grut ol' big uns that come a-purpose for the corn. With his shotgun he went after them. But today now he, Robert, must walk in without flinching, and plunge his hand straight into the corn bin; and not let Grandad see he was afraid. Because Grandad would know.

Maize trickled through his fingers, cool little nuggets. He closed his hand. Enough. He plucked at the loop of string and swung the door open. Out now. Sun struck him, hard and dry, in the eyes.

The hens scattered, squawking, as he came through their gate, chicken-wire nailed to a ramshackle frame. They got no wits. He threw the maize angrily at them, a flinty shower that sent them scuttling about in greed and fright. There was a last nugget lodged under the edge of his shirt-cuff and he drew it out and gripped it in his teeth. Impossible. You couldn't crack them. Never.

But hens had gizzards. Bags of gravel in their necks, and the corn went round and round and was crunched up like the concrete in a mixer. Nanny showed him when she plucked the chicken last time, putting her hand inside the parson's nose and pulling it inside-out, empty. 'That's its gizzard,' she said, cutting the bird's neck open so he could look at all the bits of grit inside it.

Nanny was very brave.

Gizzard. That's what Grandad. O, that's what Grandad had said that day about the horseradish. 'Git a forkful down into your gizzard.'

And then he caught sight of the bottles, and went over to the heap by the hedge. Because Rectory Farm had no dustbins, of course, and they threw all the tins on a bonfire so they'd be burnt blue and then they'd rust away, and they dumped them into a pile with all the bottles and jars and this is where it was.

You could find all kinds of interesting things there. Paste-jars that had held crab, and salmon and shrimp, and bloater, O! and lots of others. Thick little glass pots with ribbed sides. Bottles with rotting corks in their necks and strange oily brews trickling inside them. Medicines, and things for asthma. Because of Grandad. They shifted as he groped among them, toppling rainwater orange with rust across his fingers, a crumbling ziggurat of rotted tins and glass. Grandad's.

There was a sound of motors, and voices. 'Bobby? Bobby?' Marie and Margaret, his cousins coming to look for him, back from church.

And they were younger than he was, but they'd been allowed to go. He stood among the nettles by the hedge, looking down at his rust-ruined hands. His mother hadn't let him go to church. He'd be too upset, she said. That's why he'd got his best clothes on, out playing in the yard. Because.

He crouched down again, and emptied old water from a jar across his hand, scrubbing away what marks he could with a dock leaf. Green streaks replaced the orange. They were calling him, round by the hens, girls' voices.

'Coming,' he cried. 'I'm coming.'

No hide-and-seek today.

The cars were back now, lined up along the cobbled pathway, summer-dusty. And the flowers were gone. Now that they were all back home again from church.

All in black clothes. Because of.

Because Grandad was.

Dead.

*

The parlour was filled with chattering. Aunties were going round with pieces of cake, sandwiches, teacups, not even waiting to take off their hats and coats. Strangers were sitting there, eating hard, gobbling down mouthfuls in a roomful of clatter and noise.

'Well, I declare! Is that baby Bobby? He *hev* grown!'

Unknown aunties squeezed him against their corsets. 'You remember aunt Edie, don't you? Of course you do.'

They smelt of face powder and mothballs, and there were crumbs of seedcake on their whiskers, and they had great glass baubles skewered through their hats. Unknown uncles sat balancing a plate on one knee and a cup and saucer on the other, red farmworker's faces swollen with the effort. Uncle Lionel and uncle Sim kept springing the glass of their fob-watches open, and asking each other what they made the time. Grandad was in a nightshirt in a box in a hole in the churchyard, and here they all were eating and talking and auntie Eva was bringing in the jelly now.

He sat in a corner by the window and stroked the flowerpot that Grandad had dipped in cement and decorated with little bits of broken china, blue and gilt and rose-patterned. He'd never thought before how beautiful it was. Flies were buzzing in the windowpanes, and there was a smell of geraniums.

*

They planted a briar rose on Grandad's grave by the east wall of the church. And when next he went to Cambridgeshire, Nanny and the aunties and uncles were settling down in a bungalow four villages away, with electric light, and mains water in a cast-iron pillar outside the gate. Before a dozen years were out, the Red Lion had been deconsecrated, and Rectory Farm was a bulldozed ruin of clunch and chimney bricks and plaster. The wooden privies and the rose-briars smoked together in a bonfire, and the apple trees of paradise were stacked in logs for the landlord's hearth. Only the chickens remained where the farm once stood, penned in their grizzling thousands in a row of corrugated broiler houses.

PC Robert Kitchener Druce

7

UNDERTONES
OF WAR

And now the daily truths of death and sex were edging closer, try as his parents might to protect him from reality.

Back in the playground at Consort Road with a black diamond stitched to the sleeve of his coat in remembrance of Grandad, he became matter-of-fact about the facts of death, a consultant on its mysteries. Wasn't his father a policeman? And wasn't it his father's job to lug puffed-up bodies out of forest pools, and faces beefsteak-red out of the hiss of gas cookers? It was, it was.

And I bet you never knew that before they gassed themselves, people put cushions on the floor and inside the oven. That was because then they could crouch down and die in comfort. And it's true about the beefsteaks: coal gas colours your blood bright red. Not that his father discussed such matters in front of him. But you eavesdropped, you overheard, you listened, and you put two and two together.

In Standard II there was girl called Janey who sometimes fell down in frothing fits on the floor. One playtime she wandered away and nobody missed her until third lesson. Mrs Baldwin sent groups of older children along the roads and into the forest to look for her. She gave PC Druce's son a party of five or six to lead.

All an October afternoon long they quartered the near and not so nearby forest, their brains fraught with the dread of finding Janey dead. He marshalled them beside the forest brook, and sent them to poke with sticks under overhanging roots where a corpse might lodge. He forewarned them of the ravages a water-rat could make on flesh — O, a policeman's son could tell you things about *that*! From Sandpit Plain to the Hollow Ponds they tramped alongside the noisy waters.

At the Hollow Ponds he ordered them off to search for a glimpse of sodden clothing or the gleam of a naked limb beneath the floating leaves and duckweed. Moments later Kenny Woods ran back to him in panic; he reckoned he'd seen a three-foot-long jack pike smacking its lips.

With empty hands and a skullful of nightmares apiece, they trailed back to school and still no word of Janey. At assembly next morning it all turned out to have been a false alarm, and Janey had just wandered away and caught the bus to her auntie's.

Well, all right. Janey was just one that the rats and the crows and the old men and the water hadn't got. So far. There'd still be plenty to come who weren't so lucky. You ask Roy Shotley. He'd tell you the same, his dad was a policeman too.

*

And anyhow what about that shopkeeper who gave all his ice cream away?

There was a shop at the foot of St Anne's Hill that had a curse on it. Wedged between a baker's where the yeasty warm air made you swallow your spit, and a boisterous, joke-cracking greengrocer, the middle shop changed its name and identity every few months. Wool shop, cycle shop, newsagent, outfitter: each metamorphosis seemed equally, pointlessly doomed. It was as if there wasn't a shred of goodwill for sale. *Ill-wishing*, more likely.

For weeks and months at a time it stood empty, with paint flaking, dirt and spiderwebs clotting the window. Then suddenly a pair of cheery newcomers would be scouring the place from roof to cellar and getting a new name painted over the door — 'Regency Outfitters', 'Sweets and Smokes', 'The Gold Mine', — and setting out the shiny displays that the commercial travellers carried inside in armloads.

But even the names the newcomers chose had the smell of failure about them. The bright crêpe-paper window-dressings faded and sagged in winter fogs and the fumes of cooking from the living-quarters at the back. Bluebottles fizzed in the window for a day or two in summertime and lay there, lodged against the glass with their toes turned up. Before long the shopkeeper and his wife were quarrelling openly in front of the customers. The stock grew stale, unsaleable. *He* would appear unshaven, *she* with her hair in curlers. If either were loitering in the doorway when the children pelted down the hill to school, they got a wide berth.

And then it wouldn't be many weeks before the place reverted to its abandoned state, with a window full of dead insects among the torn paper and cardboard, and a litter of dereliction inside the empty shop.

In 1937 for perhaps half a year, the place struggled slowly downhill towards bankruptcy as a sweetshop — how could it prosper, rank with the smells of shag tobacco and boiled cabbage? — until the afternoon of the miracle. As Bobby rounded the corner past the Royal Arms, children were running back down the hill, bringing the glad tidings to their friends and then turning back up the hill again. He ran on among them, and fought his way into 'The Gold Mine', where the shirt-sleeved and collarless proprietor was putting ice-creams into fingers as fast as they could snatch them.

But *why?* There had to be a reason. Shopkeepers? Twisters, the lot of them, his father said. They wouldn't give you the smell of an oil-rag.

When his turn carried him to the front and he came face to face with the shopkeeper, he knew that something was wrong. Their eyes met, and the man's eyes were bright with tears. At his own side and over his shoulders fingers were stretching out to clutch and voices calling. 'There you are, son,' said the man, pulling two ribbons of paper apart and making a cylinder of strawberry ice-cream strip itself naked on the counter top.

He looked into those eyes again, as the man prodded a cone over the cylinder, and held it out to him. 'Ask me, ask me why,' begged the tear-filled eyes. But he answered, bracing himself among the jostling shoulders, 'Can I have another for my friend?' He took it, elbowing his way out of the shop, and hurried back down the hill to look for Roy.

By the time he had found Roy and they were back at 'The Gold Mine', the riot was already over, sweet-jars and refrigerator emptied, the blind behind the door pulled down. He was cross that he wasn't there when the fun came to an end.

But he could not shake off a foreboding. Nor free himself from the guilt of refusing to answer those tear-filled eyes.

When he got home, he told his mother about the man, wanting her to ask about it all and understand. But she could only be angry that he had demeaned himself by taking charity.

'When you want an ice-cream we will buy it for you,' she said. 'What would people say? Think of your father's position!'

Days later his own name caught his eye in the *Clarion & Weekly Advertizer* before his mother had had a chance to read the paper and hide it. And then he learned how the story ended.

What with the miraculous debauch and then hearing no sound from the neighbouring shop, the greengrocer grew suspicious and telephoned the Police Station. It was PC Robert Druce who broke a pane of glass in the back door and found the shopkeeper's body dangling from the banisters.

*

Now nine months later a huddle of mothers stood amongst swaggering children here in this same shop, commandeered and freshly distempered by the Council. With his mother he joined them, coming to be fitted for his gasmask.

For days air-raid officials had been going from house to house showing parents how to fit the masks. Was it their demonstration masks, wet with condensed breath and passed on from child to child, which spread the sudden outbreak of diphtheria? A letter-writer to the *Clarion & Weekly Advertizer* thought so, though the notion was scouted by the powers-that-be. Yet by mid-November there were forty-six cases and three children dead, Eileen among them.

That afternoon he wrenched away from his mother's grasp, to giggle among his school mates at their fat-pig cheeks and tin-can snouts and misty oblongs of celluloid to squint through, as they all sucked noisily in and blew out hard to make the rubber fart. A few still maskless children were fidgeting in line while their mothers watched and waited.

His own turn promised to be a long time coming, and he edged his way to the inner door and out into the back of the shop, to see for himself where the man had hanged himself. He was studying the stairwell and the darkly-varnished banisters when his mother snatched him away to take his place to be transmogrified.

With buckles and rubber straps in his Strewelpeter hair and a brand-new cardboard box on a string, he rejoined the farting roisterers.

Throughout the late summer and autumn of 1938, the daily talk was all of war. Air raid shelters and static water tanks of brick and concrete were mushrooming up in streets and playgrounds on every side, and soldiers came to dig trenches opposite the Plume of Feathers. For the children of Sparrowfield Lane here were new and exciting playgrounds. Utterly forbidden, all of them.

In late October there was another novelty to contemplate at Consort Road. The authorities laid on school meals so that mothers would be free for war work. The meals cost twopence a head, and there was no longer any need to traipse home and back at midday.

Every afternoon the reek of cabbage and boiled mince lingered on the classroom air. Twice a week, with clockwork regularity, boiled rice was ladled out for afters. Watery thin as it was, it always tasted of burnt milk. But there were bloated sultanas adrift in it, and Tomlins and Milligan always counted theirs and punched each other over who got the most.

Still chewing the last mouthful, he would mumble through the second Grace and escape with the others out of the gates and into the forest for the rest of the dinner hour. Unless it was raining and they were sent to sit in the cloakrooms.

At the turn of the year three lectures on Air Raid Precautions, Entrance Free All Welcome! were advertized at the Regal and stirred up a public row. Letters to the *Clarion & Weekly Advertizer* signed 'Pro Bono Publico' and 'Major, MC, Retired' deplored even the mention of ARP. The populace would panic, the Major asserted. What measure had the authorities in mind to cope with *that?*

The local Council drew up plans to evacuate children under fourteen, mothers of children under five, the elderly, the infirm. But who would go first? And where? In the Village anger and anxiety ran high, and the public meeting called to discuss the matter broke up in disorder.

O, the cowards and the bullyboys were showing up in their true colours, make no mistake, said PC Druce.

It wasn't long before their journeys to and from Consort Road were taking its pupils past walls of sandbags, and shops whose plate-glass windows were varnished and criss-crossed with ribbons of canvas.

Shopkeepers — 'What did I *tell* you?' growled PC Druce — stood in front of emptying shelves and practised how to fold their arms and be disobliging, while housewives hurried from shop to shop and bought three times the provisions they needed, and hoarded them. When a man came to read the gas-meter at 99 Sparrowfield Lane, he couldn't see past the barricade of flour and sugar and dried fruit that Mrs Druce had built in the cubby-hole under the stairs. He stood tapping his foot while she made a gap in the stack for him to shine his torch through.

What was going to happen? Why? Nine years old, he wanted to know.

'When you need to know something, your mother and I are the people to ask,' his father constantly reminded him. 'We are the only true friends you've got. It's a waste of time going to other people. They'll fill your head with any old lies that suit them.'

But, unflinching in their aim to protect him from anxiety, and truths that might prove dangerous, his parents brushed his questions to one side and made up comfortable falsehoods.

There were hints and threats enough in the newspaper headlines. But when you turned to the cartoon page, Hitler and Mussolini were goose-stepping grotesques, figures of fun, while General Franco was a fat little man with a bell on his hat. Asked about *now*, so many adults harked back to 1914 as if their world had begun and ended then.

Old Mr Ramper leaned on his front gate one afternoon telling Betty's dad about Kaiser Bill. He said, 'He started it orf. Someone should have stuck a bayonet up that old bugger's bum.' Mr Ramper giggled and said it again.

Billy Saxon's mum suddenly announced one morning that she'd lost three brothers on the Somme in that last bloody lot, and ran out into the scullery. She came back wiping her eyes on her apron and told them how she'd seen a German Zeppelin burning in the air. He and Billy shivered, and grinned at one another, and hoped they'd see the same.

But he could find nobody who was prepared to explain the *what* and *how* of war, if it sprang up along St Anne's Hill and Consort Road and Sparrowfield Lane.

'You've got too much spare time on your hands,' his father told him. 'That's your trouble. Leave the worrying to those whose *job* it is to worry. *Your* business is to pass the Scholarship and get to University. Think of the future, my son.'

But it *was* the future he was thinking of. Last week workmen had been going round painting the tops of the scarlet pillarboxes yellow. If Jerry dropped poison gas, the yellow paint would turn blue, said the men, so then you'd know.

As the months passed and rumours multiplied, Village people grew more and more aware of the tiny handful of miles that lay between the Village and the London docks. Those who could afford it sold up and took themselves off to safer places.

And that was how he came to learn the piano.

*

'And you want to learn, don't you?' said his father. 'It's a social asset, you realise that?'

So one afternoon he raced home from school to stroke the veneer of the iron-framed upright his father had got as a bargain at £14 with the stool thrown in. He bruised the chilly front-room air with thuds and twanglings until his father stormed in to put a stop to the din.

'What were my *explicit* instructions? Not until it's been tuned.'

Outwardly it was a handsome enough instrument, with a fretwork of foliage on its panels, and 'Grout, Maker' in gold leaf curlicues. But it needed more than tuning. The hammers and dampers were wormed with mothholes, and the floor inside was littered an inch deep with fluff and rotted felt. While the works were away, he sat creaking the pedals and reaching underneath to strum the wires, whenever PC Druce was safely out of earshot.

After a month the works came back with fresh bright felt glued into them, and elderly Mr Hackamore turned up. Bald and bright-pink faced and grinning with concentration, Mr Hackamore spent from midday to early evening twisting a handle and twangling, and downing endless cups of sugary tea and saying, 'No, thankee' every time Mrs Druce asked him if he'd like to wash his hands.

When at last the old man was out of the front gate, Bobby fisted his way up and down the keyboard until bedtime, trying to match the black and white patterns to the sounds they made. Twice his mother came in and went round the room lifting the fern pots out of their vases, convinced that Mr Hackamore had piddled in one.

*

He started piano lessons every Wednesday after school with Miss Hilda Shuttle LRAM (so the brass plate on her gatepost said), sitting at her side in a roomful of potted ferns and lace curtains and feminine smells. She sold his parents a set of practice books. They were fingered on the antique 'English' system with a '+' to tell you where to put your thumb, and '1, 2, 3, 4' for your fingers. They were as out of date as her parlour.

He couldn't fathom Miss Shuttle. She sometimes seemed reluctant to admit him into the house, although when he was perched at her side she drilled him through Czerny's exercises determinedly enough. But when she welcomed the girl who arrived for her piano lesson immediately after his, Miss Shuttle's lips flew into a smile and her voice was different, throaty and caressing. The older he grew, the odder Miss Shuttle's attitude became. One afternoon he told her it would be his eleventh birthday in five days' time, and she asked him to wait while she wrote a note to his mother.

'Have you been misbehaving yourself?' his mother demanded. 'If not, why *this* all of a sudden?'

Miss Shuttle wished to discontinue the lessons; she had taken Robert as far as lay in her power.

It was an obvious lie.

One by one as their time came she served each of her boy pupils the same jade's trick. But he was glad to be quit of Hilda Shuttle and the musky smells of her parlour and of the accusing way she clutched the neck of her dress when he swivelled round to look at her, as if she had caught him peering into its bony depths.

So he passed on to no-nonsense Miss White, whose pink scalp gleamed through her hair and who fussed like a scalded hen and had her early work cut out to teach him Continental fingering. 'Attack, *attack!*' she insisted, and gently whacked his limp wrists with a ruler until he braced them correctly.

'Any Tomfool can listen, but few know how to hear,' Miss White would say.

She taught him to love Bach and Mozart, though he knew he could never make their magic sound the way he heard it. Years later, when the war was over, Miss White invited him to escort her to the Wigmore Hall. There twice for an instant he would hold the miraculous fingers of Myra Hess in his own.

But here and now, as 1938 slid into 1939, he sat on Tuesday afternoons beside farouche Miss Shuttle, slewing round when she corrected him, blushing and trying not to stare at the whiskers in her armpits, and prodding his way through Czerny. There was a further price to pay in the hours of daily practice. A price unduly high, it seemed, when schoolfriends came to the door and asked if he could go out to play. While his mother turned his friends away, he listened to their voices and plodded through arpeggios and tried to see it all as a social asset. It didn't feel like one.

*

Piano practice for half an hour before tea. An hour of homework before bedtime. But listen to me, my son, as his father never tired of impressing on him, in less than a year he'd find himself in the scholarship class, and the rest of his life would depend on what he did there: 'Now, what time is it? Quick! Good God, boy! here you are already — How old? Nine? — and you still can't tell the time reliably. Let's see how good you are at pounds, shillings and pence.' But fast as he was at words and infallible at spelling, his stomach sank when it came to mental arithmetic. He made a ruin of it, and his father went red in the face.

Night in night out, his father or mother set him sums, and rattled him through the multiplication tables and the Kings and Queens of England and their dates, and demanded to know how many gills there were in an imperial gallon, rods in a furlong, roods in an acre. His handwriting was appalling, a mess of spluttering pothooks where he'd crossed the nib.

His father told him, 'If you are to succeed at University, my God, you'll have to pull your socks up.'

His father's 'if' was not a conditional. It meant 'because'. As long as he could remember, right back to when Bobby ate his meals in a highchair, his father had talked like that. *Asserting* his son's future. '*When* you are at University.'

Each evening now for half an hour by the clock on the mantelpiece — 'And before you start, what's the time now? Quick!' — he dipped his nib and copied line after line of sloping copperplate calligraphy, his tears of childish despair splashing across the paper more often than not.

But copperplate calligraphy, like playing the piano and telling the time, was a social asset. Well, wasn't it?

'One day you'll thank us for all this,' his mother said. 'Now, dry your eyes and try again. For *me*.'

*

All this while the old dispensations had been turning themselves inside out at Consort Road. Where gas mantles had wheezed and flared, electric bulbs now glittered. After twenty-six years, Moggy Jenkins was gone into retirement with a presentation clock. The occasion was reported at length in the *Clarion & Weekly Advertizer*. 'In my eight years on Mr Jenkins' staff, I have never seen him annoyed,' said Mr Parrot in his valediction, closing ranks. 'He has had very little trouble. The boys always rally round.'

The Senior Boys and Senior Girls had all left too, transferred to a brand-new Senior School on the newly flung-up River estate half a mile away. And within a month or so of Moggy's leaving, Mrs Baldwin scrambled together the few hundred Junior Girls and Boys and Infants who were left.

She set to work cautiously. One Monday morning they discovered the wire fence uprooted which had separated the boys' playground from the girls'. By Friday, a few adventurers were dashing back and forth across the invisible boundary before the bell for playtime had stopped ringing.

After a few weeks of playtime on a common stretch of asphalt, the classes themselves were mingled and regrouped according to age. Girls — alien creatures who once they left the Mixed Infants had been consigned to a separate fate — now appeared in the boys' school, and began to jostle for space on the school stairs and among the cloakroom pegs. Mr Evans took himself off to another school where he could enthral his pupils with strip farming and Channel Packets. And Mrs Nightingale arrived at Consort Road to face a newly-named 3A, perching at a high desk in a roomful of giggling, blushing, skittish nine and ten year-old girls and boys. There were fifty-five in the class, Bobby Druce among them.

8

THE LAW OF THE JUNGLE

Girls were a problem and womenkind a mystery, the more so when you didn't have a sister around the house. Vice-versa, too. And that was the way most parents wanted to keep things. For as long as possible.

Girls were forbidden guests in 99 Sparrowfield Lane, and in the other homes the Druces moved to. 'When you are twenty-one, and at University, we will be delighted to welcome the girl of your choice into this house,' said PC Druce from time to time, his head still awash with memories of West End Central and his service in the Vice Squad. 'But not before.' He kept his word almost to the hour.

But you couldn't wander in the Forest for many summer days and not somewhere come across a couple lying under a raincoat. Hadn't PC Druce frogmarched Dodger Warren to the Police Station, for creeping close to a courting couple, and hooking away the woman's handbag with his walking-stick? But Dodger Warren's goings-on were secrets that only Roy Shotley, a policeman's son, was qualified to share. And it still didn't explain what 'courting' meant.

The day came when Roy and he lay in the long grass of Maze Hill, hooting like owls through their cupped hands, a skill they'd only just acquired. You could imitate a cuckoo, too, once you'd caught the trick of squeezing your palms towards one another, to alter the shape of the hollow space. Luxuriously, they lay in sunshine, listening for the afternoon school bell. They pursed their lips against their thumbs, and savoured every passing minute.

When the bell began they rose and ran up the flank of the hill and down towards the pollard hornbeams and the holly bushes. Suddenly Roy flung out a hand to stop him. There was a couple lying under a holly tree ahead of them who hadn't covered their nakednesses with a coat. Roy and he stood stock-still to watch. Then Roy suddenly went crazy and called out, 'Mister, do you like what you're doing?'

The man sprang up, fumbling with the front of his trousers, and shrieking, 'Get out of it. Get out of it.' The woman made no attempt to cover herself but lay where she was and opened her eyes and shut them again and suddenly squealed with laughter. Roy and he lingered an instant to stare at her long bare legs and the clump of darkness between them. Then they took to their heels as her lover ran towards them, wrenching up feeble sods of moss and raining them at their vanishing backs.

All through the afternoon they caught each other's eyes across the classroom and ducked down under their desklids to giggle. Mr Evans was bewildered by what had got into them, and kept them in after school. When he demanded to know, they could only collapse in mirth. At last he let them go, and they went back to the holly tree again, and stood there meditating, until their hunger told them it was time to hurry home.

But something had to be done to advance into the mystery, and one Saturday they blarneyed Elsie Charlock, two years younger than they were, to pull her knickers down in the hollow oak in the hilly fields. 'All right,' she said, and brushed aside any further talk.

Roy and he took turns to look and to keep guard, and he was first. Elsie wouldn't pull her navy-blue knickers down, and only prised them to one side. 'There. See?' she said. A lump of dough, he said to himself. Then it was Roy's turn to look and his own turn to keep guard.

He climbed up onto a hunch in the oak-tree bole, and gazed out across the meadow. Bottle Atkins's cows were mouthing the stream less than ten yards away, strings of their spittle curdling down into the water.

A lump of dough.

Roy took a long time looking. Then he straightened up. 'All right, Bob,' he said. 'I seen it.' And they all three scrambled out of the hollow tree.

Elsie tugged her skirt straight and skipped away along the path that ran at the back of Mrs Slade's chrysants, while Roy and he made their way to the cesspit field and Sparrowfield Lane.

A lump of warm, pale dough. 'You took a long time,' he said, grudgingly.

Roy stopped and slowly turned towards him. His eyes were stretched wide. 'I kissed it... she pulled down her drawers and said kiss it.'

A lump of warm, pale dough, with a slit in it.

*

Girls couldn't keep secrets, he should have remembered that. The forbidden knowledge brought guilt and violence in its wake. A few days later Alfie Charlock accosted him.

'Give us a ride on your bike, or I'll tell your Dad you fucked my sister,' he said.

Alfie Charlock didn't own a bike.

'I *never*,' he answered. But he couldn't be sure he *hadn't*. 'Fuck' was a word that people wrote on walls, and who was to say what it really meant? He felt his face flooding with incandescent guilt, as Alfie wrenched the handlebars out of his grasp and pedalled away in triumph.

The blackmail went on for a month. Alfie wanted bike-rides, sweets, money: while his own pathetic counter-threats were of no avail. Alfie had a trick of wrestling you down and banging your head on the ground. But one day it all came to an end.

It was getting close to teatime and Alfie Charlock was sitting on his chest and pounding the back of his head onto the dried-out earth under the oak tree near the hilly-fields stream. It was the second time in less than a week, and the twentieth time in nightmare. But then at last fortune took a hand.

Suddenly, as Alfie leaned back for an instant, he found he could curl his own legs up around Alfie's body and, getting a purchase, slam him backwards in his turn against the hardened earth. While Alfie was still winded he was kneeling astride him, crouching forward beyond the reach of Alfie's writhing legs as he tried to use the same trick. Now his own knees were bruising Alfie's arms and shoulders into the ground, and he had a grip on Alfie's ears and Alfie's head was thumping down into the dust and the litter of acorn cups.

A dozen bangs for the weeks of blackmail. Another dozen for his sister's betrayal of the secret. A dozen bangs for the navy-blue knickers that she wouldn't pull down for him, though she'd pulled them down for Roy and told him to kiss her. Crash and crash and crash for the sweets and the pennies and the blackmailer's bike rides. Crash and crash for the scratch and dent in the mudguard where Alfie had deliberately banged it against old Bottle's gate hinge. Crash for the way that Alfie grinned when he saw his victim coming.

Thud and thud and thud of Alfie Charlock's skull among the acorn cups, until his own wrists ached and tears were spurting out of Alfie's eyes and splashing into the dust, and Alfie had given up trying to wrestle himself free. Thud and thud until his own anger had rinsed away into disgust and he thought he might as well stop.

He stood back and watched Alfie clamber along the ground like a newborn calf in its struggle to stand, and stagger forward. Then Alfie turned and shrieked at him, but his voice was blurred and the words made no sense. So he rushed at Alfie again with his fists clenched and Alfie turned and ran away diagonally across the field, ignoring the path, running on blindly through the thistles and buttercup stalks that clattered across his boots, sobbing bitterly, his eyes still spurting tears that splashed down his jersey. His conqueror ran ten feet behind him, shouting in triumph, bending down to rip dried cakes of cow dung from the brittle white grassblades that grew up through them, and running closer to fling them so that they burst apart and spattered Alfie's neck with crumbling filth.

He abandoned the pursuit when Alfie drew level with Bottle's yard and perched himself, out of breath, on the front gate of number 99. He kicked the fencepost to set himself swinging, and watched Alfie blindly lurching along the pavement, his still-jangling head throwing his legs out of balance.

He fetched his bike from the shed once Alfie had vanished indoors, and scooted it up and down past the Charlocks' alleyway for ten minutes at a stretch, ringing the bell. Nobody came out. After piano practice he went down to Roy's to tell him he'd bashed up Charlock, and there'd be no more blackmail.

*

He became a choirboy at St Anne's. He wore a cassock and a starched white surplice and carried a candle at Mattins and Evensong as the all-male choir processed out of the vestry and into the echoing spaces of the church. His senses tingled, as pious talk and its admonitions were all swept away into the music and the great tides of his pounding blood.

He longed to carry the great brass cross and lift it high among the roof-beams. Or, better still, to be thurifer and swing the incense-burner on its chains, wreathed in sweet smoke. A public, incantatory role. To move through the focus of, but himself looking away beyond, attention. Nine years old, he fumbled among words and tried to pinpoint the mood that possessed him then. Exultant. Sanctified. Sacred.

To him it was sheer theatre, abstract in its purity. And the massy candlestick, and his fingers clasped about it and the flame lolloping high above the level of his eyes, were a beginning.

Sunday by Sunday it was a fearful exultation, treading the razor-edge of terror. For somewhere, anywhere, God's shiny china eyeballs were staring down. And God knew what you were up to, at every moment of the day or night, inside your head.

All the younger members of the choir were in the Wolf Cubs. He joined too, scurrying off every week to St Anne's church hall to play boisterous games, and learn about knots, and sit on the floorboards looking up, as Akela puffed his pipe and told a yarn.

It was his second public membership of an exclusively male society. On Church parades, the cubs marched back and forth from St Anne's church to St Anne's church-hall through a gate in the graveyard wall, moving from high ritual to horseplay and licensed farce. He savoured the freemasonry of both.

Akela taught them campfire songs with roaring choruses. 'Wi' a rum-tum-taddle 'um, Old John Braddle 'um, Hey! What country folks we be!' You didn't get lyrics like that in Singing lessons at Consort Road. Or in the English Hymnal. 'Number twelf, number twelf: If you want any more, you can SING IT YERSELF.'

And then it was time to say the Lord's Prayer and they all made a circle round Baloo who, when he wasn't dressed in his Scout's uniform, was the black-suited curate at St Anne's. 'Hands together, eyes closed. Our Father' — and he glimpsed God again with the white china eyeballs staring out of His head — 'Who art in Heaven…'

His own gaze always fell to Baloo's kneecaps, hairy round bones, naked below the man's shorts. Invariably, with each stressed syllable the kneecaps jerked upward and dropped back again, punctuating the text. The sight was faintly disgusting.

Each week the thought of it disturbed him afresh. And he wondered if Baloo played the same game in church, under his trousers.

Half a lifetime later he thought about Baloo's kneecaps as he stood in school assembly every morning watching 2B's form master, a religious-minded man, punctuate the 'Our Father' with yawns. Every morning, without fail, his scattered words and phrases blurred into an open-mouthed inward snore. And none too quiet, either.

*

Assiduous in acquiring stars and badges, by the summer of 1939 Druce R. had been promoted to Senior Sixer, and flaunted three yellow stripes on the left sleeve of his jersey.

He was invited to play the part of Mowgli, human-child fostered by a wolf-mother, in a show put on by the Scouts. His mother appliquéd patches of woolly brown cloth all over an old undervest and, adding button-holes and buttons back and front in the bottom hem, made a stage costume of it.

Garbed in his camiknicker version of a leopard's pelt, with his elsewhere naked body stained the colour of cocoa, he trod the boards of the church-hall stage, Mowgli the man-cub and cock of the walk. A frame of mind properly to be deplored. But Senior Sixer and master-to-be of the Indian jungles, he was boyhood's pattern — thanks to Lord Baden-Powell and Rudyard Kipling — of every member of a Wolf Cub pack.

But 'a man-cub is a man-cub, and he must learn *all* the Law of the Jungle', Kipling had insisted. And in 1939 as the summer holidays drew near, the St Anne's pack was torn apart and nothing was ever the same again.

One evening he was dressed for cubs and anxious to be off, when his father, still in uniform, sent his mother upstairs and sat down in an armchair behind the table. 'I want the truth,' he said. 'Now stand up straight and look me in the eye. Has this Akela of yours, or whatever he calls himself—'

'Akela.'

'Don't interrupt me!' His father was shouting. 'Listen. Has this Akela ever tried to touch you?'

'Touch me?'

'Touch you. *There.*' He gestured. 'On your private parts. Look me in the eye. *Has* he? Tell me the truth.'

'No.' He felt the blood rush into his face.

'No? Is that what you are telling me?'

'Yes.'

'Yes, *what*? Yes, he touched you? Or no, he didn't touch you?'

'He didn't touch me.'

'Never? Are you telling me the truth? If you're lying I'll find out, you can be sure of that, my son. Stand up straight and take your hands out of your pockets. Now, I'll ask you again, did he ever touch you? Well? Well? Did he ever ask you to touch *him*?'

And so the interrogation continued, circling over and over, circumstance after circumstance, as the hands of the clock moved on.

'Are you telling me the truth? I'll ask you once more: did he ask you to touch *him*? Did he touch *you*?'

And 'No' and 'No' and 'No', he answered, standing to attention before the table. He felt himself choked by the coloured scarf around his neck, and his body was burning hot inside the jersey with its badges and tawdry yellow stripes.

The violence of his father's manner made him weep.

'What's the matter with you? You're telling lies, aren't you? Aren't you? Aren't you?'

His father was enraged, out of control, and he was terrified of what he might do.

'If I thought that swine had so much as — I'd swing for him. I'd smash him to pieces.' And he could. He'd boxed for his Police Division and was an instructor in ju-jitsu. 'Now, I'll ask you once again. Has he ever touched you? Has he ever asked you to touch him?'

He *hadn't*. O, *please*. It was the truth. *He hadn't*. And finally, when almost a quarter of an hour an hour had passed, his father accepted what he said.

'Very well, I'm prepared to accept your solemn word. Now you can go and get that uniform off. There'll be no more cubs for you.'

*

He heard from the others what had happened. Akela had put his hand up Bobby Gutteridge's shorts one night and felt his johnny. Bobby Gutteridge had told his dad and his dad had gone to the Police station about it. So *that* was it. That was why his own father had interrogated him like an executioner whose obsession makes him crave to hear the worst. That was why he himself had had to swear on his bible honour that Akela had never touched him.

But Akela *had*.

Is it likely that, when he went to change into his Mowgli vest, the man wouldn't follow and fondle him? Of course he did. They had been undemanding caresses, in no way menacing although unasked for and unreturned. What had been truly terrifying was his father's almost slavering inquisition. For days the memory of that voice went on hammering questions inside his head.

With his back against the wall as it was, he had not dared to answer 'Yes'. He had had to hide the truth for, nine years old as he was, he knew that his father could not be trusted with it. In that half-insane state, what might he not do? For his own sake, he must not know.

No criminal charge was brought against Akela, but he silently vanished from his post, and Baloo took over until another Akela could be found. And after a fortnight of pleading, PC Druce relented and allowed his son to go to the cub meetings.

Mr Cutler, the new Akela, was a married man, with a thirteen-year-old daughter. Austere in manner, he barked out orders every week with no show of friendliness. But he asked the Sixers round to his home one Saturday, and there they met his wife and daughter. Faced with a gaggle of boys, both were as pimply-faced and as cool and distant as the man of the house. At some point during the visit, Mr Cutler told the boys that he took a cold bath every single morning of the year.

One by one he looked them in the eye. That was the sort of discipline that sorted out the strong men from the weaklings! In winter he broke the ice on the tub before hopping in.

Was he asking for their admiration?

His Senior Sixer looked at Mr Cutler, with his blue chin and bobbing Adam's apple, and pictured him naked, all bluish gooseflesh amid slivers of ice. He shuddered and was appalled.

*

Soon love was to strike him down like a bolt of lightning.

When the new Autumn term was only two days old at Consort Road, and the boys and girls of 3A were still strangers to one another, he came face to face on the stairs with Dawn Andersen, the blonde and blue-eyed only child of a Danish sailor and an English mother. Forgetting the world around him, he fell fathoms deep in love.

Her scribbled note, 'I love you, too', passed on by a go-between in answer to his, almost split his senses apart with joy and terror. After school that day he snatched a kiss among the coats in the cloakroom, and then walked home with her, trailing half a mile to the River estate and loitering in talk with her as the daylight faded, before traversing Consort Road once more on his way to Sparrowfield Lane at the opposite end of the Village.

He was distraught and feverish at teatime, and quite unable to account for himself. His mother put him to bed with a cold compress on his forehead, and rubbed his chest with Vick, in case he'd caught a germ. It was hours before his lovesickness would let him get to sleep. How could a look and a voice send you up in flames like a handful of straw?

Days later Dawn was sitting at his side on a bench drawn up to the table in the dinner hall. They had become inseparable at morning break and dinner time. Between mouthfuls of sultana-studded rice, she whispered, 'Shall I show you where I had my siss cut out? Look!' She slid her skirt up to her waist and turned to him, touching the tiny scar where a cyst had been lanced, high inside her thigh.

'See?'

To his dazzled eyes her skin seemed to glow from within, as though it were some sort of magic metal or condensed sunlight. His heart was suddenly pounding, and his breath caught in his throat.

'What's a siss?'

'Don't know. The doctor said it was a siss. Go on, feel it.' Her voice caressed him, a husky lilting. 'You can feel a little lump there.'

He was unable to move or speak, dazed by the silent miracle of her flesh.

His passion was sudden, an utter, bitterly consuming thing, not to be shrugged away, or changed by a month's reflection. Daily his eyes dogged her about the classroom, his soul brimming, adoring her. By night, he cocooned her with his thought. When school broke up for Christmas, for three long weeks he pined away, gazing into the exact quarter of the skyline

— hadn't he set the direction with his father's compass and a map? — across Bottle Atkins's meadow and just to the left of the hilly field thorn, to where she dwelt three miles afar as the lucky crow could fly.

He responded to Dawn with nothing less than worship. Only child and fierce misunderstander of sibling treacheries and reconciliations — How *could* those sisters ever forget such spiteful words? How *could* those brothers stroll off arm in arm before the blood was dry on the noses they had punched? — he was damned from the start. That Dawn should forget his love for an instant was a vision not to be borne: for didn't he centre his waking world upon her, doing whatsoever he did to her great love and glory?

It was a pattern he was to repeat.

*

When she passed him in the playground one morning some months later and did not greet him, his world imploded in a thunderclap. She would not meet his eye in class, and made herself scarce at break and dinner-time. That evening he trailed home late, silent and feverish, having cast himself into the forest leaves to weep. His mother felt his forehead and tucked him into bed with an aspirin and hot milk.

The next day, the innocent flames which consumed them both flared up into a bitter and possessive quarrel such as brotherless and sisterless children, unused to give-and-take, are most inclined to wage, when gentleness turns all to greed. Day by day from that time on they would catch one another's eyes across the classroom but, such had their anguish grown, neither had skill enough to smile. Then at last it was August, and the long summer days gave them a respite from one another's presence, while daily he craved to see Dawn as much as he dreaded meeting her: a frame of mind which he was not to be rid of, all through his adolescent years. Nor, it seemed, was she.

There was a second respite when his last term at Consort Road came to an end, and he took the train each morning to a distant school. But in less than a month the German sea-mine — one of the batch that Herman Goering requisitioned from the German navy — floated down on its parachute and shattered the roof, and the Druces moved to Auckland Drive on the River Estate, not seventy yards away from the Andersen's identical three-bedroom semi in Tasmania Gardens. Standing in the boxroom he could crane his neck and see the pillar-box outside Dawn's gate and her bedroom window above the porch. And the teasing tortures began again.

Sometimes he might make a blind dash down Tasmania Gardens on his bike, but he *never* walked there alone, *never*: however convenient a short cut it might offer. Sent to post a letter, he chose to travel three quarters of a mile in the opposite direction. She, he was to learn, took equally elaborate precautions to avoid *him*. More than once, through chance or through not paying attention, they came face to face in the Village, and each time his bloodstream seemed to explode within him. Later yet, when both were seventeen, they met at a youth club social and were forced to respond.

So he asked her to the Regal and she accepted, and afterwards he walked her home to her door and they talked for a minute or two and kissed goodnight. Both knew it was a mistake. Where lightning had flickered along their nerves, now there was only yawning boredom for both of them.

9

MRS NIGHTINGALE

In 1939 it seemed as though the summer holidays would never come to an end.

Consort Road school broke up on 4th August, and its pupils did not come together again until 30th October. Preparing for war was the first priority. Primary education was not. As far as the authorities were concerned, that is. Mrs Nightingale, as her scholarship class discovered, had other views.

As the year-long breathing-space which followed the Hitler-Chamberlain Munich pact drew to a close, regulations and emergency measures proliferated at every level, and so did the temporary civil servants whose task it was to enforce them. Jacks in office everywhere grew more and more obtuse and fussy: 'It's more than *my* job's worth to authorize that... *I* didn't make the regulations... *I'm* only obeying orders.' Their inward glee was apparent even to a nine-year old.

'Man, proud man,/Drest in a little brief authority,/Most ignorant of what he's most assured,/His glassy essence; like an angry ape,/Plays such fantastic tricks before high heaven,/As make the angels weep!'

He looked on with anxious pride one afternoon as his father roared the text, word perfect, into the astonished countenance of a bloody-minded clerk at the Gas Light and Coke Company Office in the High Road.

Those late summer weeks, and the bitter winter months which followed them, held out a final, teasing chance to explore a vanishing landscape, an occasion to take a lingering last look round. Before all the road and footpath signs were uprooted and stacked in the Council yard. Before the name of the Village was painted out wherever it appeared on shop facades. Before barbed wire, deep ditches, concrete pill-boxes, and anti-tank traps made once-open woodland unapproachable.

Now all the day long he had an eager companion, yellow-haired, bright-eyed and intelligent. Pat. She curled up in an armchair, and eyed his fingers all through piano-practice time. She laid her head on his foot each summer morning and evening as he muttered his way through the homework set by his parents and Mrs Nightingale. She crept onto his bed at night and thumped her tail when he spoke. She fetched her lead in her mouth at intervals during the day and, whenever she could, tugged him out across the hilly fields and into the forest.

Pat, still less than a year old, had been PC Abbott's dog. But, living alone in a furnished room and filled with dread of the coming violence, Mr Abbott had taken to drinking heavily.

Soon close upon a million and a half evacuees would be on the move throughout the kingdom. Already compulsory military service had come into in force for every British male aged between 18 and 41 and not in a reserved occupation. Already the animals Jack Abbott loved were suffering. Soon the strays — and Pat had been a stray before he rescued her — began to vanish from the streets of towns and suburbs. By the 16th September, ten thousand dogs and cats would have been destroyed at Ilford PDSA alone, less than ten miles away from Sparrowfield Lane.

As for PC Abbott, it was only a matter of time before he was officially reported drunk on duty.

The Disciplinary Board gave him no choice: he was ordered to move into the Police Section-House, a barracks for unmarried men. No pets were allowed in the Section-House.

But, as luck would have it, PC Druce was looking for a dog for his son, to act as his bodyguard, and keep him out of solitary mischief. So one evening PC Abbott brought Pat round to Sparrowfield Lane. As parting gifts, he had bought her a new collar and lead, and a bowl of her own marked 'DOG'. When Bobby had promised on his honour to look after Pat and love her, Mr Abbott gave his dog a last hug in the front garden, and turned away through the gate with tears streaming down his cheeks.

*

Less than a month later, at a few moments past 11 o'clock on the 3rd September, tears equally disturbing were streaming down his own mother's face.

German troops had invaded Poland. Adolf Hitler had returned no answer to Neville Chamberlain's ultimatum. Britain and France had mobilized. The breathing-space was at an end at last. Europe, and Sparrowfield Lane, were at war.

His father was on duty, and that Sunday morning Bobby sat in the kitchen with his mother's arm around him. Together they wept, staring at the fretwork veneer of the wireless set, and listening to the voice of Neville Chamberlain.

As his mother switched off, Pat whimpered and jumped up to lick the tears from their faces. Then the Air Raid Warning siren started to wail from the Police box on Silver Hill.

Then nothing happened.

Then the All Clear sounded.

His mother went out into the garden where the neighbours were talking and calling to one another across the garden fences. He and Pat played on the lawn with a ball, but his mother wouldn't let the pair of them outside the gate.

A day or so later, his father came home off duty wheeling a bundle of wooden strips and a roll of tarred paper balanced on his bike. That evening he set about nailing wooden frames together for blacking out the windows. 'The black-out will be official any day now. You can't have a police officer's house showing lights,' he announced. 'Caesar's wife must be above suspicion.'

'Caesar's wife' was a phrase often in his mouth. His own house was the first he checked on Blackout Practice Night in mid-October, peering at it from every angle. Then he went out on his beat, blowing his whistle and shouting, 'Put that light out! Don't you know there's a war on?' and banging on doors. As the war continued, he would ceremonially break in and extinguish the light himself if nobody answered; and declare it all in evidence when the offender was brought up in court and fined.

*

September dragged on, and still the end of the summer holidays seemed nowhere in sight. On October 3rd, Mrs Baldwin was faced with yet another delay, as air-raid shelters were dug in the playground at Consort Road, and the Military and ARP Headquarters moved into the Infants' and Boys'

School buildings. It couldn't be helped. There was a War on. Mrs Baldwin would just have to cram the Juniors, boys and girls, into what had been the Girls' School building as best she could.

When the autumn term began at last on Monday October 6th, she read out her plans for dividing the classes into morning and afternoon shifts, and sent the afternoon shift back home.

Pat, who had slunk away that morning, tail lowered when Bob left the house without her, leapt about in ecstasy when he re-appeared at one o'clock. His father, off-duty, did not. 'If you think you're skipping off out to play about all afternoon, you've got another think coming, my son. Playing is something you can put right out of your mind. You've the scholarship to pass. Don't ever forget it. Your whole future is at stake,' he said. 'And haven't you got homework to do for Mrs Nightingale?'

Sighing, his son fetched the mauve-printed list of questions.

For Mrs Nightingale, faced with forty-six pupils in her Scholarship class, had love and skill enough to cope with harder problems than half-time working. Three or four days a week throughout September, she travelled back and forth, teaching small groups of pupils gathered in the home of one of them. She divided her attention between the River estate, Station Approach and Victoria Road in the middle of the Village, and — a sometimes muted bliss — Mrs Druce's front-room at Sparrowfield Lane.

Whenever it was time for Mrs Nightingale to arrive, he had to show what a help to his mother he could be. It was his task to wax the front-porch tiles with Cardinal Red, and dust the front room, and polish the table and the piano, *and* stop tinkling the keys and close the lid before she had to tell him a second time: this was serious, this was his future, not an invitation to show off, and Pat had better be shut in the kitchen.

Soon the scholarship children from Sparrowfield Lane and Silver Hill and the Lower Road would be straddling in one by one across the scarlet-gleaming tiles, while he watched to see they didn't tread on one on their way to the front room. After a bit they'd hear Mrs Nightingale hanging up her hat and coat in the hall while Mrs Druce welcomed her. His mother always took a last look around the front-room door to see that Mrs Nightingale had everything she needed, and to give Bobby a final frown as a warning. They all settled around the front-room table while Mrs Nightingale handed out their red-ink marked exercise books and her mauve-printed sheet of questions, and told them things to remember. At the end of an hour, Mrs Druce flustered in with a pot of tea for Mrs Nightingale and a plate of cakes and biscuits for everyone. Then they brushed the crumbs off their fingers and settled down to work again.

On one occasion — and he thought it had promised so well! — he stood his latest contraption on the mantelpiece as soon as he heard Mrs Nightingale wiping her feet on the mat. He was itching to demonstrate it.

It was an empty shoe-box with a halfpenny-sized hole cut in one end and, inside, saucers of weak hydrochloric acid and ammonia as a source of smoke. Tap the lid and a fat white smoke-ring shot out straight across the room, continually rolling itself inside-out as it went. Tap again in swift succession, and a second ring shot out and passed, unbroken, through the centre of the first. His mother had forbidden him to bring it down from his bedroom, but he bided his time and smuggled it past her.

When he sent the first ring sailing across the room, Mrs Nightingale smiled and seized the opportunity to discuss the phenomenon. Aha, you *see*? as he knew she would be, she seemed pleased.

Mrs Nightingale's pleasure faded as she passed on to other matters while he still sat there firing smoke-rings at faces across the table, until she snatched up the box and slapped it back on the mantlepiece. He had to be content with nudging eyes across the table with his glances, not willing to let the matter drop.

'*She* seemed in a funny mood when she left,' his mother said later. 'What have you been up to *this* time? Don't you *want* to pass the scholarship?' But Mrs Nightingale was far too courteous a guest to carry tales.

Back at Consort Road, she pinned up progress charts on her classroom wall, divided her scholars into teams, and set them challenges. She drilled them in mental arithmetic and general knowledge until they got the answers right. She taught them how to capture their ideas on paper, and how to punctuate and spell. Even the litanies of collective nouns and threadbare similes that the scholarship required them to get by heart she wove into the magic of her enthusiasm, and they took on new shapes and sense.

'A murder of crows, a deceit of lapwings, an exultation of larks. Just think about those three birds for a minute; and you'll realise how their collective nouns make sense... Now, what about *this*? As bright as a button: I think that must be a button on a soldier's tunic, don't you? As lively as a cricket: how many of you have ever seen or heard a cricket?'

Sitting there on the edge of his seat he thought to himself: hadn't his granny said that his dad was 'as smart as a newly-scraped carrot.'

It seemed exactly right for PC Druce who, razored and spruce, always looked as if he had just sprung out of a bandbox. Who — and only years later did the truth come out — now that his son was old enough to get his hair cut on his own, had instructed every barber in the neighbourhood to listen amiably to the boy's instructions; and give him a short-back-and-sides regardless.

'As smart as paint' seemed dull by comparison with PC Druce. And — no, but *listen,* carrots did look *smart* when you scraped them: and when you scraped *yourself,* the graze *smarted,* too. Well, didn't it?

Above all else, Mrs Nightingale taught them to use their eyes and ears: to look at and listen to the world, and question what they thought they saw or heard. She led them out into the forest to look at trees — beech, hornbeam, alder, ash — and set them to sketch their leaves and fruit and the patterns their branches made when November had blown the leaves away. She had them drawing maps of the streets they lived in, and knocking on doors to find out why houses had been given the names they had.

'Hersanmine', 'The Shieling by the Burn' — that was a Scottish lady's bungalow in Water Lane — 'Enfin'. He thought *that* one must be a mistake for 'Elfin' — hadn't Enid Blyton called *her* house 'Elfin Cottage'? — until Mrs Nightingale told them no, it was French for 'At Last'.

She set them competitions in finding out, and paid for the books she gave as prizes. And for half the books in the classroom library that she arranged in a corner of the room. She paid out her own pennies, too, for the coloured stars which she kept in the pink and gilt tin in her desk, and for which each team struggled so desperately. She paid for the pale slabs of jelly in the meat-dish that she called her 'jelligraph'. She used it for copying their homework assignments and fortnightly tests, and sometimes allowed a chosen few to use it to make a class news sheet.

In a school that lacked even a typewriter, Mrs Nightingale's jelligraph was a casual and worldly magic. It worked with special violet-coloured ink. You wrote onto shiny paper; and where the ink dried out on the paper and your pen-nib, it left a glittering green-gold crust. You had to lay the paper glittery ink-side down on the jelly in the meat-dish, and wait for the jelly to absorb some of the ink before you peeled it off again. Then you smoothed a new damp piece of paper onto the jelly, and it came off again with the writing copied in pale mauvish-violet.

You could make a copy for everyone in the class.

Then Mrs Nightingale melted the jelly down and used it again. As the weeks slid by, the jelly slowly changed colour through a dozen meltings until it was violet all through, and it was time for Mrs Nightingale to buy some more.

*

The winter months of early 1940 were harsh. Saturday 20th January was the coldest day for fifty-nine years. In London the overnight temperature dropped to 3° Fahrenheit — 'would you credit it?', said PC Druce: 'that's 29 degrees of frost.' In the countryside, ground temperatures were as much as nine degrees lower. Stretches of the Thames froze over, and at Dungeness, Folkestone and Bognor Regis, even the sea froze.

By Friday 19th, the playground lavatories at Consort Road had frozen and now were choked and unusable. In the boys' side, the drains were blocked with glass-hard yellow ice, and icicles hung from cisterns burst by frost. Half-way through the morning, the classes were assembled and sent home through the falling snow. 'I expect you all back next week,' Mrs Baldwin said, dismissing them. 'Scholarship class, remember your homework. Now, hurry home. And stay out of the forest, all of you. You can't risk falling into a snowdrift.'

He and Roy Shotley risked it. Plodding home on slushy pavements was too much to ask when each forest twig was piled with snow, and the brook had been transmogrified into fantastic combs of ice. 'See, you could easy break yer leg on the pavement goin' up St Anne's Hill, couldn' ya?' they agreed. 'Nah, it's *safer* in the forest, innit?'

They plodded alongside the brook all the way to Gregories and the reservoir, losing their footing every few yards. Twice they floundered thigh-deep into drifted snow.

At Gregories, the reservoir was frozen a good foot thick; perhaps more. They halted at the edge and peered down through flawed glass at suspended methane bubbles, and at what Roy decided was a motionless pike, and ribboning water weed. Then yard by yard they crept out towards the middle, aware of death underfoot and nervous of the treachery of ice, each daring the other on. Roy trotted a few steps and braced himself to slide.

Soon — in that enchanted place it seemed soon — there was a narrow lane, darkly gleaming across the frost-whitened crystal of the reservoir. Heedless now of danger, alone in the landscape, they both went racing back again and again to run and launch themselves and skim across the surface. Their woolly gloves and coats, sodden with snowballing up and down Consort Road ever since Mrs Baldwin had let the classes out of school, and drenched again in the drifted snow along the brook, now froze as the east wind rose and grew colder.

The ice sang under the thin leather soles of their shoes, and snow-dust sprayed their ankles through the check and turn at the end of each breath-taking slide. Their toes and fingers froze and ached and then grew burning hot. Their noses snivelled with cold and they wiped them as best they could on the back of their gloves. Their cheeks flamed.

As dusk fell, the darkness between the beeches rang with their shouts and the hollow, reedy cry of the ice. The grassy slopes of Gregories flung that music back in interlocking echoes.

The stars had risen and hung above the trees before the spell was broken. Then cold and hunger reminded them of tea-time, and of the fury of worried mothers. And then there was only time for one last slide before they panicked and scampered through the snow-covered leaves towards Almshouse Green and Sparrowfield Lane.

After tea, his mother packed him straight off to bed as a punishment. But he went on skidding and sliding by starlight in his dreams.

The cold brought the the phony war in Europe almost to a halt. But winter had not done with them yet. On the morning of Sunday, January 28th, people stared out through frost-ferned panes at a world once again transformed. All through the night there had been an east wind and a gentle rain, sifting down onto frozen surfaces. Grass-blades, branches, telephone wires were all coated with a shell of ice — 'frozen frost' or '*verglas*' the daily papers called it — half an inch thick in places, as though they had been embedded in molten glass. The ground beneath trees was littered with broken twigs and branches, torn off by the weight of ice. Telephone lines sagged in impossible curves, or lay along the ground, ripped away from the insulators.

When Consort Road school officially reopened, the roads and pavements were already choked again with a fresh fall of snow, and there was a freezing fog that grew white whiskers on your eyebrows and on your woolly scarf where you breathed through it. Few children turned up at Consort Road. By the end of the week, the playground lavatories had frozen again, and the school was closed once more to all but the scholarship class. For them the examination was fast approaching, and there followed a week of shivering lessons in an otherwise deserted building. They shared the staff lavatories: an intimate privilege, Mrs Baldwin made it clear, which they were on no account to abuse.

*

With the thaw and the spring, the war began again in earnest.

Mrs Nightingale hung a map on the classroom wall with little coloured flags on pins that marched along in lines. Different patterns of red, white and blue in the Union Jacks and the flags of France and Holland; black, red, and yellow for Belgium; black swastikas on white and red for the enemy. Day after day and inch by inch, the little coloured flags changed places as Mrs Nightingale's pupils plotted their paths across Europe.

Then at last and too soon for 4A, their own day of reckoning arrived. Alongside scholarship candidates from adjacent villages, and according to sex, they trooped along in their Sunday best to the Girls' High School at the centre of the Village, or the High School for Boys at Monkswood, a bus ride, then a train ride and a half-mile-long walk away from Sparrowfield Lane.

Roy Shotley and he stuck close together. They were over-awed by the red-tiled locker rooms and glittering parquet floors of Monkswood County High School; by the rituals of the scholarship examination; by the grave speech of the black-gowned masters who guided them. *But where were their mortar-boards? Had they left them in the cupboard with their canes?*

Once inside the building, the candidates spoke, if at all, in whispers.

'It's your future and your livelihood that are at stake today: remember that.' His mother's kiss and his father's parting words echoed along his nerves as he slid into his place, and waited for the signal to begin.

At lunch-time — and *that* was a new word to notice: at Consort Road the midday meal was called 'dinner' — at *lunch*-time they swallowed their sandwiches and were sent out to play. Roy and he, striking back against the awe they felt, interlaced their arms and tied their inner ankles together with a handkerchief and galloped three-legged around the playground.

A blue-chinned and black-gowned figure strode across the asphalt and ordered them to behave themselves.

'Well? Well?' said his father when he got home, draggled and dusty and with his brain ablaze. But all he could coherently remember was his answer to the English composition topic: 'A journey by train'.

That had been the most promising subject on the list of topics. See, he could describe the travellers and their talk as the carriage, lit by a dim blue bulb, went a pilgrimage through unmarked wartime stations. When you ran short of ideas about a character, you could put him off at the next halt, and bring somebody else aboard. You could stop the train in a smoky tunnel and set all the travellers chattering. Or hold them up with an air-raid. He was still scribbling at top speed when the invigilator's voice broke in, telling them they had a minute left.

His carriageful of character-sketches arrived unscathed at the terminus; and he had used 'extremely' — the current favourite among all his adverbs — an impressive number of times, he thought. He glowed as he knotted his additional answer-book to the first, with the scrap of whitey-brown string a black-gowned master fetched for him.

'I see,' said his father. 'And what do you think are your chances? Are you going to be riding the new bicycle I promised you: *provided* you pass?'

There were weeks to get through before anyone would know for sure.

On 8th and 9th April, Hitler's troops invaded Denmark and Norway, and now the pins and little coloured flags streamed northwards. Exactly three weeks later, a new railway-station was officially opened in the Village. It was fashionably aerodynamic, built in streamlined concrete. 'Go and take a good look at it,' sneered the voice of William Joyce, broadcasting from Nazi Germany a few nights after the ceremony. 'It won't be there much longer.'

'Aw, you don't want to take no notice of old Lord Haw Haw,' said Mr Ramper. 'What does that treacherous bugger know about it?'

But wasn't it enough that he *did* know? And that somewhere in the Village there must have been an enemy spy to tell him?

On May 14th, the leading troops of Hitler's Panzer columns crossed the Meuse and stood gazing into France. Faced with obliteration city by city, Holland had no choice but to surrender on May 15th. A fortnight later

King Leopold of Belgium made peace with the invaders. And now it was the turn of the little black, yellow, and red flags to be popped back into Mrs Nightingale's cardboard box.

In May Mr Hackett, sole proprietor, printer and reporter of the *Clarion and Weekly Advertizer*, could congratulate himself on a scoop in his one-man war on crime. Alfred Charlock, aged 33, was found staggering along St Anne's hill, drunk and with his clothing heavily soiled with mud. He was taken into custody and spent the night shouting and kicking the door of the cell until they took his boots away. In that same month, in another world, the gates of Auschwitz-Birkenau first stood open. But who was there in the Village to write or read about *that*?

Across Mrs Nightingale's map the swastikas swept on through Picardy, reaching the Channel within a week.

Picardy? But, please Miss, *that* was a favourite song of his father's: 'Roses are flowering in Picardy; but there's never a rose like *you*'. 'Yes, quite,' said Mrs Nightingale.

Through Picardy and Normandy the Union Jacks converged towards the blue of the English Channel at terrifying speed, while German troops crashed on through Calais and Boulogne, and headed towards Dunkirk. But when at last they entered the town on June 4th, the evacuation of the British Expeditionary Force was miraculously complete, and the beaches were littered with piles of abandoned equipment.

Six days later, Mussolini picked a promising moment to enter the war on the winning side, and now there were more pins and bright new flags to slither around in the cardboard box. On June 22nd, German and French officers signed their armistice.

By Hitler's orders, the same carriage on a railway siding at Compiègne was used for the ceremony of surrender that had been used for the signing of the previous Armistice, an armistice that had brought to an end 'the war to end all wars', ten years before the oldest child in Mrs Nightingale's class was born.

'He's rubbing salt into the wounds,' Mrs Nightingale explained. 'He wants to wipe out Germany's humiliation then.'

*

Four of them, Roy Shotley and the Gutteridge girls and Bobby Druce, were toiling up Black Mutton Hill, a selvedge of gardens and houses fifty yards distant from Maids Hill and the forest. They were larking about in July sunshine, trailing home from Consort Road.

Half-way up its length, the steep hill flattened for fifty yards or so alongside an orchard of quince trees where Bobby had gone with his mother the previous autumn to buy quinces for quince jelly. Today the four of them paused at the same spot to draw breath and skirmish again. In a yard beside the orchard, Mr Petts the barber had cut his hair from time to time in a garden shed that smelt of fart, making him wait while men who came in after him got their hair cut first: 'You're in no hurry, boy, are you? No, *you've* got all the time in the world, *you* have, at your age.'

And now a white-faced woman was running up the yard, waving her arms and calling them: 'Quick, quick. Get in here under cover. O, do be quick!'

It was only then that they heard the tiny typewriter rattle of gunfire in the sky, no longer masked by their laughter and the squeals of the girls. Above their heads fighter aircraft were wheeling and diving, signing the air with vapour trails. Fascinated, like rabbits gazing at a stoat, they stood in the road and craned their necks to stare.

The woman ran through the gate and dragged at Roy's arm: 'Quick. Get out of the road before you all get killed. Didn't you hear the air-raid siren? Why didn't you take cover?'

It wasn't into her house that she hustled them, but into the wooden hut that still smelt of fart and hair-oil. She made them sit in a row on the slippery bench, and sat herself down in the barber's chair and watched them in the mirror.

'If Mr Petts was here he'd have something to say to you. He's had to go out for the afternoon. What am I to do if it gets dark before the All Clear goes? I suppose you haven't thought of *that*. I don't know what they teach children these days.'

They sat quiet and tried to listen past her nervous babble for gunfire in the sky.

There were magazines piled on a table. They were ragged and greasy with fingering, and half of them were ripped across, almost back to the staples. The bench was upholstered with woven horse-hair. Where it had frayed, the loose strands stabbed the back of their knees. Every few moments, 'Hark!'

the woman said, suspending her monologue. 'Is that the All Clear?'

After half an hour or more at last it *was*, and they raced away without a thank you, freed from her nagging anxiety. Up to the crest of Black Mutton Hill and pell mell down the other side across Almshouse Green, to Silver Hill and Sparrowfield Lane and home.

To teatime and a romp with Pat, and music-practice and no homework now that the scholarship exam was past. Perhaps he'd get out his conjuring set later on and do a bit of prestidigitation, and after that there might still be time for some chemistry before bedtime.

10

THE YOUNG CHEMIST

Auntie Eva had started him off with chemistry on his ninth birthday, with her present of Sherwood Taylor's *The Young Chemist*. Could she have ever looked beyond the cover? The book was a revelation, a straight-talking, pragmatic manual that nowadays would be hounded off the bookshop shelves by every Safety Committee. It was in the pages of *The Young Chemist* that he'd found instructions for his smoke-ring contraption. But smoke rings were namby-pamby stuff, scarcely worth attention, compared with what the author had to say about fireworks, with all those naked threats like NEVER GRIND POTASSIUM CHLORATE WITH ANYTHING THAT WILL BURN!

There was a whole chapter devoted to fireworks. You had to make cardboard tubes out of glue-soaked paper rolled round a broomstick, and plug one end of each tube with a pellet of clay. You concocted flaring or explosive powders from Dr Sherwood Taylor's recipes, and rammed them down into the tubes.

He made Bengal Lights that briefly lit up the night-time garden of number 99 with an acrid blaze of colour. You had to mix in barium chloride for green, and strontium nitrate for scarlet. His father promised to put the book in the dustbin if he ever caught him at that game again.

You could make gunpowder from a grinding of sulphur, charcoal and potassium nitrate.

Ah, but the problem at ten years of age was to lay your hands on the ingredients. Ask for potassium nitrate and sulphur in one breath, and any pharmacist would read your mind and throw you out of the shop. No, the trick was to distribute your custom among the local chemists, and call potassium nitrate 'saltpetre'.

That was another of the exciting things about chemistry: the changeable names. In an old book his nanny had at Rectory Farm, 'spirits of hartshorn' meant ammonia, 'spirits of salts' meant hydrochloric acid. 'Saltpetre', 'potassium nitrate', 'KNO_3', 'nitrate of potash', 'nitre': all those names meant exactly the same thing. But the last two were old-fashioned; and KNO_3 was too knowing a term: all three could give your little game away.

'Saltpetre? What do *you* want with saltpetre?'

The lady dispenser in the chemist's shop at the foot of Silver Hill glared at him over the flopping gas flame that she used for melting sealing-wax.

'*I* don't want it; my mother wants it for pickling ham.' That was the diplomatic response which got you what you wanted.

'*Charcoal?*' said the man at Boots in the Village.

'Yes. It's for our dog. My Dad says he's got wind.'

'Sulphur?' said the Co-op pharmacist. 'We only sell flowers of sulphur.'

'Ah. Then yes, please, that will do.'

But it didn't. *His* gunpowder never exploded properly. Well, once it did. But without proper rock-sulphur and hours of grinding with a pestle in a mortar — and who could afford a pestle and mortar? — it just flared up and wouldn't go off with a bang.

Empty treacle tins did, though, upended on the gas-stove and filled with gas, which you lit at the little hole you'd made in the lid. When the gas and the incoming air made the right mixture, the lid flew off and clanged against the ceiling.

You could write a message on blotting-paper with a solution of saltpetre: your parents didn't have to be out of earshot for that. When the writing had dried and was invisible, you borrowed a glowing cigarette and touched the spot where you'd pencilled a cross. Or you could focus sunshine on it through a magnifying glass. Then you watched a spark and a smouldering black line retrace the words.

The Young Chemist even took ammonium iodide in its stride. Simply dissolve crystals of solid iodine in concentrated ammonia solution, but NEVER LET IT DRY OUT — IN THAT CONDITION EVEN A FLY WALKING ON IT CAN SET IT OFF! That was a revealed secret as lethal as it was irresistible — if only you could lay your hands on some solid iodine. In 1945 he did, and blew a half-inch hole in an iron ladle with a saltspoonful of the stuff.

You could heat up iron filings and sulphur till they glowed, and drop the residue into acid, and make a stink that had everyone holding their noses.

That was the best thing of all about the book: it understood a schoolboy's cast of thought; and it taught you how to make shift with simple substances and apparatus: spirit lamps in place of bunsen burners; a jam-jar and a sand-tray instead of a flame-proof flask.

TO ETCH ON GLASS: First you hammered a piece of thick lead over a cricket *ball — yes! wasn't there was a strip of lead in the shed? —* to make a dish. He didn't possess a cricket ball, but there was a round stone in the rockery that would do. Next you had to paint a piece of window glass with warmed-up pitch, and scratch your name or a drawing through the pitch once it had cooled. Then you'd be all set to rig it up over your heating apparatus and warm up some hydrochloric acid in the dish with a few teeth, but DO THIS OUT OF DOORS — THE FUMES ARE DEADLY! You rested the piece of glass on top of the dish, and the fluorine fumes would etch your design into its surface where you'd scraped the pitch away.

It was a compelling text. It made him feel grown up, trusted with secrets of chemicals that he must never grind together, and fulminating explosives and lethal fumes. But *teeth?* Hydrochloric acid and *teeth?* 'Beg a few from your dentist,' Dr Sherwood Taylor advised.

With a premonition of the school dentist's likely response, and a vision of hollowed-out stumps spat bloodily into a basin, at this point he always gave up the idea of etching on glass, and thought about something else.

And of course he had the conjurer's black arts to think about and practise.

*

Only a week or so before the day they watched the dog-fight in the sky above Black Mutton Lane, he had been romping with Roy and the Gutteridge sisters in the forest after school as usual, rolling and kicking like puppies in deep drifts of leaves. He snatched up a handful to stuff down somebody's neck, and realised he'd grabbed a pebble along with the leaves. When he shook it free, he saw that it wasn't a pebble but a gold wristwatch on an unfastened strap. 'Ooh, you lucky thing,' said one of the girls. 'Finders Keepers: Losers Weepers.'

'No, if you find anything you've got to hand it over at the Police Station,' he said, and Roy echoed him, and they both marched off through the leaves, the girls trailing behind.

At the Police Station the desk Sergeant received them with grave courtesy. 'You're young Bob Druce,' he said. 'And what can I do for you, sir? And, wait a minute: aren't you PC Shotley's lad?' He took the watch and asked exactly where and when it had been found, inscribing his answers in a book. If no-one claimed it within three months, the watch would become young Bob's property.

That night his father came indoors from Late Turn and demanded the truth. 'What's all this about you going to the Station behind my back? A gold wristwatch. Why didn't you bring it to *me*? I come along off duty, in all innocence, and find my own name in the Lost Property book.'

'O, no. What's this?' chimed in his mother. 'What have you been up to this time?'

'I only did what you're always saying people *ought* to do if they find anything,' he said, and marched off to his bedroom, closing his ears to the pursuing voices.

Soon after that, he received an official letter notifying him that the lost property had been identified and claimed. His father told him that an engaged couple, on holiday in the Village, had lost it more than a year before. O well then, that was that.

But a few days later, there the couple were at the front door of number 99. They'd already collected the watch and taken it to a jeweller's. Despite the winter snowdrifts and the thaw, it was in perfect working order; not a speck of rust was to be found. His mother gave the visitors tea, and the lady told her they were married now, and the watch had been an engagement present. It was far more than her fiancé could afford, really. She smiled at her husband and he squeezed her hand. Losing the watch had seemed such a dreadful ill omen, she said. And then she had to dry her eyes on her handkerchief.

When shortly afterwards PC Druce, still uniformed, came in, they overbore him in their insistence on giving his son a reward. 'A Police Officer's son does not do things in the hope of a reward,' he told them. But, however diffidently, they insisted, and the husband laid a £1 note on the table, and put his wallet away. 'Very well,' said PC Druce, capitulating at last.

'Now, what are you going to do with all that money, eh? I'll *tell* you, my son. You may spend half of it straightaway, but not a farthing more. Ten shillings goes into your Post Office book first thing tomorrow morning.'

It was wealth untold. He needed no prompting from his father to thank them properly. He lay in bed that night with his thoughts whirling. And the following morning, he stepped out of the Post Office with ten shillings in his pocket and, for five shillings each, he bought a camera and a conjuring-set.

Only when the war had come to an end and there were films in the chemists' shops again, did the little black bakelite camera come into its own. But that very morning he set to work to acquire sleight of hand, legerdemain, prestidigitation — what words, O, with what *words* the book of instructions flattered the future adept!

With the exam behind them, Mrs Nightingale's scholars had leisure to relax and applaud one another's party pieces, and it wasn't long before he was posturing at the front of the class. His conjuring-set was full of a mountebank's trickery.

There was a scarlet ball than stopped at command as it slid down a thread from a hand held high to a hand held at the height of his knee. Child's play: there were holes drilled into the ball which met at an angle to one another, and the thread ran through them. Pull the thread tight and the ball was halted in mid air by friction. 'Halt! Proceed… Halt!' Then you swapped over the position of your hands and did it all over again: 'Proceed… Halt!' If you chose your background carefully, the audience couldn't see the fine black thread.

There were cardboard tubes that you passed through one another, showing them turn by turn to the audience. 'You observe, ladies and gentlemen? Empty, entirely empty.' But with each pass you collected the wire-hooked container full of coloured scarves, or paper flowers, or the water they'd watched you pouring in. After practising for a week or two, you could palm a penny convincingly: 'You agree with me, Sir? There's nothing up my sleeve?' Then you leaned forward, and took the penny out of your victim's ear.

There was a magic wand to tap and wave to distract people's attention. There was a set of cups which the prestidigitator upended and squeezed, turn by turn, to grip and carry away, unseen, the ball he had told the audience to watch so carefully. 'Thimble-rigging', PC Druce called *that* pastime. If you were an adult and he caught you placing bets on it in public, he'd arrest you.

Then there were cards printed with columns of numbers: 'Now, Madam, kindly think of a number between nought and a hundred, and be so good as to write it down. No, *don't* tell me what it is! Now, is your number on that card? And on which other card?' All that the Lightning Mind-Reader had to do was to add the number in each left and right top corner of the chosen cards… Or something of the sort.

Gaze at the ceiling. Close your eyes. Frown, and pass your hand across your brow. Pause.

'Madam, the number I see in my mind's eye is 87. Now would you be so obliging as to read out the number you wrote down?' (O, if only mental arithmetic and pounds, shillings and pence could be as foolproof as that!) 'Ladies and Gentleman: the Magic of the Mind. I thank you.'

He harnessed the resources of chemistry to his sleight of hand. In Dr Sherwood Taylor's book, there was a chapter on indicators: litmus-like compounds that changed colour when you dropped alkali or acid on or into them. Try red rose petals, or red cabbage, the book advised: and before he'd read to the end of the paragraph, he was off and away through the back door to raid old Ramper's cabbage patch again. There was a complex double formula for a conjuring trick: you held up a jug of what you told the audience was water, you rang a bell at it and suddenly it turned blue. But the *Young Chemist*'s intricate formulations of *that* were beyond him.

Phenolphthalein was a lot simpler: you could pour 'water' from a jug into a glass and watch it instantly turn deep magenta. You could paint your nose with phenolphthalein solution and pretend to sniff an ammonia-soaked rose, and your nose would turn bright red. Of course, you couldn't do that trick at the front of a classroom: they'd smell the ammonia. Anyway, how could you keep your eyes tight shut and still watch to see your nose turn red?

He called at Boots the Chemists for half an ounce of phenolphthalein. 'Can you spell it?' said the dispenser, folding up the white powder in a sheet of paper, and sealing the overlap with a blob of sealing wax. He couldn't get it right and was mortified. The moment he got indoors he found the book and practised it, preparing to rattle it off like a machine-gun next time; but nobody ever invited him to spell the word again.

At the close of his act, he twirled his magic wand, 'Abracadabra, Hocus Pocus' and tipped half a jugful of 'the purest water' (primed with phenolphthalein) into 'the purest water' (a weak washing-soda solution). Obediently, the liquids mixed in a swirl of magenta. 'Ladies and gentlemen, I thank you.' He bowed to the applause and the rattling of desk-lids, and blundered back to his own desk, unable to stop grinning, aware that all his skin was flushing crimson in a sudden unbearable joy.

And then one Saturday morning he was trooping off with his parents to Oliver's the Outfitters in the Village High Street, to be fitted out for the grammar school. He had to have a school blazer and football socks and a football shirt striped in Monkswood school colours, yellow and blue; and another football shirt in white and, and, and... Yes, all in good time! He squirmed as Mr Oliver in person looked back and forth from the official list to young master Robert, and whipped his tape-measure into service: 'And, Dad! What about the school cap?'

'You heard your father. All in good time, young sir,' said beaming Mr Oliver.

And a yellow-and-blue-striped tie, and football shorts, and football boots, and gym shorts — 'Ah no, Sir, Madam: I'm afraid it's against the rules of the school to use football shorts for both; or *vice-versa*' — and a gym singlet, and gym slippers. And a dark-blue raincoat, and football socks, and plain grey socks, and plain grey shirts, and *two* new pairs of short grey trousers. And a pullover? 'I'll knit you one,' whispered his mother; 'and I'll knit you a pair of woolly gloves and a scarf.'

'Which just leaves trying on the house shoes,' said Mr Oliver.

House shoes? His stockinged feet rebelled against the dancing pumps that Mr Oliver called 'house shoes'. He wanted to open up the other box again and put on his football boots with that lovely leathery smell and their tight sides and their studs that hobbled across Mr Oliver's carpet. Mr Oliver had slipped a complimentary tin of dubbin into the box for him to grease them with.

But *house shoes?* That was the rule of the school, Sir, Madam: pupils were not allowed walk on the parquet flooring in outdoor footwear. 'And marking-tape and marking-ink, Madam?' That was another rule: every item brought into school must be marked with the owner's name. 'More work for me, sewing in all those tapes,' said his mother, giving him a passing hug.

'Cash, Mr Druce? Or credit?' asked Mr Oliver, totting up the bill. But his father was already waiting, wallet in hand. 'Cash. Of course, cash.'

The grand total sounded monstrous, as huge as the heaped-up pile on the counter. And all these things were *his*.

'Never say we don't look after you,' said his father, as they walked home with the parcels. 'Never say we don't make sacrifices. And your new bicycle last month, just as you were promised. No, never say we don't keep promises. And it's all paid for, eh Dorothy? Down to the last penny.'

That was the way of the Druce household. Nothing on credit. Nothing on the never-never. No mortgages. No millstones round your neck. Every weekend his father brought his wage-packet home unopened, and in consultation he and his wife slid notes and little piles of coins along the table. Rent-book, insurance man, housekeeping money, burial club, Post Office Savings book. His son looked on and waited. Holiday money. Bobby's music lessons. Father's tobacco. Last of all Bobby's pocket-money: a whole shilling. Sixpence for his Post Office book. Sixpence to finger in his pocket and not spend all at once.

Back indoors again from Mr Oliver's, he stretched his eyes at the plunder on the table. All *this!* And the school fees for Monkswood were going to be £9 a term, almost twice what his father earned in a week

'Never you mind about that,' his mother told him. 'It's for your future, and it's money well-spent. You did your part and passed the scholarship: this is your reward. Now, go and dress yourself up nicely in your new uniform, and I'll take a snap of you in the garden.'

*

The school uniform, although not yet to be publicly worn, signalled the arrival of new allegiances, and an end of the old. 'When you are at University…' Nowadays the phrase was constantly upon his father's lips.

Before the coming term was out, his fiddlings with meccano and its clockwork Magic Motor would begin to metamorphose themselves into Physics. In another year or two the walks with Pat and his mother, naming wild flowers, would be eclipsed by his solitary searchings through the French dictionary, getting lists of plants and trees, and birds and colours and things mechanical, by heart in another language.

Practicalities becoming theory, things becoming ideas. But in September 1940, there was a long way to go.

And not least in the practical acts of daily life. He hadn't learned to do up his shoelaces until he was nine years old and on the point of joining the Cubs. With grammar school and his eleventh birthday looming, he still couldn't tie his own tie. Left to himself, he could only make a hard little knot with a loose end dangling down below his belly button. 'Don't ever let me hear you say that word,' said his mother. 'And for heaven's sake, stand *still* while I tie it for you.'

His mother still flannelled him all over on bath nights, until he begged her to leave him alone to wash and dry himself. It was high time he learned, for there were only days to go before he'd be flung into the hurly-burly of a boys'-school changing room and communal showers.

And however much he might soak himself in books, intellectual independence was even further out of sight, did one but know it.

'In *your* opinion? And who asked *your* opinion, Druce?' Well, *my father* says; *the headmaster* says; *the dictionary* says; *the Bible* says; *the law* says; *the poet* says. O, before long you'd have to keep your eyes peeled and your wits honed, and argue every inch of the way.

At present it was farewell to Consort Road, farewell to the presence of girls. 'Good riddance to bad rubbish,' he and his mates said among themselves. Good riddance even to girls as disruptive of his peace of mind as Vicky Snell.

Vicky arrived at Consort Road when the last day of term was only weeks away. She smiled around at the boys in the class and, surprisingly, only giggled when they travestied her name. 'Not *Snail*, silly,' she said. '*Snell*. My mummy says it means *quick* in German.'

He was one of a handful of boys, lounging against the playground arches one dinner-break, grinning and sniggering, as Vicky laid bare the facts of life. 'You just be quiet and listen to me,' she said. 'My aunty told me what you have to do.'

Her command of the facts was amazing. The man and the woman had to lie down in a ditch... 'A *ditch?*' he said. 'In the *water?* They'd drown.'

'A *dry* ditch, silly. And then they have to take off all their clothes. And then they do it.'

He was lost in images. Frogs did it in ditches full of water, of course. But not people. Still, if it was dry you *could* lie down in the leaves, perhaps.

But did you really have to take all your clothes off? *All of them?* Out in the open? Suppose there were nettles. Suppose it started to rain. Suppose a policeman came along. Supposing his dad came along when *he* was doing it.

The thought flung an icy handful of ditchwater down his spine.

'And then the man ties a knot in it and throws it away.' Vicky was still holding forth to a ring of wide-stretched eyes. Sharp little Mistress Quickly.

Now that really *was* silly! Ignorant of contraceptives, pulling into his mind's focus only known things, it wasn't till a few years later that he learned *what* it was that the gratified lover was supposed to knot. But in 1940, narrowing his eyes in July sunshine, he was convinced that Vicky Snell was making it all up. *Knot* it? How could you tie a knot in your Johnny? *Throw it away?* Trust a girl to think up an idea like that.

'And then they kiss each other's bottoms and get dressed,' said Vicky Snell as a parting shot, as her audience lounged away across the playground, reluctant to quit her company, grinning into one another's eyes, up the steps and into afternoon school.

*

Then suddenly the time had arrived for a final Assembly.

Time again to create a school hall out of three classrooms. He helped to push the juddering partitions back against the wall, and paused for the last time to stroke the crystalline structures that sweat had etched into the brass finger-plates. Time to pay attention while Mrs Baldwin gave out notices and wished the leavers success in their new schools and in their lives. Time not to think about the whippy canes in Mrs Baldwin's cupboard, and the spilt and wasted hours they'd had to sit mumchance, hands on their heads, as a punishment.

First the photograph. And then at last it would be the end of school and time to pelt out of the gate with Roy, into the forest and up across Maze Hill. To polish the bleached knuckles of the climbing thorn with their scuffling shoes, and sprawl over tree roots where rain had scoured the clay away from under them. To drag their hands through leafmould, and dabble their fingers in the fluid that lurked in the crook of each pollard hornbeam, and smelled of toadstools. To jump the brook and paddle in the cold pond, its waters lapping the goose-flesh of their knees. To pummel one another into the leaves for the last time.

It was saddening to admit that, after the summer, all this would belong to other children, and then to the newcomers who in turn ousted them. And O, after the summer, Roy wouldn't be one of the lucky ones catching the bus and train to Monkswood. Though, of course, they'd go on seeing one another at weekends. And Roy could always wait, couldn't he? for Bob to do his homework in the evenings.

But now at this minute it was time to carry benches out into the playground for a last group photograph. Forty-six scholars, posed in ranks, not all of whom had qualified for a scholarship; although, and largely thanks to Mrs Nightingale, an astounding percentage had.

Accountant, teacher, doctor, writer, economist, businesswoman, businessman. Out of the fading print the faces frown and squint and grin, beckoning with them suddenly remembered snatches of speech and tones of voice.

Pudding-basin haircuts, short-back-and-sides, ribbon-tied plaits; mother, father, ancestor, nothing, prize-winner, ne'er-do-well, thief. Perched between smirking University teachers of fifteen years ahead, behold the disarming smile of the future recidivist.

And out of the camera's field of vision, hovering at the photographer's side that afternoon: proud of her scholars, sad, and loving; preparing now to forgo their affection and defiance and looks of amazed pleasure and acts of thoughtlessness; saying, 'Say *cheese*' to make them all smile for the last time: Mrs Nightingale.

A murder of crows, a deceit of lapwings.

An exultation of larks.

A watch of nightingales.

Dorothy Druce and Robert senior

11

MONKSWOOD

In the late autumn of 1939, water-filled holes and heaps of raw clay had begun to appear throughout the Village in back and front gardens alike. Suddenly there were council workmen riding around on lorries, stopping wherever there was a hole, and clanging out sackfuls of nuts and bolts and silvery piles of corrugated iron. Free to households on low incomes, £5 to those who could afford to pay for their own safety, these were the Anderson air-raid shelters the Government had been promising.

The Ridouts' Anderson shelter was the first in Sparrowfield Lane, and one Saturday and Sunday young Bob strolled across the road from time to time to watch. For hours at a stretch, Fatty Ridout's two elder brothers and his dad took turns to dig, slopping about in wellington boots in the flood of yellowy water that welled up through the subsoil, while Fatty and his sister scooped it up by the pailful and flung it across the flowerbeds.

All day long, onlookers hung around the Ridouts' garden to offer advice and stand about in the way. Mr Ramper leaned against the fence, rolling cigarettes in his earth-stained fingers. 'Bloody rabbit-burrow, that's what you're a-goin' to be livin' in,' he said from time to time, wagging his head and coughing smoke.

Every time a newcomer strolled along, Mr Ramper repeated his offer to the Ridouts to send a ferret down to chivvy them out when they overslept. The Ridouts grinned, and went on taking turns to dig and to scoop up water and souse it across the michaelmas daisies.

'Why haven't *we* got a shelter?' Bob asked his mother when he got indoors.

'You've not been across the road again, have you?' she said. 'Didn't I tell you to keep away from there?'

'Mr Ramper is still telling everybody his joke about ferrets,' he answered. 'O, well, I just thought I'd see how they are getting on with the hole. Why aren't *we* digging a hole? Why, mum?'

'Why? Because.'

That's what she always said when she didn't want to give you a straight answer.

But the reason was simple enough, though neither his father nor his mother thought fit to share it with him at the time. On his pay of £250 a year, Police Constable Druce was not entitled to a free air-raid shelter. Nor did he have five pounds to spare at that moment, saving every halfpenny as he was for the coming expense of school fees and school clothing and piano lessons — not to mention what he'd already forked out for the piano.

Before twelve months had passed, PC Druce would pay the price of his devotion to the interests of his son, in a night of anguish which would almost cost him his reason.

*

All through the summer months of 1940, the Luftwaffe kept up its attacks on Britain's airfields and factories. On September 7th, the Blitz began. Day after day the tiny silver aircraft dived and spiralled in and out of the clouds above the Village, and throbbed at night through the searchlight-pencilled dark beyond the rafters and the roof tiles.

The Ridouts were the lucky ones now, creeping down the garden every night to their waterlogged earth. Next door at number 97, so did the Thompsons, elderly newcomers who had replaced Bob and Alfie's family: they too had an Anderson shelter of their own.

So had Mr Ramper at 105. Early in the spring of 1940, his son-in-law had helped him bury the galvanized arches among his cabbages. 'You can send a bloody ferret down for *me* this time,' Mr Ramper called to anyone who'd listen and, 'John, John, for God's sake watch what you're doing to them bloody plants,' as the harvest he had looked for vanished under a heap of clay.

Since they had no shelter of their own at 99 Sparrowfield Lane, PC Druce pushed the heavy oak dining-room table up against an inner corner of the room, barricading the third side with a cupboard: well, that little lot ought to protect them against anything but a direct hit, surely?

And then again, even an Anderson shelter couldn't cope with a direct hit, could it? No, mark my words: the only thing you'd crawl out of a shelter in the garden with was waterlogged socks and double pneumonia. 'Dorothy, isn't that right?'

Nightly now Mrs Druce tucked her son in to sleep on a mattress under the table, and huddled there beside him when his father was on night-duty. Pat catnapped on a blanket close to his feet, shivering at the thud of bombs and anti-aircraft guns, and trying to nose her way under the blankets.

*

A bare week after the Blitz began, the morning came when his mother stood over Druce R.C.L. and commanded him to hold his tongue for once in his life while he swallowed a proper breakfast. Then it was high time to peer into his ears and prod him back upstairs again and scrub them scarlet for him. Time to scrape a comb through his hair and prink him out in his new school uniform, and tell him to admire himself in the mirror. Time to ride with him on the bus to the railway station. As if he couldn't have found his own way blindfold.

At the top of St Anne's hill an unknown boy, with a Monkswood cap and a raincoat and satchel as brand-new as his own, stood alongside his mother waiting for the bus. All the way to the station they side-spied one another, while their mothers exchanged polite smiles.

By the ticket barrier — 'O, stop it, mum,' he raged, 'everyone's *looking!*' — she knotted his tie all over again, and tugged up his socks, and made him produce his ticket and his lunch-money and his handkerchief, and gave him a hug, and waved him goodbye. He turned away and climbed the stairs to the platform side by side with the other boy, trying hard to conceal his upwelling joy behind a show of nonchalance. 'What's your name? You didn't go to Consort Road. I'm Robert Druce,' he said.

'Eric Travers. We only moved here in July.'

Solemnly they shook hands, and gazed down for a moment at Mrs Druce and Mrs Travers who now stood side by side, waiting to see the train carry their sons away to Monkswood. Along the platform, there were voices and faces familiar from Consort Road: John Robbins, Bren Slaney, Ron Heron, Ronny Bellows; and he swept Travers along to join them.

Three miles and a boisterous ride away, blood-brothers now, they piled out onto the platform among slamming doors and a hiss of steam. They jostled their way up and across the footbridge two steps at a time, through a crowd of bright-capped fellow first-formers. They clung to one another's company, and were elbowed aside in turn by senior boys. And now a single knot in a sprawled-out swarm, they squabbled and chattered their way like starlings down the half-mile-long lane and in through the gates of Monkswood County High. Beginning all over again at the bottom of a new pecking order, privileges and responsibilities all stripped away, cocks of the walk no more.

A black-gowned master marshalled them in a separate area of the playground and followed them into the school in silence, a hundred of them, marching over red-tiled floors to the locker rooms, where they hung up their coats and locked their outdoor shoes away in wire cages. 'Those of you who wish to be excused, go now. There will be no further opportunity until break.' A hundred boys scuttered out to the lavatories in elastic-sided house-shoes.

J. H. Rhodes — it wasn't long before they learned to call him 'Dusty', but not when he or any other master was in earshot — welcomed them in the hall. Mr Rhodes was not only gowned, but scarlet-hooded, too — a sign of his Headmastership.

It was a privilege to be joining the school, Dusty told them. A privilege which they had earned by their own efforts, but which future laziness or indiscipline would cause them to forfeit. A privilege which was symbolized by the school colours and the school uniform. When a boy wore that uniform, Monkswood School would be judged by his conduct in public.

Then Dusty Rhodes took them through the school rules: a copy was to be found in every classroom, remember, to the left of the door.

Rules? — he and the others from Consort Road glanced along the line and caught one another's eyes — *they'd never had printed rules at Consort Road, had they? Cor, no. Moggy Jenkins or ol' Ma Baldwin just used to make the rules up as they went along.*

Dusty strode away to his room and the Senior Master mounted the platform, hitched his gown across his shoulders, and contemplated them.

Druce recognized the gesture with a qualm. Did the Senior Master remember *him*? There was the blue face that had peered into his own the day they sat the scholarship, the face that told him and Roy Shotley to behave themselves. You could recognize that face a mile away by its blue cheeks and its horn-rimmed glasses and its tight-lipped smile.

'My name is Black,' the face announced.

At the end of the year, Mr Black told them, in icily sardonic tones which would come to be familiar — an examination would take place, on the results of which would depend each boy's final placing in an academic stream for the remainder of his school life. Now pay attention.

Those happy enough to enter 2A a year from now would learn Latin. The folk in 2B would make a start on German. For C-streamers a single foreign language was deemed sufficient. In every other respect, all three streams would follow parallel courses. Until a boy entered the sixth form: if ever *that* day dawned. Mr Mason here was in charge of French and tomorrow every boy there in the hall would begin his adventures in that tongue.

Eyes slewed sideways to rest upon Mr Mason.

'You will attend to me,' said Mr Black.

Each boy had been allotted to a House on the basis of where he lived, and to a position in the first-year on the strength of his scholarship result. The thin lips enunciated their way through the lists, while Mr Black let his eye dwell on each boy as he held up his hand and answered, 'Present, Sir'.

Then he glanced down to tick off the name, and confer on its owner a shiny new identity of first-year stream, and House. 'Hmph,' they could hear him mutter in the pin-drop silence.

From now on, there'd be no more childishness of first names. They'd be known by their surnames. Whoever and whatever you might affect to be at other times, when your uniform was on your back, you were a surname and initials.

With each jerk of his skull, light flashed from the lenses of Mr Black's glasses. Even when you were close to him, his gaze was masked by the flashing reflection: you could never tell what he was looking at. As Druce was soon to find out.

In the course of that day, Mr Black told them, they would be given exercise books and course-books for every subject, together with a hymn-book and a dictionary. Tomorrow morning an inspection of all the course-books would take place, in order to ascertain that each had been neatly covered with brown paper.

At the end of the week, when the sheets came from the printers, they would be given the words and music of the School Song. This they were to paste onto the flyleaf of their hymn-books. After which they would do well to get the words by heart as soon as possible. Had he made himself clear? The blue face still smiled its thin-lipped smile, as Mr Black dismissed them, stream by stream, into the care of their form-masters.

Enlisted into 1A and Forest House, grinning and bubbling with excitement, Druce R.C.L. scrambled into line with Travers and his old mates out of Mrs Nightingale's class. Mr Mason strode out of the hall and down the corridor. 1A, coalescing for the first time into a self-conscious entity, trooped along behind him.

*

Their form-room was to be Room 1 — the French room, Mr Mason's room. These were their desks, these places theirs. Pinned around the walls were posters of unknown places into which you could wander in a daydream, and lose yourself.

Beneath each was a caption that Druce R.C.L. could make no sense of. Not yet. Not yet. But France, her landscapes and her language, lured his eyes. He craved to think and speak in words and phrases alien and arcane: already he was fretting to enter into those mysteries and master them.

They paid over their lunch-money. Mr Mason appointed monitors for chalk. The blackboard. The cupboard. Milk. Ink. Someone was put forward as form-captain, and triumphantly elected.

Every detail of the day burnt itself into his senses. And would again in a year's time, and again and again for almost every year of his life. Perched in a desk in the front row of 1A, he found himself swamped by that same forward-looking wistfulness he had felt in Mrs Nightingale's classroom. And now intensified. Impossible to put it into words, impossible to frame the paradox of so strong a premonition of future nostalgia. He knew only that he yearned for the rituals of this day which was already slipping away into the past. And yearned, with an equal nostalgia, for occasions still far in the future, for those rites which would come to shape his life.

Year by year, the pattern would remain the same. A day that opened with a different journey, or a journey with changed companions. Autumn, a hunter's moon, the harvest gathered from orchards and ploughlands. The whiff of bonfires. Frosty air, the magic of early morning mists, dew-beaded cobwebs in the hedgerows.

The unfinished or false moves of a past season all discarded. A clean start now. New clothes on his back as often as not. Altered class-lists, unfamiliar companions. Fresh fields of thought. New visions. Minds as yet unknown to reckon with.

Rooms that had stood silent through the summer weeks now re-allotted, pungent with floorwax. Empty desks and shelves, blackboards washed free of chalk. The smell of print and new bindings and unsullied paper tugging at your senses.

Here at Monkswood today and then for ever after, he found himself caught up in the rituals of learning. He smoothed unread pages with the side of his hand, rejoicing in the feel of glazed paper. He snuffed up the smell of fountain-pen ink, inhaling its metallic scentedness worlds apart from the tang of the fluid that froze in the inkwells at Consort Road when the frost came down.

And the exercise books. They were colour-coded, their bindings sewn. Black for English. Yes, of course, of course: there was Mr Black's sardonic touch. Red for Geography, with a salmon-pink drawing-book for mapwork. Greeny-brown for Science: earth-colour. Dark violet — the colour of Lent, and mysteries, and magic — for French. With only the subtlest of changes he would keep to these colour-codings throughout his academic life.

*

At half past four that afternoon, he climbed down from the bus at the top of St Anne's hill, and walked along with Travers to look at where Travers lived. It was a muggy day, threatening a storm, and they stopped to fold up their coats and blazers and drape them over bulging satchels. Travers asked him in, but Mrs Travers didn't, and he walked on alone across the hilly fields and old Bottle Atkins' pasture, trying to recall if Travers' house was one of those they'd bombed with balls of clay or where they'd swung on the electric flex in the hallway: it was certainly on *that* estate.

But more important matters were on his mind. He needed breathing-space to savour the day's events. To set his thoughts in order, hugging his excitement to himself, before he faced the onslaught of his mother's questions.

Such joy was all too fierce to be constrained. As he leaped the hilly fields stream there was a sudden gush of blood from his nose. Before he reached his own front gate, his shirt and tie were wet with it, his handkerchief sodden.

His mother ran out of the front door to meet him.

*

She had washed his face and put his shirt and tie in soak by the time his father came in. 'Well? Well?' he said. 'How did you get on?'

He lay back in the chair, with the iron back-door key dangling on its string against his spine. 'Don't squirm about or it won't stop bleeding,' his mother said. 'You can answer your father from where you are. He's had a nose-bleed. It's over-excitement.'

'Look on the table, dad,' he said, 'look at the books. They've got to be covered in brown-paper by tomorrow without fail. And when it comes from the printers, I've got to learn the school song by heart. And I'll play you the tune on the piano. We got roast beef and steamed pudding and custard for lunch. Wait till you see the science labs. And there's a special room for dissecting frogs and Mr Fitzroy's made a machine out of an old alarm-clock for finding out why plants grow up and down and not sideways and Dad, listen, I shall soon be saying things in French.'

'Who gave you the nose-bleed?' said his father.

'Nobody! It just started all of a sudden. I think it's stopped now.'

'Are you telling me the truth? Has anybody been hitting you?'

'He's over-excited,' said his mother. 'All the excitement's been too much for him. Now listen to me. I can tell your father all about it while you lie down for an hour or two.'

'But the books, the books. They've got to be *done*.'

'Do you want your nose-bleed to start again? Do as you are told this minute. Your father and I will cover the books for you.' She prodded him out of the kitchen, calling up the stairs after him, 'Put on your pajamas, and try to get some sleep.'

Tugging his vest over his head, 'He didn't sleep a wink last night, I know he didn't,' he heard her say. 'He'll have to come down again soon enough when the siren goes.'

He lay on his bed with the whirl in his brain slowly subsiding, and heard the clank of his father's bicycle and his mother whispering: 'Get four or five sheets: better be safe than sorry.' Later he heard their voices and the sharp rustle of paper and the snip of scissors, and then his waking self ebbed and he fell into a blaze of dreams.

Next morning there was the pile of books miraculously covered in that lovely tough brown paper that has a fine pinstripe of darker ridges in it. On each book his father had lovingly inscribed its title, inking tall capitals between feint-ruled pencil lines.

'O,' he said, 'it's like Rumpelstiltkin spinning all the straw into gold. I couldn't ever have made them look as good as that. Thanks mum, thanks dad.'

'Well, give us both a kiss, then,' said his mother.

'What a wealth of knowledge, eh Dorothy?' his father said, washing his fried bread down with a gulp of tea. 'I've been going through some of them. All that learning waiting for you to master it. My God, if I only had had *your* opportunities.'

*

First period: double English, and they stayed in Room 1 for it. They had to lay out all their English books on the desk-top. He tingled with pride, waiting for the Senior English master's praise when he approached his desk.

'Name?'

'Druce, sir.'

'Druce? Very well. Let me see what you have done.'

'Here, sir.'

'I see. Hmph! Look at *that*.'

Mr Black's fingernail was pointing to the first title, trenchant between its pencilled guide-lines:

COLLINS DICTIONARY

'Well?'

'Sir?'

'Druce, you are a foolish little person, are you not?'

'Sir?'

'Has it not yet come to your notice, Druce, that we do not dot our capital I's?'

He stared up into the blind flash of Mr Black's spectacles, hot with shame, brimming with a great protective love of his father, his fury murderous.

'You can take that look off your face, Druce,' said Mr Black over his shoulder, passing on along to the next desk.

But he did not.

Half-an-hour later, when Black set them to write an essay in silence, he snatched the opportunity to catch his neighbour's eye across the gangway and risk a whisper. 'Can I lend your ink-rubber?' The uncouth capital dots were burning his eyes.

'Did you speak, Druce?'

'Yes, sir.'

'You will recall, no doubt, that I asked for silence.'

'Yes, sir. I was only—'

'You will take a detention. Come to me at the end of the lesson.'

As the others filed out at break, he made a second attempt to explain. You can whisper in church, he thought to himself, for someone to pass you a prayerbook, that's not chattering, and you don't get sent to hell.

'But, sir.'

'Hold your tongue, Druce,' said Mr Black. 'Take this detention slip home, and write out twenty times in your best handwriting: *It is high time that I learned to pay attention to the instructions which I am given.* You will bring me the slip tomorrow morning signed by your father.'

Contempt mingled with his fury. Black was unfair, an enemy. And Druce knew where he stood. In seven years he would not forgive, while Black and he were never reconciled to one another.

How diametrically opposite proved Mr Mason's approach, though no less disciplined. Where Black issued instructions and demanded conformity, Walter Mason encouraged his pupils to learn, sweeping the tongue-tied along with him, boosting their confidence, sharing a joke, keeping his promises, making even the grind of syntax worth the achievement.

In the corner of the room he rigged up a shop, and they chaffered over empty bottles of wine and lemonade, counted out quantities of haricots, camembert, empty cream cartons, tins of sardines, rehearsing the partitive article. They bought tickets for the metro, sang songs, booked hotel rooms, played gin rummy with cards which instilled vital vocabulary, answered the telephone. Anyone who forgot himself and spoke English without demanding permission: *Comment dit-on «sausages», Monsieur? Monsieur, que veut dire: «entre guillemets»?* had to pay a half-penny *sou* for every word. It went into the end-of-the-year French party fund. If the fund looked none too healthy, Walter Mason forgot himself on purpose and *vingt, vingt-et-un, vingt-deux, vingt-trois…* 1A kept the score.

*

Often several times a day, the air-raid warning sounded. Then whoever happened to be teaching them scurried them out into the concrete shelter tunnels. Travers and Robbins shot off like dutiful rabbits. But six or seven always hung back, Slaney and Heron and he among them, craving to see sudden smoke burst open among the tiny aircraft glittering and swooping at one another. Sometimes pieces broke away from one. What was left fell out of the sky, and your heart swooned in a horror shared. German or English? No matter which, the shock was the same and would not quit you, and you hoped for a parachute unravelling.

Day after day in the shelters, they polished their French and chorused defiance at the Huns with *Au clair de la lune*, and *Il était un petit navire*. Then, if a weak master let them get away with it, they caterwauled a defiance of high-school proprieties and Black's prune-and-prism English and the Luftwaffe alike with *Any old i-ern, any old i-ern*; and *Hi'm Enery the H'eighft, Hi ham*, rounding off with *Beer, Beer, glorious Beer, Fill yourself right up to 'ere, up to 'ere*. Whenever their riotous Cockney carried to Black's ears he would bustle across from one of the other shelters, and order them to sit in silence. So then they stretched their ears to the sound of anti-aircraft shells and machine-guns in the sky.

At unoccupied moments he and his classmates scrawled every spare scrap of paper with crowded skyscapes. Spitfires and Hurricanes veering in to attack, Nazi invaders spiralling earthwards in a gush of smoke and flame. No space was left vacant, but filled with shellbursts and dotted lines of tracer. British squadrons, *vice-versa*, roundels on their wings, unloaded bombs onto targets across the Channel, unscathed by enemy fire.

Spells. Sympathetic magic. Paper images to reinforce the voices on the radio and the throbbing in the sky. Victory. *There'll always be an England.* Bom-bom-bom **BAM**, *b-b-b* **C.** Hollow drumbeats, rapping out a tune in morse. *We shall never go under.* Victory. *And England shall be free.* Machine-gun fire in the sky. *Qu'un sang impur abreuve nos sillons!* Blood of an alien tribe quenching the thirst of our furrows: O, the French national anthem had the words for it.

*

On September 26th 1940, three weeks, two days and half a night after Druce had joined Mr Mason's class, his father was out on night-duty and his mother lay beside him under the table in Sparrowfield Lane. Beyond the roof the sky was full of aircraft noise and the hollow bang-bang-bang of pom-poms. Suddenly there was a strange swishing they'd never heard before. Pat whimpered, and nuzzled her way under the blankets and into his arms.

The air in the room sucked in and out, the ceiling fell down, glass clattered across the furniture and floor, and there was a stink of soot.

Then there were voices shouting in the street and whistles screeching.

Boots came crunching into the house over broken laths and plaster. His mother crawled out across the drifts of glass and chimney soot and grit, and he followed, with Pat cringing behind them. They found themselves shepherded along, barefoot, their ears singing, blankets slipping off their shoulders. Out to the street and round into the Thompson's shelter, hudging up along the wire bed-frame in the hours that followed before the All-Clear, trying not to let their legs dangle into the water.

How could they have stumbled barefoot over broken glass without gashing their feet to the bone? When they returned at early light in borrowed rubber boots, to gaze at the roof tiles spilling down the staircase and laths hanging by a shred of wallpaper, it seemed miraculous.

More puzzling still had been the dance of the doors. Somehow the front door now leaned against the frame where the kitchen door had been, the kitchen door had lurched sideways into the back-door's place, while the back door hung through the shattered frame of the kitchen window. He never could picture, though he tried to imagine it, the panicky waltz of the doors in that rush of time.

His mother boiled water and made tea in the wreckage of her kitchen, rescuing a can of condensed milk out of the litter of jam and milk and broken glass. They gulped it turn by turn out of an enamel mug, wondering why his father hadn't appeared.

Then PC Druce burst in, flinging his arms around them both, white-faced and weeping. He had taken the telephone message at the Police station that night when the news came in: a string of German parachute mines had fallen across Silver Hill. The full extent would not be known until daylight, but a woman and two children were missing, believed dead. Sam Alcock relieved him at the desk, and PC Druce had pedalled like a maniac the length of the Village.

Past the foot of Silver Hill, where a snow of glass from the shattered hothouses of Jordan's Nursery lodged in the gutters, and rescue workers were huddling people towards the deep shelter at Gregories. On into the chaos of Sparrowfield Lane. He had raced back and forth the length of the street crying 'Dorothy! Bobby!' until he lost his voice and damaged his reason. Mrs Shotley had heard him, fetched him in and put a mug of tea into his hands, and had tried to calm him.

Soon after PC Druce's homecoming, PC Shotley arrived, bearing the latest news. Four parachute-mines had fallen. Jordan's Nursery in Silver Hill had received a direct hit. Mrs Jordan and her two daughters were dead. The authorities were trying to contact Sergeant Jordan, somewhere overseas. Up at the top of Silver Hill, Sandsted Hall was still alight. Lord Sandsted was likely a goner, lying in a coma in St Katharine's emergency ward, not expected to last the day out. But his Lordship and his sister had been alone in the place, thank God. There was another crater away across in the water-meadows. No casualties there. But Bottle Atkins would find himself a few cows short next time he was sober enough to count them. (Oh yes, Druce R.C.L. remembered, *If a bomb fell in a field. and a bull swallowed it, what would be the result? Abominable [a bomb-in-a-bull]!* Mr Hackett's contribution to keeping the civilian population happy, in the previous week's *Clarion & Weekly Advertizer's* 'Humour of the Week'.)

St Anne's churchyard was cordoned off, said PC Shotley. Special Constable Hardiment had reported an unexploded mine, its parachute lines caught in an elm, dangling above the graves. The silly sod, now would you credit it? only assumed it was somebody's washing blown off the line, and had kept an eye on it for half an hour. Then he'd strolled up to take a closer look. He'd buggered off quick enough then, eh?

But PC Druce and his wife weren't smiling. 'Well, if you need a hand, Bob, let me know.' Roy Shotley's dad thumped his colleague on the shoulder, and took himself off to his own, happily undamaged home.

United now, the Druces explored the house. Bob ignored what his parents said, and scrambled upstairs behind them over the rubble to a landing and bedrooms largely open to the sky.

He pushed the door of his bedroom till it jammed against a heap of books and toys and fallen plaster. His bed and Pat's basket were littered with glass.

He went through into his parent's bedroom. The middle of the front wall was gone where the bay window had been. The window-frame and floorboards were broken through. Over everything there was a litter of splintered wood and crumbled brick and mud and glass. The iron frame of his parent's bed had been folded double, headboard locked against bedfoot, by a great cannonball of clay flung by the explosion out of the crater in Jordan's Nursery.

He peered down through the gap in the floor. A tile slid down the roof, and plaster fell from the ceiling into his hair.

His parents were motionless, holding hands, their faces turned towards him. If his dad hadn't been on night-duty, they would both have been sleeping there.

He stared at the clay-filled bed, trying to thrust the bloody images away.

12

AUCKLAND DRIVE

There was no question of staying on in the house. That night he and his mother lugged suitcases full of blankets and spare clothes to the public shelter at Gregories, while PC Druce took Pat to the Police Station with him.

To his fastidious mother, the hours in the shelter were a season in hell, and an amazement to his own innocent senses. Coir mattresses had been laid out across the concrete floor. In the flickering darkness, families and their belongings were huddled around them, sprawling over into the gangways. People came and went, and there were snarling disputes over territory and who had staked or failed to stake a claim. 'Look, that's *your* place *there*. If you don't like it, you can sod off outside.' 'You bleedin' what?' 'Don't you speak to my wife like that.' 'Listen, mate: if you want trouble, you've come to the right address.' 'Put a sock in it, you noisy bastards, will you?' 'Right! 'Oo said that?'

'Don't listen to them,' his mother said. 'Close your ears and say your prayers.'

The air was rank with the stench of hurricane lanterns, sweat and wet clothing and beery breath, fartings and snores and whisperings, babies crying, drunken mutters, furtive gasps and shufflings of married men who would not be balked of their nightly congress, voices of people who started awake with a shout, or whimpered in their dreams.

In the small hours of the second night, a voice spoke loudly from the sandbagged doorway: 'Aye, laddie, I've come to fetch Mrs Druce and her boy away hame. You can cross them off your wee list.' Then boots tramped among the bed spaces, and the light of a torch came flickering across the rows to rest on his mother's face. 'And what d'ye suppose you're doing here, lassie? Yon's nae place for you. Up with the pair of you now and out of here.'

The instant he'd heard where they were, Police Constable Sandy Turnbull had driven his patrol car to Gregories to escort them away from the stench and the fading curses of men and women — 'Oo's *that*? Woss 'e want?' 'Soddin' copper.' 'Yers, see? That's coppers for ya. Alwiz knows 'ow to look after their own, coppers do. Yers, alright for some, innit?' And the ancient quarrels resumed: 'Ah, for Jesus Chrissake, put a sock in it.' 'Wos you addressing my 'usband?' 'An' you can pipe down too, you noisy cow.' 'Right! 'Oo said that? If I find aht 'oo said that…'

'That's nae company for a decent family,' said Constable Turnbull, opening the door of the patrol car. 'You're away hame wi' me this minute.' They arrived to find that Mrs Turnbull had turned herself and her husband out of their own bed. Sandy and she could sleep in the girls' room for as long as it took Rob to find another house, while Bobby and the wee lassies could make shift on camp beds in the parlour.

*

The report book, under my hand here, fixes the dates. Ten days off school for Druce R.C.L. and compassionate leave for his father who pedalled off every morning looking for a house to rent. Meanwhile workmen arrived at number 99 and the other houses in the row, and got the windows glazed or nailed across with plywood. They lashed tarpaulins over the roofs, and screwed the street doors back on their hinges.

The Druces couldn't sleep at number 99, what with ceilings liable to come down, and bedding thick with soot, and glass splinters everywhere, but from morning to early evening he and his mother camped out in the shell of their old home, clearing up the mess, smearing the furniture with wax where the rain had mottled it, hanging batches of washing out to dry. Everything that had not been ruined by filth and the rain, or looted in those first few hours, they packed in borrowed tea-chests and orange-boxes from the greengrocer, ready for the removal van. His mother never saw her best cutlery again, nor her home-made wines in their stoneware jars, nor ornaments, and pictures. Some of his toys, and those of his own books not ruined by the rain, had vanished.

He scurried across the hilly fields with his tea-caddy full of Young Chemist's gunpowder. He handed it to Travers's mother, asking her to pass it on to Eric for safe keeping. No no, it wasn't dangerous and it would never explode. Well, see, the trouble was he didn't have a pestle and mortar, so even if you *could* manage to light it, it only flared. Mrs Travers didn't look happy, but she accepted the tea-caddy and he hurried home.

Minutes later, the removal men arrived and they loaded up and set off for the River Estate and number 66 Auckland Drive, at the opposite end of the Village.

*

The elderly owner had fled from the Blitz to the West country, taking his housekeeper and his furniture with him. He left behind him a garden shed full of ironmongers' stores, a greenhouse with its glass amazingly intact, a garden serried with apple and pear and plum trees, and most important of all, an Anderson shelter.

Bob wrenched the wooden blast-door open and peered in at a lake of water a yard deep. 'Don't you concern yourself about that. That's a mere detail,' his father said. 'We can soon bale that out. In fact, you can fetch a bucket and make a start now, my son.'

Before a month was out his father had concreted the shelter floor, and cemented a five-gallon can in the corner to act as a sump. He painted the walls and lined them with trellis, to keep anyone from leaning against the condensation that streamed down them.

He sank a sixty-gallon oil-drum nearby in the garden into which the shelter sump would drain, scrounged a hand-pump from somewhere, and rigged it up on a post. His son — it was time the boy took on some responsibility — was allotted the task of pumping out the bilge water every day, so that the floor, now carpeted, would remain as dry as a bone.

He got hold of a coil of lead-covered cable, and ran in electricity for a light-bulb and the wireless. The Druce family laboured through an afternoon filling sandbags with earth and dry cement and piling them up to make a right-angled entrance tunnel. 'Well, Dorothy?' his father said at last. 'It's a little palace, eh?'

From dusk to first light they sat or lay on their narrow bunks, Bob busy with homework and his mother knitting or sewing, pushing past one another to peer sideways along the tunnel when parachute flares lit the sky, and cringing back when the earth shook. PC Druce preferred to sleep in his own bed, only joining them during heavy raids or when his wife implored him to think of her for once and come down out of danger. On the night of 29th December, when London burned all along the horizon, they all climbed out into the garden, to stare at their own townscape washed in orange and scarlet light.

When the raids grew less frequent, they only slept underground when the moon was full and unobscured — a bombers' moon — and raiders flew along the silver flarepath of the Thames. But they returned to their cave-dwellers' life when the doodlebugs began to arrive in June 1944.

*

After a fortnight's absence, he went back to Monkswood, now only a bike-ride distant from Auckland Drive when the meadows weren't water-logged or the field-paths greasy with mud.

He was aware of an altered self inside his skin. Back in the quotidian rituals of school he was just as exhilarated, just as enthralled with the vistas opening out all around. But he was conscious of having passed unscathed through a confrontation with murder. The Druces had been spared, a family still surviving and united. But only yards away, the Jordans — twelve-year-old Aileen, her mother and her sister — had been obliterated among the shattered glass of their hothouses.

At break times now, he had tales to tell, visions to pass on: the crazy dance of the doors, the mound of clay hunched in his parent's bed, the looted house, the parachute-mine dangling over St Anne's graveyard, the Druce's new shelter with all mod. cons., their walk unscathed over ribbons of glass, the night hours at Gregories. So much to think, and talk about: if this was what growing-up meant, he was more than half-way there. It was October already, and on 21st he'd be eleven.

He reclaimed his gunpowder, freeing Travers' frightened rabbity eyes of the responsibility, as they swapped it from satchel to satchel. He had outgrown childishness, he told himself. And anyway the stuff never did explode. He'd get rid of it in a final flare, and turn his interests to other matters.

He waited till his parents were out of the kitchen, then fetched the tea-caddy over to the Ideal boiler where his mother hung towels and teatowels to dry in the rising warmth. He lifted the lid of the boiler, and tipped his useless gunpowder in.

Falling onto incandescent coke, it finally lived up to its name. It detonated in a crash that flung open the boiler door in a roar of sparks, charred his eyelashes away, frizzed the hair on his forehead, and set the tea-towels smouldering. When his parents burst into the room, he was still sprawled in the corner where the shock had sent him reeling. 'Don't punish me,' he wailed, 'don't punish me. I've been punished enough.'

His father heard his appeal and stayed his hand. For weeks he retailed the story of his offspring's latest escapade to anyone who'd listen.

*

'No, you don't want to join the Cubs again at this end of the Village, do you?' his mother told him.

St Anne's was more than a mile away from Auckland Drive. He felt no urge to join the rival pack attached to All Saints, his new parish church. He didn't want to be a newcomer, entangled in alien allegiances, having to take orders from a leader not himself. In any case, the days were drawing in and his parents kicked up a fuss if he wasn't indoors while it was still light. That was a good enough excuse for quitting. Get out while you were on top.

With a change of newsagent, he gave up reading the *Children's Newpaper* and *The Scout,* and spent the money his father gave him for weekly magazines on sixpenny, sky-blue Pelican paperbacks instead. Jean-Henri Fabre's *Social Life in the Insect World*, and a book on German 'Decadent' Art: those were the first to stand between bookends on the shelf above his bed. As the months went by, he went on picking out at random any title that caught his eye: Leonard Woolley's *Ur of the Chaldees* and *Digging Up the Past*; *Hydroponics*; *Human Physiology*; *Watching Birds*; *Mediaeval People*; *Man, Microbe and Malady*; and, the first to sport the orange livery of a novel amid his blue non-fiction, *Poet's Pub*.

At Monkswood, ideas and words — how could you prise them apart? — were exploding in all directions. Daily, 1A were confronted with unknown terminology, the jargon of each subject-lesson. *This we call the 'stigma'; this is known as 'pupation'; as 'convection'; as a 'peninsula'; as the 'passive voice'.* It was a joy to be vouchsafed names you could use to possess the world around you. Here were words as ready to hand as knives and forks, or picture-hooks. 'Inertia, sir,' he confided to Walter Mason one afternoon, jerking the bottom sheet from under a stack of papers without disturbing the rest. Then blushed, sensing his favourite master's gaze dwelling upon him for a long instant. But it *was* inertia, wasn't it, which let you do that?

The chant of French and Latin verbs escalated into incantation. Once part and parcel of your thought, words became more than a ceremony of naming, more than incantation, and began to exfoliate into clusters of concepts and hypotheses. Behaving like ice-patterns on a window-pane, creating structures and syllogisms of their own, breaking bounds, slipping and sliding, contradictory.

Reading and the joy of words possessed him. Homework set aside, he scoured his midget French dictionary and copied out lists of colours, trees, animals, plants, metals, getting their French names by heart, drunk with words.

He worked his way through the volumes in his father's bookcase, swallowing them whole. Foxe's *Book of Martyrs*. *The Posthumous Papers of the Pickwick Club*. *Sylvan Winter*, packed with engravings of skeletal trees and catalogues of the uses that each kind of wood could be put to. *Half Hours with the Best Authors*. *Plain Home Talk and Medical Common Sense*, by E.B.Foote MD. It was a collection as random as his father's and his own curiosity. The flow of words acted like a drug, dazzling in its power to conjure images.

He loved *Plain Home Talk* for its browbeating text and its steel engravings. The diagram of a woman's body crippled by tight-lacing. The sketch of a self-opinionated patient trying to lift himself by his own bootstraps and forever doomed to fail. The treeful of monkey-faced infants, wizened and brutalized in the womb by improvident mothers: 'fretful Peter', 'Benny, the child of sensuality, liquor and tobacco', 'poor little scrofulous Job, whose parents ought not to have had him'. He pored over the coloured lithographs bound in at the back, delineations of fat pink limbs defiled by ulcers and vivid sores. *Chancre. Syphilis*. Turning the pages, he could recite the titles at the foot of each, as it opened a door into a nightmare as comic as a fairground freak-show and as far beyond his understanding. He acquired the nomenclature of sex, parrot-fashion, glib.

A day or two after his thirteenth birthday, the memory of what he had absorbed paid off. One evening out of the blue, PC Druce caught his wife's eye, and gestured to her to leave the room. 'Sit down, my son,' he said. Then he went in search of his tobacco-pouch, and elaborately filled and lit a pipe. 'It's time,' he muttered between puffs, with the match-flame leaping and dipping, 'it's time you knew about the facts of life.'

'I know all that,' said his son, blushing hotly and dreading what was to follow.

'Know? What do you mean, *know*? How do you *KNOW*?' His father was red in the face and shouting.

'From books.'

'Books? What books? Come on then, Mr Clever, let's see how much you've learnt from books.'

'Well,' answered Druce R.C.L., searching his memory for a suitably impressive fact, 'the clitoris is erectile tissue.'

'My God,' said PC Druce. 'Very well.' He went to the door.

'Dorothy! You can come down now. We've finished our little talk.'

*

At 66 Auckland Drive the toolshed was a treasure-house. Not only of the landlord's ironmongery and tools, but of cardboard boxes stacked full of books and journals.

Volume after volume, Bob devoured Zane Grey. 'Yup, Maw, ah guess ah'll jes' mosey down to th'ole corrall, git mahself a Western tuh read in the bunkhouse.'

'You'd better not let your father hear that sort of talk,' his mother would say. 'We pay for you to learn how to speak properly, not to fill your head with American rubbish. Just leave those books in the shed alone, or your father'll put a padlock on the door.'

From Zane Grey he moved on to Sax Rohmer. For weeks his dreams were haunted by the fiendish Dr Fu-Manchu, who murdered his victims with poison injected under the fingernails, or with venomous spiders; and slid them into the Thames through secret trapdoors in the floor.

In one of the landlord's cardboard boxes, there was an unbound set of *The Handyman's Cyclopaedia*, the issues neatly piled in order in their rust-red covers. It was fascinating, a ragbag of random information. 'To Cure

Warts', 'Unblocking Waste-pipes', 'Choosing Timber for Household Joinery', 'Preparing a Picnic'.

The advice was insane at times: 'Burns should be rubbed at once with soap, lanoline or castor oil, or bathed with strong washing soap. Next day, puncture the blister.' The ingredients of the recipes — 'muriate of potash', 'sugar of lead', 'Condy's crystals', 'salts of lemon', all of which were to be 'readily procured at the drysalters' — were unlike anything Fitz Fitzroy wrote on the board in Chemistry. But words, words for the hoard in his brain.

He fetched a stack of issues into the house, and in an idle moment his father leafed through them. 'Dorothy? Dorothy! Listen to this. I'll have a go at this.'

PC Druce had lighted on a recipe for hair-oil, a mixture of liquid paraffin and oil of citronella. The result stank of over-ripe lemons and filled a half-pint bottle. Snarling, his son was compelled to anoint his own locks with it. That morning Alwyn Black BA paused alongside Druce's desk, snuffing the air like a fox. He leaned nearer.

'Is it the stuff on your hair that is reeking the classroom out, you messy little person?'

'My father made it, sir.'

Black curled his lip, looked at the ceiling, and sighed. Dutifully, 1A followed his cue, and tittered.

*

Nightly the air-raid sirens wailed as the Blitz intensified. In May the Luftwaffe made nearly 100,000 sorties, many of them attacks on London. Each morning now, while his mother cooked breakfast, it was his job to wrench the handle of the shelter bilge-pump back and forth, back and forth, until the gush of water trailed away. When the siren went at dusk, he would shut down the lid of the piano, collect his homework together, and trail down the garden after his mother.

Week by week he searched the *Clarion & Weekly Advertizer* for a mention of his father. 'PC Druce forced entrance for lights' was the usual tale. All reference to bomb-damage in the Village was suppressed: 'Be like Dad — Keep Mum!' the posters warned on walls and hoardings. When a warden was blown to bits across the street from the police-station and PC Alcock had his arm torn off by the shrapnel, Mr Hackett reported the incident as taking place somewhere fifty miles away.

PC Druce saved his colleague's life that night and Mrs Druce laid her husband's uniform in a bathful of cold water to soak out Sam Alcock's blood. But the vision of Sam's spouting artery lingered in PC Druce's mind, never to be washed away. Sam Alcock's suicide a decade later plunged his saviour into suicidal despair.

As the days lengthened towards the summer of 1941, Bob rediscovered old classmates from Consort Road in the River estate around him. Brendan Slaney and Ronnie Bellows in Hawkswood Road. Ken Heron in River Parade. Girls, too. Not that *girls* counted for much: except for Dawn Anderson, and she was a nightmare to avoid. Just round the corner lived Daphne Ring, a tree-climbing tomboy, and the Nicholson twins. From time to time, when he practised on the piano, frizzy-haired Barbara — whose tray of pencils he had once kicked up into a blood-red fountain — came to listen, lurking outside the privet hedge, before knocking on the door to giggle and ask Mrs Druce if Bobby could come out to play.

Most people in the neighbourhood seemed to own a cat. At night and in defiance of the raids, rival toms dashed through the Druces' garden while queens sat yowling on the fence. (*Humour of the Week: Why are cats like cannon? Because they mutilate [mew-till-late].* Another of Mr Hackett's space-filling attempts to keep up public morale.)

He filled a garden syringe with whitewash, and lay in wait one afternoon behind the air-raid shelter. When a cat scrambled onto the fence, he gave it a good squirt. There was a squeal, the cat vanished, and the face of a girl appeared in its place, whitewash dripping from her ginger hair. Before she stopped squawking he recognised her as Doreen Delacy, who'd sat in the desk behind him at Consort Road. She was Dawn's bosom friend and had never liked him. He hadn't set eyes on her since the previous summer and had no idea that it was *her* garden that backed onto his in Auckland Drive. 'I'm telling my mum all about you, Bobby Druce,' she promised, running indoors. Well, he'd owed her one, anyway, for always hanging around with Dawn.

But he heard no more about it, so that was all right. And soon the Delacys moved away, and a war-reserve policeman came to live there, with his two hulking daughters and a mentally defective son. From his bedroom window Bob watched the boy mouthing earth that he'd scrabbled up in the garden with a Golden Syrup tin. He was huge for his age, and when he threw a tantrum, his grown-up sisters together could hardly pin him down. So Bob gave up whitewashing cats in that quarter of the compass.

*

On June 22nd, Hitler's troops invaded Russia, and Stalin suddenly became good old Uncle Joe in the newspaper cartoons. But the Blitz went on.

Clothing was rationed, so many coupons per item. 'You can give up using your handkerchiefs to mop up ink and clean your bike, my lad, if you want a shirt to your back,' his mother said. 'And don't tell me some rigmarole about you couldn't find a rag.' Within a year the Monkswood rule about house shoes fell into abeyance, and steel segs scarred the parquet floors.

On December 6th the Japanese bombed Pearl Harbour, and at last the United States entered the war. Now victory was assured — the staff at Monkswood told them — however far away it might be, and however great the struggle.

*

Two months earlier, after the summer break, the survivors of 1A had come together for the first time in a new form-room and gazed around at their fellows. Heron gone. Travers gone. Both relegated to 2B, along with five others not of Consort Road vintage. Walter Mason and room 1 no longer theirs to claim. Here they were in room 32, at the farthermost end of the top wing.

'2A?' said PC Druce when he heard the news. 'Good boy…

'And now be good enough to hear me out for once in a while, my son. Be guided by me. Don't rest on your oars. Take pride in what you have achieved. But don't rest on your oars…

'No, no. I don't say abandon your hobbies. But if you're serious about going to university, First Things Come First. There'll be ample time for less important things, *after* you've done your music practice and your homework.'

The members of 2A stared at Mrs Rivers, their new form-mistress, weighing her up. Bluff, white-haired and motherly, she allotted desks and handed out homework schedules with swift efficiency. This was her room, a maths room. Tee-squares, blackboard compasses and rulers clattered out of the corner cupboard when you opened the door, and the walls were bare of posters.

But at the back of the room there hung a framed reproduction of van Gogh's *Pont de Langlois*, opening a door, hot as an oven, into a vision of a sunlit Provençal landscape.

13

HOOLIGANS

Throughout Druce R.C.L's first five terms at Monkwood, the weekly double-period of Art was a misery. 'Spoils work by inattentiveness… Does not do his best work always… Should be more careful to follow instructions…' His report book can only hint at the sorry tale of spilt paint and smudged paper, of the red-bearded Art-master's fury, the detention slips and the whacks across the ear.

For weeks at a stretch, 1A drew nothing but the groups of cylinders, blocks and cones stacked on a table in front of them. Mr Cavanagh prowled along the rows while they scratched away in silence, concentrating their attention on the fall of light and the shading. Then for weeks they laboured to construct a two-inch-high roman alphabet, inscribing each letter into a square with a ruler and compasses.

The thought of Thursday morning and double Art made him sick to his stomach. With his father safely out of the house, he malingered, persuading himself and his mother that he had a raging headache. She let him stay in bed and fussed over him, never questioning the miraculous recovery that occurred at midday, nor his desperation not to miss afternoon lessons.

One day in 1941, after he'd loitered all the way to school, plotting to play truant but not daring to, his fear turned itself inside out in an instant. At the start of the lesson, Mr Cavanagh gave them eight minutes to trot outside, find something to serve as the basis of a pattern for a plate, and then to come back and get on with it. Druce brought back a sprig of Herb-Robert from behind the bike-sheds, and drew and coloured its ferny leaves and pink flowers with elaborate care, winding them round on a stem that spiralled to the centre of a circle. He was lost, aware of nothing around him, when the bell rang and Mr Cavanagh tapped his shoulder. He looked up at the man's red-bearded face.

'Excellent work, boy! See what you can do when you put your mind to it? I'll put your name down for the Art Club Competition, shall I?'

His heart brimmed over. In an instant, Mr Cavanagh had cast off his mask of enmity, and declared himself an ally.

He won the competition and the prize of a water-colour box, more through eccentricity of approach, than skill in drawing. There were two set topics: 'Queueing up', and 'Industry'. Where the other entrants depicted a queue of housewives outside a shop, workmen waiting in line to collect their pay, or something of the sort, he filled the diagonals of his sheet with a sky-scape of sloping wires, and swallows gathering to fly south. For 'Industry', he painted a straw bee-skip against a sky alive with more than life-sized bees.

From then on every week he fretted for the Art period to come round. Swamped with his new-found enthusiasm, he looked for occasions to indulge it. Overnight he began to flood the dry diagrams of chemistry and physics with irrelevant colour. When there was Geography homework to be done for Miss April, he hastened through the written work, absorbing little or nothing in the way of geographical facts. Then laboured for an hour, transforming a sketch-map into a rainbow.

In the landlord's shed, he had come across a collection of builder's plans, drawn in waterproof black on tracing linen and tinted with coloured inks. The compass rose in the corner of each plan was a tiny work of art in itself. A barbed arrow-head with a two-inch shaft and a feathered tail; a cross-bar not quite halfway along the arrow; at its centre a roman 'N' set in a circle. There were four fine parallel lines on each side of the central axes, clustering like the rods around a fasces.

He laid out pocket money on tiny bottles of coloured ink, and a ruling pen with a knurled screw that you could adjust to make lines as thick or thin as you liked. From now on he created a north arrow in the corner of every map he drew.

'Yes, yes. It's very pretty,' Miss April admitted, when pressed. 'But it's facts that count.'

He found her indifference hard to accept.

During the summer holidays, and at the weekends in term time, he carried his prize paintbox with him into the forest and along by the river. Pat rested her head on his foot while he tried to paint water that didn't look like a stretch of brown or sky-grey pavement, and autumn foliage that didn't churn itself into a muddy brownish mess on the paper. When December came, he painted snow-scenes on Christmas cards so that his mother could choose one for herself and send the others to her sisters, and he sparkled them with glue and the mica dust that you could buy in a little packet from the newspaper-shop.

'He can take pleasure in his efforts,' the Headmaster wrote in his end-of-term report.

PC Druce repeated Dusty's words aloud on December 28th, contentedly re-reading and signing the page.

'But don't forget, my son: never rest on your oars.'

*

New Year's Day 1942.
Once again in the daily newspaper cartoons, a senile and skeletal Old Year shuffled away into the darkness with his hour-glass and scythe, while a smiling baby in a nappy toddled into a dawn-lit landscape.

Across in Europe, the Nazi leaders met at the wooded lakeside of the Berlin Wannsee in January to discuss 'the Jewish problem' and endorse a 'final solution'. Three weeks later, British-controlled Singapore — ill-prepared and ineptly commanded — was over-run by Japanese troops. On March 9th, Java capitulated to the Japanese.

Slave-labour camps. Extermination camps.

In the Far East, prisoners-of-war, men and women, dying of heatstroke and starvation. In occupied Europe, night and fog, *Nacht und Nebel*. Boots kicking down doors, neighbours huddled away to die under torture, or to choke and burn: horrors yet to be made known to the British public at large. In England and all over Europe incendiary bombs and high explosive raining down.

But No News is Good News.

'Are We Downhearted? No! Let 'em All Come!'

Here in the Village, *Merrie England,* the operetta by Edward German (*GERMAN?*), is packing out All Saints church hall, and Elizabeth the First (*Ooh, look., mum! It's that Mrs Lapwing in a ginger wig*) mounts guard over her sleeping subjects (*Shhhh!*). 'Sword and buckler by my side, here on the shores of battle-tide,' Mrs Lapwing warbles in her booming contralto. Safe in her care, let the English sleep, and in their slumbers, *smile*.

Take heart of grace, and banish fear! The ghost of Sir Francis Drake will arise and drum the enemy up the Channel, as he drummed them long ago.

'Business as Usual,' chalked on the walls of blitzed shops. 'Careless Talk Costs Lives! *Your* Britain — Fight for it Now!'

'Britain Can Take It! Hit Back With National Savings! Dig For Victory! Make Do and Mend!' 'We Never Closed!' That war-long boast of the Windmill theatre, where the girls posed naked and even when the building shook stood as stock-still as they could, in deference to the Watch Committee's rules of decency. 'Keep Smiling Through! Be Like the Kettle and Sing!'

'There'll be Blue Birds Over, The White Cliffs of Dover,

Tomorrow:

Just You Wait and See!'

*

He spent part of the Christmas holiday making himself a model theatre, slotting plywood sections together according to a plan he'd come across in a book, and he fretsawed a proscenium arch to finish it off. His dad painted it white-and-gold as a surprise, and his mother sewed curtains that drew up on a drawstring at the start of a scene. He tugged the curtains down again with his fingers after he'd tilted the players forward to take their bows. He unscrewed the bulb holders from the model railway station that his dad had made him for his previous birthday, and wired them up behind the scenes, swaddling the bulbs in the scraps of coloured cellophane that you could unwrap from Christmas chocolates. At school he swapped a pocketful of assorted treasures for a tiny six-volt dimmer which would make the lights fade or glow bright. He cut out cardboard actors, to slide in and out of the wings on strips of plywood. When it was complete, he took the whole contraption round to demonstrate to Mr and Mrs Moon.

With the black-out curtains drawn from early afternoon onwards so that Mr Moon could have his midday snooze, the Moon's front room was a perfect setting. The tiny actors glided in and out of a puddle of coloured light as Bob stood behind the table and ventriloquized their lines. 'Bravo. Encore!' said Mr Moon.

Then Mrs Moon glanced at the clock and had to hurry off to the Village, before the shops shut. 'Come round this side,' said Mr Moon, 'and sit on my lap, and show me how you move the actors and work the lights… Good, good, that's marvellous. Yes. Yes,' said Mr Moon in a voice grown husky, as his fingers slid over his visitor's knee and under his short trousers.

*

Finding an anecdote in a book of jokes, he saw in it an occasion to write a three-minute dialogue for 2A's French lesson: a woman, buying a hundred eggs (where else but in France?), and chatting with the grocer, as he counts them out.

> — *Un, deux, trois, quatre — et quel âge a-t-il, votre fils, Madame Martin?*
> — *Eh bien, il a douze ans, Monsieur Lebrun.*
> — *Douze ans? Déjà? Sacrebleu! Alors, reprenons: douze, treize, quatorze…*

And so on, counting out more eggs again, and pausing to ask another and another and another question, while Madame Martin answered him patiently, and didn't notice how he skipped the totals. It went down well.

A year later, the whole class collaborated in writing a French play. The afternoon arrived when he and Michael Grace got themselves up as Gallic housewives: *Ah! Bonjour Denise — Bonjour Marthe!* They pranced about an imaginary *cuisine* in high heels and silk stockings and suspenders borrowed from their mothers, and made a batch of cakes. They beat eggs in a bowl and in place of flour, ho! ho! tipped in the plaster-of-Paris left lying around by M. Gaston, the husband of Denise. And so on to the dénouement of rock-hard buns, visitors breaking their dentures, howling with toothache and calling in the *gendarmerie*. PC Druce spent several evenings perfecting a batch of plaster-of-Paris rock-cakes, varnishing them to lifelike perfection: a collaborator and craftsman at his happiest.

But if French was living up to its promise, and flinging open fresh doors into thought and meaning, at other times his mentors failed him. In the space of an afternoon in his second year, he wrote off both Dusty Rhodes and his own mother as sources of certain kinds of enlightenment.

Dusty took 2A for Religious Instruction, week by week expounding biblical texts and inviting discussion. One afternoon, Dusty was called away to the telephone for a quarter of an hour, leaving 2A on their honour to sit quietly and read the Bible. Druce R.C.L., always one to read the last chapter first, plunged into the closing pages of The Revelation of St. John the Divine. When Dusty returned and the class filed out, Druce had a question.

'Sir, please Sir, what's "whore?"'

'What makes you ask, Druce?' However grim the look on his face, Dusty was unfailingly courteous.

'It's here, Sir, look, Sir: chapter 21 verse 7, Sir:

But the fearful, and the unbelieving, and the abominable, and murderers, and whoremongers, and sorcerers, and idolaters, and all liars shall have their part in the lake which burneth with fire and brimstone which is the second death...

Sir, I know "monger" means somebody who sells something; like a fishmonger sells fish, and an ironmonger sells, well, iron and stuff like that. But I don't know what "whore" is. Sir, why should God put you in a lake of fire and brimstone for selling whore, Sir? What is it?'

'A whore, Druce,' said Dusty, 'is a very wicked woman.'

Well, that's a great help, isn't it, I *don't* think, thought Druce, watching Dusty's gown fluttering as he strode away down the corridor. I mean, how can you sell a *woman*? So after school he looked for 'whore' in a fat dictionary in the Library. 'A prostitute, a strumpet' and 'NOT IN DECENT USE,' the dictionary told him, hiding behind words. When he got home, 'Mum, what's a prostitute?' he asked.

'Who told you that word? I demand to know,' said his mother, and he said he'd found it himself, looking up 'whore' from out of the Bible. He didn't bother to mention Dusty.

His mother's answer, when it came, made him wonder whether she and Dusty weren't in league. 'A prostitute,' she said solemnly, 'is a very wicked woman.'

'But mum—'

'Now go and get on with your music practice,' she said. 'I'm not prepared to discuss the matter.'

A day or two later, he asked Mr Moon. 'Ha, my dear fellow, that's not a topic of conversation between one gentleman and another,' wheezed Mr Moon, rasping his unshaven cheeks with his fingers.

So it was Marsh and Bone back at school who sniggered and put him wise.

*

Lou Marsh had emerged as a ring-leader long before the end of 1A's first Christmas term. Older than his years, and speaking in a languid drawl just short of insolence, Marsh was as much a clown as he was a bully, with an equal skill in composing obscene rhymes, and inflicting casual violence. He was vain about his looks, climbing off the victim he had tripped or wrestled to the floor and, still standing over him, sleeking back his lank hair with the comb he kept in his top pocket, and smiling around for approval and applause. As he did in the changing-room after showers whenever the class was left unsupervised.

All the while facing the room and not the wall, Marsh made getting dressed into a pantomime. Sighing, first he put on socks and shoes. Then, still naked from the ankles up, squatted down to tie his laces. He sighed again, and drew on his vest and buttoned his shirt, tied his tie, and fastened the brass buttons of his blazer. If he had his cap in his satchel, he put it on. Only then did he stoop to put on his underpants and trousers, dragging them over his shoes. Last of all, he took a tender farewell of his fat sausage, leaving it lolling through his fly until the echoes of the bell had died away.

Marsh's mind, like Dogger Bone's, was a vade-mecum of sexual innuendo. When Bone made a sudden grab for your testicles, or Marsh declaimed his latest lampoon upon you, it was sound policy to laugh along with them.

At first glance Bone seemed an unlikely henchman for Marsh, but they were never far apart. Bone was smaller and skinnier than Marsh. He was grubby, ink-smeared, peering through bleary spectacles that he repaired with electrician's black insulating tape whenever he broke them, which was often. But Dogger's looks were deceptive. He fought like a street-hooligan, foul-mouthed, wiry, hard-skulled, lashing out in an instant. Throughout the term he skimped his work in every subject, but sailed through the exams with ease. Where his Monkswood class-mates hastened to acquire the King's English at least in the classroom, it was Bone's pleasure to cling to his nasal cockney speech, with its dropped aitches and its 'ffs' for 'ths'. Alwyn Black BA was not amused by Dogger Bone.

*

By the end of their first term in the second year, the twenty-eight members of 2A had coalesced into a tightly-knit group, adhering to what their spokesmen were quick to invoke as 'the schoolboy code'. They evolved an elaborate jargon of their own, erecting it as a defence against the intrusion of outsiders. It struck deep. Decades later, Bren Slaney and Bob, alone together, heard themselves suddenly using phrases from that long-discarded slang, and were amazed.

At lesson-change, it was a lengthy march from Mrs River's room to the Art Room. It was further still to Geography, where there was a staircase to descend. 2A made their journeys into a military parade, marching off two abreast and in step, while Lou Marsh strode on ahead. For a brief stretch of the lower corridor, the mouth-music and the rapping of rulers on exercise books fell away. Dogger Bone hissed the command, 'Eyes right!' and inches away from the door to Dusty's office, Marsh took the salute.

It was an effective mode of subversion. Their esprit de corps might well present a challenge to authority; yet how could 2A be faulted for moving at an infantryman's pace from one class to another? The school rules forbade *running* in the corridors, not marching — which was, was it not, Sir? a form of ambulation, as Latin and French made clear — you wouldn't want us to shuffle along, Sir, would you? or slouch? The form wits argued their case with the passion of medieval schoolmen disputing how many angels could dance on a needle's point.

Dare to be insolent, or bluster like a barrack-room lawyer, and you were in dire trouble. But state your case, however incongruous or fantastical, with wit and good manners, and Dusty Rhodes, Walter Mason, and Fitz Fitzroy were all prepared to hear you out. After which they would annihilate or accede to your arguments with equal courtesy.

One morning at lesson change, Druce seized the opportunity to swat a bluebottle. When it settled for an instant on a window at the corridor-side of the room, he snatched up a book and hurled it. The pane shattered, and Dusty Rhodes, passing along the corridor at that moment, was greeted with a shower of splinters. He irrupted into the classroom.

'Who broke that window? You, Druce?'

'Yes, Sir. I'm sorry, Sir. But — '

'But what?'

'I was trying to kill a fly, Sir, and in the heat of the moment I forgot that glass is frangible.'

'Frangible, you say?' Dusty lingered over the word.

It was enough to save the day.

'Then we will say no more about it,' said Dusty. 'You will of course pay for the glass. Perhaps that will remind you in the future that glass is indeed, as you put it, frangible.' And he marched off down the corridor in apparent high good humour.

It was not the first time that they had courteously joined issue. At the start of his second autumn term, Druce R.C.L. had approached Dusty with a grievance.

On Friday afternoons Varley, the games master, numbered off all the keen footballers of the Second year for serious matches. At the end of the afternoon he meticulously recorded their scores. The rabble remaining, the 'kickabouts,' as Varley chose to call them — anything from seven or eight to twenty-three or more of them — hung about awaiting Varley's pleasure. Which was to exile them to a distant pitch, boot a ball in their direction, and tell them to get on with it.

Mooching up and down with the kickabouts wasn't Druce R.C.L.'s notion of a fruitful occupation. He knocked on the Headmaster's door.

'Sir, I think the school has a problem.'

'Indeed? And what might that problem be, Druce? Enlighten me.'

'Well, you see, Sir, people walk up and down Monkswood Lane all the time. They look over the hedge and watch us on the field. When they walk past on Friday afternoons, they can't avoid seeing me, Sir, shivering and running up and down, Sir, and suffering. It can't be a very good advertisement for the school — can it, Sir? — seeing me suffering.'

'But you have a remedy in mind, Druce, no doubt.'

'I thought, Sir, if I could read in the Library, every Friday afternoon—?'

'Hm.' Dusty smoothed his hand over his bald skull. 'I am, I may say, reassured to know that you have the good name of your school at heart,' he said. 'Very well, Druce, you may sit in the library. But make just one false move, and — do I make myself clear?'

It was an arrangement honoured by both parties.

In 1947, when Druce left the school and Dusty endorsed the final page of his report book, time's whirligig brought Dusty the opportunity to exact a price. 'Not a sportsman,' he wrote in the space allotted to *Games*. But smiling, and ever courteous, he was sportsman enough to add, at Druce's reminder: 'Captain of Chess.'

*

In September 1942, 2A was metamorphosed into 3A, with Miss April's Geography room as their form room.

It had been their home for barely a month when, snatching a moment while Miss April was elsewhere, Lou Marsh darted into her store-room. He emerged with the globe — a heavy black-lacquered hollow sphere of fibrous plaster — hoisted above his head. He struck a pose in front of the blackboard.

'Behold,' he proclaimed, 'Atlas!'

Then Dogger Bone made a feint at his mate's unguarded testicles.

Atlas sprang out of arm's reach and lost his balance. The terrestrial globe toppled from the heavens, and splintered into shards.

The destruction of the Geography-room globe was a serious matter. It forced into public view the rifts that lay between the teachings of 'the schoolboy code' and what the School rules implied about damage to property.

Miss April ordered 3A back to her room after school.

She had come out of retirement in 1941, to fill the gap left by the conscription of the geography master. She was tiny and bespectacled. Winter and summer she wore billowing directoire knickers clamped with elastic just above her knees. Sitting directly in front of her for Geography, Humby couldn't keep a pen or pencil on his desk for more than ten minutes at a stretch. He would nudge it off the table, duck down to pick it up and gaze up at Miss April's knickers as she presided at her open-fronted desk five feet away from his nose. He invariably returned to the world above red in the face and snorting with suppressed laughter.

After a lifetime of teaching girls, boys were a trial to Miss April. Horrified by the vandalism that had destroyed her globe, she hissed with rage as she questioned the members of 3A one by one.

'Did you do this?'

'No, Miss.'

'Are you aware who did?'

'Yes, Miss.'

'Give me the culprit's name.'

Silence.

A shaky silence once or twice. But the others turned in their desks to glare a warning, and the code held.

Marsh and Bone lied. But that was their affair. It wasn't 3A's place to sneak on them.

Miss April launched into a diatribe fast becoming familiar.

'I will not permit my equipment to be interfered with. You are all criminals, all accessories after the fact, you realise that? In any court of law your refusal to give evidence would make you equally guilty. Marsh! Fowler! if you utter one more word about there being nothing in the school rules to forbid your keeping silent, I shall report you to the Headmaster for gross insolence.'

She was enraged, stamping her foot at them.

'It is the *spirit*, not the *letter* of the law which is to be followed. Well?

'Robbins? What have you to tell me?'

Robbins, her favourite pupil, blanched. But he lowered his eyes and did not speak.

'Very well. Never, in all my teaching experience, have I ever encountered a concerted refusal to name the culprits in any affair.'

Well, she wouldn't have, would she? — teaching in a girls' school.

3A's glances at one another, shame-faced as they were, were eloquent. Miss April didn't understand the schoolboy code.

The trouble was that there were teachers who always tried to have it both ways. They constantly dragged in 'courts of law'; but refused to see that in any court of law it was *precisely* the letter, not the spirit of the law which counted. Just ask Blain in 4A: his dad was a solicitor.

Look, if teachers wanted to see themselves as prosecutors in a court of law and find you guilty of being 'accessories after the fact', then it was the letter of the law that they would have to go by. Nothing in the school rules said you weren't to touch the globe: therefore no rule had been broken. Neither Marsh nor Bone had *intended* to cause any damage. It was an accident. So, as long as the damage was paid for, that should be the end of the matter.

Well, yes, all right, Marsh and Bone had lied, saying they hadn't done it. But was there so much difference between that and pleading 'not guilty' in court, if you knew you perfectly well that you *were* guilty? Judges didn't charge you with lying to the court, for pleading 'not guilty', did they? No.

And hey! what about Plutarch's story of the Spartan boy, who stole a fox-cub? Holding it under his clothes and letting it chew his belly, rather than cry out and show that he was both a thief and a coward. You were all supposed to admire him for his courage.

That was a story they'd read in the scholarship class at Consort Road. And again, at Monkswood. Keep your mouth shut under interrogation: that was the moral of *that* story. A moral for a time of war.

So what it came down to was this.

Either insist that the spirit of the law be honoured, and accept along with it the spirit of a code which declares that a sneak is the lowest of the low.

Or appeal to the criminal law, and accept the fact that any lawyer worth his fee will search for every loophole in the letter of the law.

One or the other. Take it or leave it.

That was the line which 3A's legalists took after Miss April's inquisition, PC Druce's son among them, arguing the matter in the bike-sheds before cutting off home.

When he strode into Miss April's room at break next morning, Dusty allowed no discussion. 'I do not propose to waste your time or my own. Damage has been done, to equipment which it will be difficult to replace in wartime. You will each receive a detention, the globe will be paid for in full, and you will all apologise to Miss April for the distress you have caused her.'

The Head gazed at each of them in turn.

'After that, I wish to hear no more of this childish prank. My secretary will find out the cost of replacing the globe, and one of your number will take it upon himself to collect the money and bring it to me. Is that understood?—

'Marsh, you are fidgeting. May I take it, then, that you are about to volunteer for the task?'

O, the Head was wide awake, there was no doubt about that.

*

Only once in the years between 1938 and 1947 was it apparent that Dusty had made the wrong choice on a question of discipline.

When Monkswood opened its doors in 1938 to a first-year intake of a hundred boys, Dusty had decided to put off the appointment of prefects until the lads of that initial year had reached the fifth form and maturer understanding. It was a wrong move. In the event, given the lax supervision of a wartime school, and of homes where fathers had been drafted into the forces and mothers consigned to war work, it led to pitched schoolboy battles four years later.

In September 1942, the sudden accession of power went to the heads of a handful of prefects. Their former mates became underlings overnight, and most of them found it demeaning to obey. Or obeyed with a Nazi salute: 'Heil Hitler!' or, 'Jawohl, mein Führer!' In 3A the conflict escalated from mockery into open rebellion. There were bitter fist fights on the way to and from school and in the playground. And, for a while at least, the Spartan rule of silence held.

Lou Marsh and Dogger Bone, as his lieutenant, elected themselves leaders of the third-year *maquis*. Now that the Geography Room was 3A's form-room for the year, the barricades went up at their command. Their henchmen lugged the piano and the dais to jam the door at lunch-time, once Miss April was safely out of the way. For more than a week, whenever a squad of prefects tried to batter their way in, they were repelled with boots and fists and wall-maps rolled up around their wooden poles.

When the matter came to Dusty Rhodes' ears, he enforced an armistice. The too high-handed among the prefects were given a dressing-down, and the rebel leaders caned. But not before a prefect had broken his nose against the edge of the Geography-room door, deliberately set to swing shut by Dogger as he fled through it.

14

REBELLION

The spirit of adolescent rebellion was contagious. As 1942 and his twelfth year wore to an end, PC Druce's son came more and more into raging conflict with his father. Again and again, their quarrels split the household.

For one thing, Bob had discovered Jazz: the 'barbaric and bestial music of the sub-human Negro exploited by Jewish Capitalists', as Adolf Hitler called it. Bob bought the sheet-music of Mead Lux Lewis's *Honky-Tonk Train Blues,* and in the evenings whenever the coast was clear, he snatched time from practising Debussy and Chopin, and hammered out the ear-splitting left-hand rhythms and crushed-note discords of boogie-woogie. The effect was satisfying. And even more honky-tonky, when he opened the piano lid and trapped sheets of paper behind the dampers so that they would buzz against the strings when the hammers struck them. Coming in from duty at such moments, his father would burst through the door, red-faced and shouting: 'My God, you're doing it again! You're playing that loathsome American muck in my house!'

On Mondays, when Miss White came to Monkswood to visit her pupils, both he and Humby had the right to play the Geography-room piano after school. For the rest of the week, in geography lessons and at registration, they took turns to ripple their fingers on the table-top at moments of boredom, challenging one another to identify the piece they were playing. But the piano itself remained out of bounds, and the embargo rankled. So when Druce thought he'd practised enough, he tucked slips of paper against the piano-wires one lunchtime, and belted out the *Honky-Tonk Train Blues* for 3A's entertainment.

When Miss April ran into the room, he was still only half-way through. She scurried to her desk and pulled open the drawer in which she kept her detention slips.

'Very well,' — she began to rummage through the contents of the drawer — 'you have defied my instructions — and you are perfectly — aware — of the consequences—'

'Where are my detention slips? Someone has been interfering with my drawers!'

He opened the piano lid, drew Miss April's borrowed detention slips from behind the dampers, and handed them to her. On several there were rows of triple dents where the hammers had whacked them. She signed two with a flourish: one for the Jazz and one, as she announced to the class as a whole, for wanton interference with her drawers.

Dogger Bone, mouthing the phrase over, fought to contain his merriment and choked.

*

There was a respite to the conflict with his father in October 1942, when Druce R.C.L. collected prizes for Art and History on Speech Day and declaimed the de Vigny he had been rehearsing in his sleep for weeks. He turned to descend from the platform into the applause, with the saviours of France dead and dying and his own flesh dizzy with pride and the tides of blood swooping through his skull.

His mother hugged him. 'You may congratulate yourself, my son,' said his father, walking alongside him towards the railway station, carrying his prize books. 'But don't forget: never rest on your oars.'

Three days later it was his thirteenth birthday.

With it, as adolescence and rebellion erupted within him, and his father plunged more and more often into black despair and a horror of the cancer that had killed his own mother, the most miserable year to date of the Druce family's life began. The house rang with dispute and vituperation.

'Is this what I throw away good money for? For you to play the barrack-room lawyer with me? As long as you are in my house, you obey my rules,' cried PC Druce. 'He who pays the piper calls the tune…

'*And* I'm not talking about that Jazz muck you wreck the piano with, the moment you think my back is turned.'

He wanted so much for his son to achieve great things, to succeed where he himself had failed. But he could not stomach any challenge to his own vision of society. Since the terror of the night when the parachute-mine floated down onto Sparrowfield Lane, he lived in dread for the safety of his wife and son. He suffered from a succession of gastric and duodenal ulcers and for months on end the house smelled of the boiled cod which was his staple diet. Home again from nights on duty patrolling streets amid gunfire and falling shrapnel, he slept fitfully, while his wife and son tiptoed about the house and dared not speak above a whisper.

There were times, when his mood briefly swung upwards, that he delighted in debate and conceded points or demolished them with equal glee. But when the tide turned and he sank back into suicidal depression, any questioning of anything would fire his rage. He could not bear to be crossed in argument, demanding at every turn the assurance of acquiescence, yet needling away at his wife and son until he could light on a topic for dispute. With an adolescent son so self-opinionated and so ready to argue a point, there were occasions enough.

There was so much that was contradictory in the moral syllogisms which your mentors steered towards their supposedly triumphant Q.E.D. You were constantly faced with it: at home, at school, in church and, in 1945 and after, on the hustings.

Take the Reverend Stanford's sermon on 'hope' and 'despair'. A trivial text. But the squabble about it flared on for weeks in the Druce household.

'Two men looked out through prison bars,' the Vicar told his congregation at All Saints. 'One saw mud and the other stars.' Druce R.C.L. abandoned the game of counting on his fingers how many times the Vicar would say 'Praised be the Lord' in the course of his sermon, and listened as the discourse gathered force. Happy was he, who turning aside from the thoughts of the crime for which he had been rightly punished, looked towards the stars and found hope, said the Reverend Stanford. And how fatal the despair of the prisoner who could not lift his eyes from the filth in which he had become immersed!

But who *said* which prisoner despaired and which didn't? Not the verses. You could read them the opposite way. The Vicar expected his congregation to admire the prisoner who gazed up at the sky. But you could argue that the man's star-gazing proved that his feet *still* weren't on the ground, that there he was back again at his old habit of lying to himself, reaching for the impossible.

No, let the stars wait. Mud was where you started, feet on the ground, facing the facts about yourself and where you stood. Well, wasn't it?

Which seemed to be what Yeats' poem was getting at, when Druce encountered it as a sixth-former some years later: 'I must lie down where all the ladders start,/In the foul rag-and-bone shop of the heart.'

But Yeats was no present help to a thirteen-year-old as he fumbled to make his case against the Reverend Stanford's reading, and met the intransigence of his father's own despair.

It was a single dispute in a unending series.

'When your father's in one of his moods, don't argue,' said his mother. 'Do as I do. Just agree with whatever he says. It's the only way to pacify him.' But it was not.

*

She tried to put a truce to the quarrels, carrying her son away and out of the house on long walks through the fields and the forest. Together they gathered leaves and seeds — foxgloves in the spring and summer, for digitalin; rose-hips for rose-hip syrup in the autumn — and carried them to the collection centre where they would be parcelled up and dispatched for wartime processing. Safely out of her husband's hearing, she took her son's side, and heard his opinions out at length. In her attempts to coax him closer to her, she seemed to encourage his rebellion.

Beyond her womanly persuasion and his father's violent antipathies lay the same anguish. Like so many anxious parents in wartime, both were desperate to shield their only child from the unpalatable realities of life; while he craved for knowledge, for facts to face — however horrifying — and not the ignorance of innocence.

All the while, instinct drew him towards his father, for his mother was far too eager to worm her way into his thoughts. Once she had a secret in her grasp, you never could be sure what use she might make of it.

For a brief period he turned for enlightenment to Mr Moon. With him, at least, the most private of thoughts were safe. But Angus Moon, it soon became apparent, had little aptitude for logic-chopping, and possessed few thoughts of his own, confined as he was to a sick man's landscape. Its outer limits were the Moons' back door at number 68 — for Mr Moon never ventured down the steep slope of steps to the thigh-high grass and the raspberry canes — and the front gate where he lurked on rainless days shouting, as month succeeded month, to every passer-by. 'Flaming June, eh? Ha!… Flaming July, eh? Ha!… Flaming August, eh? Ha!…' As his own thirteenth year wore on, Mr Moon and he made less and less contact with one another, beyond politenesses and platitudes.

Increasingly, as his command of French grew greater and he began burrowing into Maupassant and François Villon on his own account — 'O, don't imagine I'm unaware of the filth you read,' announced PC Druce one evening, for months in the Vice Squad had put him wise to names and titles — it was towards Walter Mason that he looked for honesty of opinion.

'What you must do — and the sooner the better for everyone concerned — is to stop behaving like a hooligan,' Mr Mason told him. 'If you *must* smash things to prove that you have a right to exist, very well then. Smash things. But don't smash up the school… How many broken windows has your father had to pay for, this term? Go out and buy some cheap crockery and smash that. *Buy* it. That's the important part. You've got to put something of value into what you smash, and punish yourself by smashing it.

'Whatever it is that you are smashing up at the back of your mind — no, I don't want to hear about it: I'd rather you thought it out for yourself on your own — whatever or *whoever* it is, smash your own property and punish yourself at the same time. That's the way to get this resentment out of your system. At present you're your own worst enemy.'

He even tried it once or twice, and in time the cure worked; although he came close to christening a vase 'Walter' before smashing it, to exorcise insights that were too close to the bone for comfort.

And there were always other ways to rebel. Against adult expectations and your own childish phobias alike.

Being afraid of heights, for instance. As the autumn evenings of 1943 drew in, Bren Slaney and he found an answer to that. He was last to take his turn in the sequence of Miss White's piano pupils. By the time he sat down at the keyboard at her side, he and Slaney had spent half an hour on the school roof as dusk deepened into twilight, after climbing through a first floor window and up a yard or two of drainpipe. The first time they went up and travelled the four-foot-wide walkway between a pitched roof and a waist-high parapet, they were almost overmastered by terror; cringing away from the gulf of darkness beyond the parapet, they handed themselves along against the roof-tiles. But within a month they could race through the dark along the centre of the walkway, from one end of the school to the other.

*

The author (circled) at Buckhurst Hill CHS, July 1943

At the start and end of every term, it was the Monkswood custom to sing the school anthem. Alwyn Black's phrases were urbane and platitudinous. But then, to be fair to the Senior Master, few school songs are not. His second stanza gazed out across the coming decades, while for a few bars the melody shifted into the minor key:

> But changeful time with restless speed
> Its silent course still runs
> And years may bring an altered scene,
> To welcome future sons…

But long before they pasted the words and music into their hymn-books, the prophecies had been hardening into reality. '*May bring* an altered scene'?
Were bringing. Had brought.

155

As the eight-and-twenty pupils of 2A shouldered their way into adolescence they recognised how far and how fast the landscapes of books and learning were stretching out beyond them, across past time and present space. Daily their frustration grew with the denials inflicted by wartime: the unexplained directives, the jammed airwaves, the daily censorship of information, the old choices restricted, the long-awaited freedoms cancelled. Just as they reached an age to travel and explore, the barricades had gone up.

The 'Keep Out!' notices began close to their own front gates. Open acres through which they had roved as children now were fenced off behind barbed wire. The beaches were sown with mines. France and the Netherlands were occupied by Nazi troops, and lay a hostile sea away, just when all that they seemed to offer had become more irresistibly alluring. Beyond a circle some ten or fifteen miles across, so much was still unknown and unmapped in their short and untutored memories. And now it was physically out of reach.

Meanwhile the world they dwelt in had become a hooligan's world, a world of carefully-constructed lies, licensed vandalism, murder.

How else explain the incendiaries and high explosive falling out of the sky whenever there was a bomber's moon?

How else explain the nightlong sobs of Doktor Koebbels in the bedroom across the alley between 66 and 64 Auckland Drive? Members of the Gestapo had torn the skin off his back, whipping him with electric flex. One evening PC Druce sat at the dinner table wiping away tears, having been shown that mutilated flesh.

It was a hooligan's world whose spitefulness and sour illogicality spread into their daily lives, and it offered them a specious justification for their own destructive acts.

What was so wicked about catapulting out the panes of a gaslamp, when adults were blowing one another's homes to pieces? Tell me that. Let *them* stop and we'll do the same. Why shouldn't you pull unexploded incendiaries out of the river clay, empty out the thermite, and carry them to school and home again at the bottom of your satchel? Finders Keepers! Why shouldn't you mix icing sugar with weedkiller, and detonate it in the forest in a home-made bomb? A boy whose argument *that* had been lost three fingers learning an answer.

Living as they did less than a dozen miles from London as the crow and the enemy raider flew, war was all around them. Who was there to notice an illegal flash or bang? In the autumn of 1944, Collins brought his father's Air Force pistol to school, while Price produced a box of stolen soft-nosed .22 rounds from his satchel. Half the members of 5A spent a period of double maths with their hands under the desks trimming the over-long leaden bullets down to size with razor-blades and pencil-sharpeners. At lunchtime a group of bravos, Druce–to his amazement — being granted a place among them, fired round after round into the steep bank of earth beyond the bike sheds. The duty master stood in a distant doorway sipping his tea, oblivious to what was going on.

On the way home that day, Price and Collins stumbled across a plank and the carcase of a dog in the ditch alongside the lane to Monkswood. They were joined by Druce, Slaney, and Verity, in the gathering twilight. Price parcelled out three or four rounds apiece, and they carved off the excess lead, and notched the flat end with a cross to make experimental dumdums. The effects amazed and appalled them: there was a quarter-inch entry hole in each case, and a cone of wood or dead dog's flesh almost as wide as a saucer ripped out of the far side of their targets

Collins smuggled the revolver back into the house that evening, and his father was none the wiser.

A hooligan's world.

Bare-knuckle fights in the playground were frequent. They began with a ring of jeerers and cheerers-on and ended with a ritual handshake of victor and victim that was somehow supposed to sanctify the conflict. Often the battles were drawn-out and vicious, and the participants staggered away with bloody noses, eyes blackened and swollen, and loosened teeth.

When Varley the gym-master left to join the army, his more slovenly successors stayed out of the changing room after gym, and let mayhem take its course. Linger a moment too long in the showers, and your towel would arrive to join you. Or you'd emerge to find your clothes pulled inside out and knotted together.

Unless you were Marsh or Bone, or a classmate too popular to be interfered with. Druce was an early victim, betrayed by his fluent gift of insult. Until he learned to flick the wetted end of a towel like a whipcrack, and plant bruise after bruise on an opponent's naked skin.

*

Almost from one month to the next, as puberty began to transmogrify him and his once-familiar body became an alien thing, his eyesight blurred. In the physics lab he had always sat in the back row. Soon he was walking further and further to the front to read the blackboard, and the new science mistress told him to go to an optician for god's sake. The tests revealed that he had become short-sighted, and astigmatic.

'Eyestrain,' said his mother. 'Poring over books and drawings hour after hour. What did I tell you? What's the point of all that reading if it only ruins your eyesight? Where's the sense in that?'

She took him for a walk in the forest while he acclimatised himself to the panes of glass at each side of his nose and the springy loops of wire around his ears. Beyond the edges of the glass, the unfocused planes of light were giddying, no matter how needle-sharp the world straight-ahead had become.

But that was not his only worry. How could you stick up for yourself and give as good as you got when you couldn't see without your goggles, and were terrified of the glass breaking into your eyes?

'Let's have a look at you,' said his father. 'Four eyes, eh Dorothy? You're the first of the Druces to be four-eyed. I don't know.'

His father intended it as a joke.

In secret he tried his hand at smoking, asserting independence of a kind. Why not? He wasn't the only one. But in wartime it wasn't easy, not even for the grown-up smoker: tobacconists and publicans kept their meagre stock of tobacco under the counter, and doled it out only to favoured customers. For a few months you might strike lucky with a railway-platform slot-machine and receive a single dry-as-dust cigarette in return for your penny. On the minuscule packet there was the picture of a butler holding a silver salver, and the caption: 'Your Kensitas, Sir.'

'Thank you, my man,' said Druce R.C.L. when he had ferreted out such treasure trove. 'And we'll have our whisky in the billiard-room.'

He made his gaspers last for a week, nipping them out after a couple of puffs, and hiding them in the aspidistra pot on the front-room windowsill.

*

Alwyn Black's changeful time raced on, and their own petty rebellions spread wider, like circles on a pond. Beyond Humby's efforts to initial the ceiling above every desk in which he sat with pellets of chewed blotting-paper. Beyond letting the classroom air seethe with flung chalk the instant certain masters withdrew their attention, or in summer with bumble-bees fetched in from the playing-field in their handerchiefs.

Beyond the winter sport of swinging open the carriage doors as their train rounded the curve into the Village station, and raking the platforms with a volley of snowballs.

Beyond Marsh's skill at stinging Miss April's fingers with a pellet fired from a rubber band as she wrote on the blackboard. Beyond Bone's trick of lobbing a nub of chalk into her shoe as she perched up on tiptoe to write, so that she squealed as her whole weight came down upon it.

Clowning changed all too quickly into horseplay, and horseplay corroded into spite.

On the way home from school in an earlier winter, Druce had pitched a snowball past Verity's head into the open window of his railway compartment. The next morning, 2A were paralysed with laughter at Verity's account. Just as the train began to move, a pompous-faced businessman had leapt aboard, muttering and looking annoyed at finding Verity in the otherwise-empty compartment. He choose a seat precisely underneath the mound of snow. As the train gathered speed so did the snow, sliding down the woodwork while Verity prayed that it wouldn't detach itself before he could make his escape at the next station. After a minute or so the snow flopped down, like a ladleful of blancmange, onto the man's bowler hat. The man sprang up and accused Verity of throwing it; he had a damn good mind to write to Verity's headmaster, and have him walloped.

It was a perfect anecdote, Chaplinesque in its gleeful realization of a childish disaster. It grew funnier every time Verity retold it or when Druce, as the prime mover, retold it on Verity's behalf. But other anecdotes were more disturbing.

Like boasts of stealing fog-signals: lead capsules of gunpowder fastened to the railway track to explode and warn an engine-driver who had passed a signal at red. *That* was so obviously criminally stupid. The thought didn't stop some idiots from finding it funny. It didn't stop one idiot — not a Monkswood boy, as it happened — from posting a stolen fog-signal down the chimney of a platelayer's hut the day after the man had chased him off railway property.

Hearing about the fire which followed and knowing the idiot's identity imposed a strain on Druce and Slaney's loyalty to the schoolboy code of silence. Nobody questioned them, and they were saved from an unavoidable act of treachery. Luckily the platelayer had been away from his hut at the time, and escaped unhurt. But they both were aware that they had no right to an easy conscience.

All too easily, anticipated glee blinded the would-be comedian. Wartime multiplied opportunities, spawning practical jokes that were less than human. Towards the end of the war, the Luftwaffe rained down tiny brightly-coloured plastic toys on Britain. They were designed to explode and maim the child who picked them up.

No, but wait now, this *was* funny, this was one in the eye for Jerry: and that was the tale of how British agents in occupied Europe had come up with an answer to a problem. How could you sabotage a factory with a well-placed bomb, and still make your getaway unhurt? Easy. Get a dead rat, fill its belly with explosive and leave it lying in the boiler room. Think now: what would a stoker, finding a dead rat, do with it? Shovel it up and throw it into the furnace, of course. Bang! Ha ha! End of furnace.

And of stoker, slave labourer or not. But let's not dwell on that.

Nor on the stinking mess that resulted whenever somebody dropped a lump of calcium carbide into a Monkswood inkwell. It was pointlessly destructive, but for a while it became a craze. If the bike-shop had run out of the carbide used in wartime cycle-lamps, never mind. You could manufacture the stuff easily enough on the gas-stove at home. The only problem was how to make your getaway as the ink foamed and spread across the desk.

Druce pondered on a solution: a mixture of yeast, and sugar, perhaps? Fermenting overnight, it would take so long that no-one could point a finger at the fleeing culprit. But the idea was abstract, an attempted answer to a logistic problem, and he did not put it to the proof.

*

It was a commonplace for members of staff to inform 3A that they were the brightest and most intractable form in the brief history of the school. The remark usually prefaced an attempt to destroy their sense of loyalty to the group. It was left to Walter Mason, revered as the master who had welcomed them into 1A, to seize upon that adolescent esprit-de-corps, and make it a motivating force in his teaching.

Their form jargon served them as a lingua franca in and out of school. As baffling to outsiders as the talk among traders in an East-end market, its significances were closely guarded and continually added to. In the French class, French itself served as the language of their freemasonry, and their lessons adhered to a disciplined etiquette. Whenever from time to time a new boy joined the form, he was admitted only after due ceremony, and behind a guarded door. Grace, «*Michel*», and Druce, «*Robert*», administered the oath of loyalty, and the novice was baptised by Marsh, «*Louis*», with a spoonful of water scrubbed into his hair, and the *nom de baptême* by which he would henceforth be addressed in class. Walter Mason's indulgence was not ill-spent. In summer 1945, no member of the twenty-four-strong form would fail School-Cert French, while twenty-two passed with a credit or distinction.

From this larger group an inner circle sprang, seven in number, *les Vrai de Vrai*. With Walter Mason as *Président d'honneur* in perpetuity, they met after school in secret for the following two years. Once a fortnight the summons to attend went out, signalled with a symbol of interlocking V's displayed on the school notice-board. In conclave behind a guarded store-room door, they clattered through their allotted thirty minutes in elaborate and gleeful ritual.

*

At All-Saints there was soon another, more public ritual to occupy his thoughts. Two months after his fourteenth birthday and two days before Miss April's end-of-term report — *He is apt to be a little thoughtless and impatient; he does not realise that attention to details is important*: huh! so much for the meticulous north arrows he inscribed for her delight — the Bishop's eighty-year-old weight drove down on top of his skull and lo! he was confirmed, welcome as a participant in the Mystery of the Lord's Supper.

He knelt alongside John Robbins with a rumbling breakfastless belly each Sunday morning, as together they pledged themselves anew. *To lead a new life, following the commandments of God and walking from henceforth in his holy ways…*

You knelt in line and waited to pick up a disc of ice-cream wafer from out of your cupped hands with the tip of your tongue. It pasted itself to the roof of your mouth, *Christ's flesh*. Then you felt the chill of metal against your lips and the wetness of wine, before the Vicar swivelled the chalice round and wiped the edge in readiness for your neighbour at the altar rail. A minute ago, he had snapped God in two and handed Him around from a silver plate, and now he was tipping Him out of a silver cup. *The Body of our Lord Jesus Christ, which was given for thee… The Blood of our Lord Jesus Christ, which was shed for thee…* The Vicar's murmuring moved away along the line. You knelt there for a moment longer, and then trooped back to your pew.

Safely back in his own place, he slid down onto his knees again, thinking: 'What shall I think about?' and glancing around through his fingers for inspiration. His eyes rested on the coloured glass that gleamed like lead on a dark winter morning, or was awash with sunlight… He gazed at columns spaced like a grove of beech-trunks, and up at their capitals. They were as fat as cushions, writhing with foliage carved in stone…

The echoes of shuffling feet faded away, and after a silence the Vicar prayed again and blessed them all. And then you burst out into the daylight and shook the Vicar's hand and went home, hungry for breakfast, awake and alive to the world.

It was satisfying, as worldly mysteries go, yet somehow not what he had hoped for. It didn't seem much of a *mystery* at all. How could it be, with the entire congregation in on the secret?

A month later, the Vicar invited him to be a Server, and his viewpoint changed as he contemplated the ritual from behind the scenes. With an old hand to show him the ropes, he lit the candles on the altar. Back in the vestry, he poured wine and water into the sacred vessels, counted out wafers into the pyx, and recited the responses as the Vicar intoned the *Introit*. Together they led the congregation in the prayers and responses, and he learned to pitch his voice up and back from the windows above the altar, so that the mumbling faithful would follow and not get out of step. He helped to wash up and dry the patten and the chalice in the vestry afterwards, before locking them away. By then the Vicar would have returned from shaking hands with his flock at the West door and be complaining again about the lipstick on the linen cloth he wiped the chalice with, while the Vicar's Warden was totting up the collection and making a note of the total in a register.

Serving at the altar, you had no leisure to let your thoughts wander. It was theatre, ritualised and holy, and a moment's inattention could ruin it. The first few times he was terrified, as stage-fright coalesced with awe and threatened to become a nightmare. Suppose you lost track, and intoned the wrong response? Suppose you forgot yourself, and started to declaim the Apostles' Creed instead of the Nicene Creed? Suppose, O my God, suppose you tripped your heel in your cassock, and spilt the Blood of Christ?

But then *his* turn to lead came round, and the Vicar asked him to show John Robbins the ropes. He watched John like a cat at a mousehole, all his muscles tensed on John's behalf. Suddenly, in the midst of chatting with him in the vestry afterwards, he realised that all his own stage-fright had evaporated in the act of escorting a newcomer through the movements of the ritual. The anguish never returned.

Not that you could relax your vigilance in the face of the congregation on Sunday mornings. Inside the sanctuary he never knelt on both knees but rested all his weight on the right, surreptitiously pulling the cassock away from the heel of his right foot and the toes of his left so that it wouldn't trip him. You had to be ready to spring up at the appropriate moment.

And, when the ageing Bishop was at the altar, at unforeseen moments, too. The Bishop lived close by in the Village and occasionally wandered along to assume the role of celebrant. Fellow guardian of the mystery, you had to be prepared to cut in fast and grab the missal — *Forgive me, My Lord* — from his trembling fingers, whenever he turned over two pages at once and was about to skip an essential prayer.

15

CONFLICT

There was a trick you could use to create a draught when the coal was damp or there was barely firewood enough to get it going. Once you'd started the fire with a match, you squatted down on the hearth-rug, opened out the double-page of a newspaper, and held it with outstretched arms across the opening of the fireplace. If you were lucky, the air sucked in and tried to drag the paper up the chimney, while you watched for a glow and the yellow light of a flame to shine through the newsprint.

Then, as the kindling began to roar, the question was how long you dared to hold the paper there, before somewhere across its surface it began to char and catch. Leave it too late and you'd find yourself grasping a faceful of flames. Desperately you scrunched them together, trying to extinguish them, while the smell of smoke spread through the house.

Police Constable Druce's sudden rages were like that, flaring up in an instant with the briefest of warning, or no warning at all.

One morning Druce R.C.L. was working at his father's side in the sunshine, clipping the privet hedge. As his father snipped with the shears, and Bob swept up the litter of leaves, their conversation turned to the landlord, whose letter from Bristol had arrived at breakfast-time: he was proposing to raise the rent. 'What, that old ponce?' said Bob. He'd learned the word from the lips of Marsh or Bone; not knowing quite what it meant, but recognizing it as an insult, and savouring it upon his tongue. He waited for his father's companionable laugh.

Instead of which his right ear exploded and he found himself sprawling across the crazy paving.

'Never let me hear you use that word again,' said PC Druce, leaning down out of the sky above him. 'D'you hear me? My god, I'm a patient man, but there are times when you drive me to the end of my tether. Who is it who teaches you this filthy talk?'

Quicksilver in his moods, his father liked to present himself as long-suffering, endowed with infinite patience. 'Beware the anger of a patient man,' he would intone.

'Your father? Patient?' Dorothy Druce would mutter, talking obliquely, glancing out of the tail of her eye at her husband. 'Him, *patient*? He doesn't know the meaning of the word.'

She did, especially when there was trouble in the offing, as so often there was in Bob's adolescent years. She didn't flare up as his father did, in a straw fire that burnt itself out as suddenly as it had appeared, if you were lucky. No, she pursed her lips and cast dark glances, and softened you up by sighing.

'What, mum? What's the matter? What have I *done*?'

'Phhh!' It wasn't so much a sigh, as a pout and a sharp expulsion of breath. As if she were blowing out a match that had had the temerity to scorch her fingers.

'Phhh!' She bustled around the table, rapping down saucers and plates, clanking the cutlery.

'Your *food* is on the *table*.'

Any appetite you might have had, sank away, out of your grasp.

'Phhh!...'

'What *is* it? What am I supposed to have done?'

'I don't need to *tell* you. *You* know perfectly well.'

She went on blowing out invisible matches while he squirmed and tried to guess which transgression it was that she had in mind. But he soon learned to hold his tongue for fear of revealing something that she hadn't even got wind of yet.

'*You* know perfectly well what I'm talking about, don't you...'

'O, yes, you *know*, all right...'

'*Phhh!*...'

'You may *think* you can pull the wool over my eyes. But you can't...'

'I can *read* you like a book...'

Could she? There were times he thought she could. But give in at that point, and within minutes she'd have turned him inside-out, and have him on his knees and promising.

*

Thirteen and fourteen years old, he wondered if it might be true that people could read your thoughts. He flirted with the nightmare fantasy of a ticker-tape screen — available to anyone who cared to look — that ran across the middle of your forehead, betraying the words passing through your mind, as they unscrolled along its length; a built-in lie detector, part of your body's betrayal. It was too anguishing to think about for long, a step towards mania.

Yet, given the duplicity of body language, the notion of a treacherous screen was not so far from the truth. And, disturbing as it was, it was a pragmatic metaphor. It suggested a way of foiling a too-perceptive inquisitor.

Think *other* thoughts: that was the trick, surely. Clutter up the screen with poems, nursery-rhymes, the multiplication table, French irregular verbs… Count the books on a shelf, the patterns in a carpet, the panes in the windows. Anything that would prevent your inner thoughts from breaking through into daylight.

Hadn't he been doing that for years, to stop himself from thinking disruptive thoughts in church?

But as adolescence hit you and twisted the world askew, even the flesh and bone in which you dwelt behaved like a mutinous animal.

Eyeballs changed their shape, condemning you perhaps to dangle panes of glass on either side of your nose. Pimples sprang up on your chin overnight, like toadstools under trees. When he scratched his own pimples open, each released a tiny hair, coiled like a watchspring. Suddenly your voice could modulate itself across octaves without warning, plunging in mid-word from a squeak to a growl. He was spared *that* indignity, thank God.

Once-familiar limbs became disobedient and ungainly, unsure of the space that they occupied. Even the furniture seemed to enter the conspiracy against some unfortunates. Just keep your eye on John Robbins: for months he seemed to be incapable of crossing a room without lurching against every object in his path.

Trigger-happy flesh erected itself as you bounced along on the back seats of a bus; and rose without warning at a snatch of talk, or a fleeting image, or in company.

Emotions of an instant could flood you from toes to scalp with a blood-hot blush, or sweep you into tears or speechless fury. In his father's wildfire rages he often recognized his own.

*

One morning he settled down at the kitchen table with his tubes of paint and jars of linseed oil and turpentine to copy a picture he'd found in a book. It was some six inches square, the portrait of a woman. She stood with her back to the viewer, naked to the hips, her flesh gleaming above a swirl of drapery. The challenge lay in catching the fall and refraction of the light from a maze of conflicting textures: pearly flesh, the sombre gleam of velvet, satin flash, the glitter of brocade. For the space of three hours he laboured over the task he had set himself, while his mother sat nearby with her knitting.

Slowly his copy came to a kind of perfection. When he leaned back from it the tiny brushstrokes seemed to coalesce into waterfalling satin and velvet, and tensed muscles under the woman's skin.

Suddenly his mother broke the spell, telling him it was high time he cleared his things away for her to set the table. He watched with horror as his hand snatched up a brush and scrubbed the painted surface into oblivion, while his eyes brimmed over with tears. His mother begged him to tell her what was the matter, but he did not know himself. She tried to console him, but could not. At last she went off into the scullery, leaving him alone in the room. He scrambled his painting things together, and carried them up to his bedroom. There, still shaking, he took a new piece of canvas, and began all over again.

He found it hard to bear himself at times like this. It was scarcely a wonder that people around him were repelled by this sudden, unfamiliar, graceless self.

*

'Self-*abuse*, *that's* what I'm talking about,' his mother announced one teatime, flinging his soiled pyjamas onto the table after a quarter of an hour of sighing and looking him in the eye.

Shame, indignation, blind rage beat in his skull. As if he'd be so grubby, or so feckless, as to play with himself in bed. But how could he answer her? — any reasoned attempt at denial would have been an admission.

167

'*Well?*'

And there were the stains. How could he begin to explain about wet dreams? 'What? That's when ya dream about girls, an' wake up wiv a cold rice pudden on yer belly!' Dogger Bone's knowingness had forewarned him of this latest, wilful joke his maleness had been storing up to spring on him, reflex, hydraulic, impossible to guard against.

'Self-*abuse*. Polluting yourself. Abusing God's gifts. You realize that?'

His mother would not listen, was incapable of listening, faced with an alien son, a changeling.

The idea of pollution preyed upon her thoughts, as it did upon the thoughts of so many of her immediately post-Victorian generation. It was all there in *Plain Home Talk*, all of a piece with the directives of Dr Samuel Foote to quell the flesh with cold baths and drive out corruption with laxatives. It lay at the heart of the muscular Christianity of the *Boy's Own Paper*, a bound volume of which he had cherished until it fell apart in the rainy ruin of his books in the roofless bedroom at Sparrowfield Lane. Its correspondence columns had been full of cryptic threats:

NERVOUSNESS: You are terribly below par. We can't tell you how to get well as you don't give us the cause, but we guess at it. No, don't go into the army. You would be a coward and get cashiered. Consult a doctor.

BAD DREAMS: It is your own fault. Have a struggle and conquer, lad. We fear for your future if you do not.

A SAD STORY: No time to take a cold tub! Nonsense. You can't even spare seven minutes? Take the advice we so often give under the head of *nervousness*, and lead a pure life, unless you want to die an early death.

He had often puzzled over the words, not understanding what they hinted at until he came to live next door to Angus Moon. But now it was 1943 and only weeks away from his fourteenth birthday.

'Are you listening to me? Just look me in the eye. No, you can't, can you?' His mother stood gazing down at him.

He sat over the meal he could not bear to eat, squirming beneath her homily and feeling himself diminished by it, his privacy stripped naked.

*

In childhood a parent's care had been so desirable a thing: 'It's all right, daddy's here… Don't cry, darling; tell Mummy what's the matter.' A cup of warm milk, a cool hand on a fevered forehead. With adolescence — and the pressure intensified amid the universal angst of wartime — that loving protectiveness seemed to have had soured into surveillance. His parent's continual supervision was irritating, an invasion of his freedom of thought and speech. Not one of the things that he could call his own, he felt, was free from prying eyes nowadays.

'Secrets? *What* secrets? At your age you shouldn't *have* secrets. There are not and there never will be secrets in *this* house,' his mother and father asserted.

They freely opened and read one another's letters, and considered doing so a virtue. If a letter came addressed to him — not that many did — whoever picked it up from the hall-mat first would think fit to open it and read it. From as long as he could remember, he had been proud of bearing the same Christian name as his father. Now it seemed less of a good thing.

When National Identity Cards were first issued in 1939, he was pleased that his membership of his family group had been formally acknowledged. 'CCFZ/273/3 Druce R.C.L.' His father had made him recite the formula. 'CCFZ/273' identified the Druce family. His father was '/1' and his mother was '/2', and Bobby was the '/3'. Druce R.K. printed the cypher in violet endorsing-ink on the canvas cover of his son's gas-mask case. A day or so later he came home with it engraved on a silver medal for Bobby to wear on a string around his neck. And here it remains indelibly inked into the hollows of his brain today.

'But what about *Pat*? If I'm the third of the Druces, Pat's the fourth,' he had protested. 'She ought to have "CCFZ/273/4 Druce P." on her collar. So when are you going get one made?' PC Druce was not prepared to countenance *that* silly sort of joke in a police officer's household. 'I didn't mean it as a joke,' said his son at that distant time.

But now, four years later, such a fixed identity was fast becoming irksome, a source of irritation and not of pride. For while you struggled with your alien and adolescent self, all around you the old authorities seemed to be weakening, the old dimensions going askew, the old imperatives crumbling away.

Willingly or not, adults were losing their divine right to be obeyed or even to be listened to. From now on they'd need arguments weightier than the years of their age. As the weeks went by, it seemed more and more natural to challenge them — all your mentors alike: parents, teachers, clergymen — to test the calibre of their thought: wasn't that what education was all about?

As you searched inside and around yourself to discover who you were, even your parents' well-meant gestures of love could be invasive. Perhaps they always had been.

'*You* have always been the most important thing in my life. When they took you away to hospital with diphtheria, I slobbered your mouth with mine so that I'd catch the germs too,' his mother told him, 'I loved you so much. I couldn't bear to be parted from you.'

He shuddered, rejecting the image, wiping his mouth. He felt ashamed to have been the object, however desperately loved, of such idiotic behaviour. Why must she insist on hemming him in? He neither knew nor asked for an answer; knew only that he loved her, but did not want to be possessed.

He'd trodden his own paths before, but now it seemed that things were increasingly out in the open, ceaselessly under scrutiny. His parents, finding their authority disputed, re-asserted it. They clung to their habit of surveillance, and affirmed it as their right.

'As long as you are living in this house, you will abide by *my* rules,' his father repeated. 'He who pays the piper calls the tune...

'And you can keep your half-baked opinions to yourself. I don't want to listen to that claptrap.'

At other times his father tried cajolery.

'Now come here and sit down, and listen to me, my son. Your mother and I are the only true friends you've got in this world. Get that into your head. Be guided by us. Nobody else is going to help you. They'll only stand by and jeer when they see you come a cropper...

'*What?* Slaney says? *Slaney* says? I suppose if Slaney told you to put your head under a steamroller, you'd do it. That boy's a bad influence on you...

'I want a stop put to it forthwith. Do you hear me? Stay away from that Slaney. He's no good to you.'

But how could you stay away from the friend you went to and from school with morning and evening? Whose thoughts were so much more in tune with yours, than those of the parents who cocooned you with restrictions?

Brendan Slaney, eldest of three red-haired brothers, lived a quarter of a mile away. His father was the dispenser at the Co-Op chemists in the Village. That was a black mark against the Slaney family from the start: Mrs Druce disliked the Co-Op on principle and wouldn't set foot in it if she could find what she wanted elsewhere. Bren's home in Hawkswood Road — Bren's younger brother Don, earphones clamped on his ears, frowning into the crystal set that he endlessly rebuilt; Frank, the youngest, chuckling over a book and reading out bits aloud; Bren's granny rocking herself by the fire and muttering; Bren's mother carrying in cups of tea; Bren's father in the front room practising the violin for an hour at a stretch — that was a place of give and take, of unprotesting acceptance of otherness.

To the half-Irish lapsed Papist that Robert Druce Senior was, the Slaneys smelt of brimstone. In his mind's eye they were axe-wielders, wild Scandinavians, Norsemen: not the gentle Lancashire Catholic stock they were.

'That Mister Slaney — supposed to be an educated man, what sort of father is he, eh? — lets those boys run wild. Dorothy, have you seen their front gate? Kicked to pieces. They use it for a goalpost, playing football in the street. The mother's no better than the father, never corrects them...

'Now I'm warning you for the last time, d'you hear me? keep away from that Slaney. I don't want him near this house.'

But he couldn't stop the pair of them travelling to and from school together, even if there were seasons when they had to meet and part on the railway station platform, or where Auckland Drive petered out and the field-path began. And soon, before many weeks were out, Bren would knock on the door again at number 66 and win Bob's mother round with his shy charm.

Stocky, soft-spoken like all the Slaneys, fearlessly loyal, hard to arouse to anger but a berseker when enraged, Bren was a companion in adventure, a counterbalance to Bob's volatile moods, Roland to his Oliver, Oliver to his Roland. In one another's company they tramped the meadows and rafted the river, and in summer dived into its depths at Bombhole Corner, where a German bomb had obligingly hollowed out a crater in the river bed. Years later and now members of the Sixth, they would go on swimming and diving at that same spot, cutting away on lesson-free Wednesday afternoons in summer, with cigarettes and ice-cream soda in their satchels.

In 1944, they saw a film together at the Regal about the Burmese jungle. That weekend, they both made blowpipes, boring down the length of a bamboo cane with a red hot iron rod. For blowpipe-darts, they glued tufts of cotton wool to sewing needles, puffed them out of their blowpipes, and watched them fly and stick in along the fence.

They saw another film and made their own *bolas*: loops of cord with a weight at each end, that South American rancheros used to fling at the legs of stampeding cattle to hobble them and bring them down. They sent their *bolas* whirling, to pinion the trunks of saplings. They'd have liked to hurl them at the cows, but thought better of it. Never mind, if the church-bells rang and German paratroops ever landed, they'd be in for a nasty shock.

They saw another film, and went scrounging around Dawson's woodyard, and made their own vaulting-poles. You could run and ground them close to a hedge or in the gravelly river-bed and, hup! sail over the obstacle. One afternoon Bob came down on an upturned broken bottle and Bren and he lost their nerve for launching out across unreconnoitred territory.

You didn't need to see a film to know how to make a catapult. Bob fashioned his in secret in the garden-shed, with bent steel rods for the yoke, a tool-handle from Woolworths, and an inch-wide strip of motor-tyre inner tube for the elastic. They looped their catapults around their necks and under their shirts to keep them out of sight. Back indoors Bob hid his on top of the wardrobe. Not his own wardrobe, naturally: his mother regularly searched around up there for what she might find. But in the no-man's land behind the architrave on top of his father's wardrobe it was safe enough. Except for a week or so before Christmas or his birthday, and then it was Bob who searched around and squeezed and shook the parcels hidden there, while his catty was tucked away at the bottom of a box of books in the landlord's shed.

*

His father had no objection to his son's friendship with David Verity.

Verity and he had much in common. Both were only children; in David's case of devoutly chapel-going, elderly parents. Both were sons of a mother whose maiden name had been Wright: it seemed to constitute a bond between them, however slight. Both were of an age to be fascinated with the world at the end of their fingertips.

They lived five miles apart, in very different circumstances. At Monkswood they occupied adjacent desks, and fraternised in term-time. But even after an interval of days or weeks of holiday their conversation somehow always seemed to resume in mid-sentence.

When they met again in the hall at Monkswood after a lapse of forty years, their talk continued virtually unbroken, almost without preamble. Neither found that surprising.

There was much to draw them together. They were both passionately involved with the physical world, both fascinated by ideas and concepts, both in love with language. For a couple of terms in their second year, they raced to be the first to make a gunpowder-fuelled rocket that would actually lift off. Verity won, and went on to design a mortar that fired tiny copper tubes. As they grew older, they argued questions of ethics and authority and discussed the role of science, and the diverging lines of Verity's Low-Protestant and Druce's High-Church faith. Both could dissect a text or turn a French couplet with facility.

On their way home from school along Monkswood Lane, they loitered in the brickfields, along with Slaney or Humby or alone together, hunting through the weeds for black-and-crimson burnet moths in late summer, and fishing in the ponds for newts in spring. Daily they both made room in their satchels among the books for plunder: fistfuls of thermite tipped out of an incendiary bomb that had failed to ignite, toadstools, twitching chrysalids, a beetle or a butterfly in a match-box, shrapnel splinters, sketch-maps of where they had located unusual plants.

They never once set foot in one another's homes, and in the holidays and at weekends set off five miles apart to rummage through the landscape or trawl microscopic creatures — amoeba, hydra, volvox and paramecium, their names alone a litany — from forest pools. And then it was Bren Slaney who came along with Bob and his dog.

Fourteen years old, David read a paper to the local Natural History Society, on the distribution of hornets in the forest. Two years later and a month or so into the Upper Sixth, he was to shatter a corner of the Senior Chemistry lab, mixing phosphorus and potassium chlorate in an attempt to invent an everlasting match. Within a further twelvemonth, he would already be launched on a distinguished career in medicine.

*

September 1943 found 3A, now become 4A, back again in Miss April's Geography room. It was unwarrantable, they agreed, an imposition. For a year they'd suffered the daily irritation of ranging their books not in a desk — there *were* no desks in the Geography room — but on an enclosed shelf under the map-table which took the place of a desk. They had to grope arm-deep to the back and along the sides and identify their books by where they had positioned them. All through the day other classes came to Geography, and people put their arms in and shoved everything to the back or, worse, glued blobs of spent chewing-gum on the shelf. Now here they were, faced with another year of annoyance!

Changing to a new form-master and form-room was out of the question, Dusty told them. Miss April would ensure that their shelves were not interfered with. But try as she might, she was helpless to prevent it.

4A deliberated over suitable anti-personnel devices. Alarm-bells or cap-bombs, triggered by a wire? Indelible ink on a sponge? Yeah, but that'd stain the desk and then you'd be for it. And there was always the danger that the only person you'd catch would be yourself.

Druce glanced across the room at the Geography cabinet, a locked, glass-topped case in which a litter of incongruous items was crowded together on display. Chunks of green asbestos rock, quartz, chert, pumice; four or five nutmegs that were really nux vomica seeds; belemnites, looking like rifle bullets; an ammonite from Lyme Regis, sliced and polished. But it was the little bottle of solid iodine that drew his eye: what about a booby-trap of ammonium iodide? A few crystals out of that bottle, and some strong ammonia. After all, EVEN A FLY WALKING ON IT COULD SET IT OFF. It was an idea to brood over, but far too dangerous, of course.

'Hey, what about mouse-traps?' someone said. Yeah, you wouldn't forget a *mouse-trap* in a hurry, would you? Nor would anyone who rummaged around in your desk, once it snapped shut on his fingers.

'Where on earth are you taking *that?*' his mother asked, when she saw him collect a mouse-trap from the larder and slip it into his satchel.

'It's for an experiment,' he said. 'We all have to take a mouse-trap for Biology.'

'For Religious Instruction,' he would have preferred to say, savouring the joke; but she wouldn't have swallowed that.

Dusty was waiting for 4A in the Geography Room, when the last bell went that afternoon and they came in to collect their things for home. 'Sit down and pay attention,' he said. Much as he sympathized, Miss April's lessons had been disrupted, and he would not tolerate their taking the law into their own hands. Other pupils might have been seriously injured. Mouse-traps formed no part of educational equipment, and the caretaker would collect them up now and dispose of them. Was that clearly understood? Very well.

But wasn't that a hint of a twinkle in his eye?

*

When Druce and Slaney carbide-bombed the urinal at Monkswood Station, it wasn't glee that moved them, nor the thought of exacting retribution: but condign indignation. Or so they told themselves.

And there was no getting away from the facts: the Gentlemen's lavatory at Monkswood station was a criminal disgrace. It was near the end of the down platform. From yards away, if the wind was blowing towards you, you could smell the reek of ammonia.

In the middle of the room stood the urinal itself, a huge earthenware bowl raised a foot or so above the floor by a hollow, cast-iron pillar. The pillar passed through the centre of the bowl, and there were panels bolted to its upper length, radiating like the spokes of a wheel: they were supposed to screen you from your neighbour's gaze. Each was embroidered on both sides with moss and efflorescence. At the bottom of the bowl, slots were cut into the central tube to serve as a drain-holes. They rarely did. They were permanently choked with sodden cigarette-packets, spent matches, cigarette-butts, bits of paper, plaster jarred down from the ceiling.

So the urine brimmed up almost to the rim of the bowl before it could overflow through a ring of higher slots, cut there for the purpose. By which time it was a foot deep at the middle. You couldn't blame the station staff for being reluctant to clean it out. What it needed was a bomb on it.

Then Druce and Slaney saw a film at the Regal, a glamourised version of A.J. Cronin's novel, *The Citadel,* staying in their seats to watch it twice round. They talked about it afterwards at length.

The young Doctor Manson, the hero, convinced that the Welsh mining village's ancient sewage tanks are the source of a typhoid epidemic. The self-opinionated town councillors who will not vote the money to replace them. The rising death-toll. The hero in desperation obtaining dynamite, forcing the issue. The night-time expedition to the septic-tanks. The climax, against a stormy sky, with the heroine's pet dog lingering close to the sputtering fuse, refusing to come when they call him. The hero risking his life to dash back and drag the dog to safety in the nick of time.

Potent images.

And here was the railway urinal a suppurating disgrace. They couldn't exactly blow it up, but a suitable outrage might force it to public attention.

Two 1-lb cans of calcium carbide, one in each hand, shot into the brimming bowl. Bren Slaney keeping the door of a compartment open as the guard blew his whistle and the train began to move. Then Druce leaping out through the doorway marked GENTLEMEN, into the carriage and away to the Village. Home to Hawkswood Road and Auckland Drive, with the conscience of a necessary deed accomplished.

The following morning's reports were graphic, all that they could have wished. Humby and Price had arrived on the up platform just in time for their train, and looked out from their compartment window at a flurry of railway staff on the opposite platform. Part of it had been barricaded off. The stationmaster was waving his arms and shouting and one of the men was running with a fire-bucket and a stirrup pump. A broad inch-high stream of foam was still swimming through the doorway marked GENTLEMEN, and a couple of porters were swabbing it towards the platform edge, down onto the ballast. One of them had put his gasmask on.

A few months later, workmen began to construct a pedestrian tunnel under the track at that end of the platform, and the offensive urinal went the way of all flesh. Druce R.C.L. and Slaney B. cherished the notion that they had played their part in its extinction.

At any event, no witnesses came forward, and there was no retribution for the blow they had struck in the name of hygiene.

16

WAR'S END

All through 1943, shrapnel, high explosives, and incendiaries went on falling from the skies on moonlit nights. Nor was there any let-up in 1944, although now the massed roar of engines above the village was likelier to be the sound of Allied aircraft setting off for another thousand-bomber raid on Hamburg or the Ruhr.

Some mornings the streets and fields were littered with inch-wide strips of metal foil backed with black paper, a sinister parody of the coloured paper strips that you could buy in the weeks before Christmas, to loop and gum together for paper-chains. Enemy aircraft released them, to flutter down and foil the radar. Slaney and he collected a satchelful apiece, thinking to make them into paper-chains, but Mrs Druce refused to let the Nazi trash enter her house.'Tip it into the dustbin, and then go straight upstairs and scrub your hands,' she cried. 'It's probably coated with poison.'

Other aerial litter was certainly lethal. There were warnings in the press about butterfly bombs. They looked like winged cocoa tins: you might come across them lying in the grass or caught face-high in a hedge. A shudder would set them off. And for months now it had no longer been safe to tamper with an incendiary bomb: the latest model carried an explosive charge designed to maim a firefighter or anybody — a thermite-greedy schoolboy, perhaps — who found one unexploded and tried to unscrew the base.

While Allied troops were moving forward into Normandy from the June D-day landings, doodle-bugs — the flying bombs with wings and a motor to propel them — began to growl through the sky above Kent and Essex. By September, they had killed 5,500 people, among them the wife and daughter-in-law of the caretaker at Monkswood School, whose house on the school drive was wrecked in the closing days of June by the doodle-bug that destroyed his family and blinded him.

The school was empty that day. Earlier that week, Dusty had declared an unwonted two-day holiday. Later he could only speak of obeying a sudden premonition. The bomb exploded in front of the school gates at lunchtime, shattering classroom and corridor windows throughout the school. A section of the front railings scythed through the dining-hall, ripping a track across the high table.

Senior Monkswood boys spent a fortnight or more of the lengthened summer-break clearing up the mess. 4A, soon to be 5A, worked among them, abandoning the books they should have been swotting up for an exam nine months ahead, and devoting their days to chopping splinters of glass from the window-frames, throwing down shattered roof-tiles, swabbing floors, and washing walls.

By September, the news from Europe was grim. The airborne landings near Arnhem had failed abysmally. A German counter-offensive had halted the Allies in the Ardennes. Meanwhile the flying-bombs kept on coming, and early in the month, the first V2 rockets began to fall on Greater London.

For many people, the V2s were less terrifying than the doodle-bugs. They travelled at supersonic speeds, swooping up into the stratosphere before falling back to earth. They announced their arrival with a crash which blurred into a rumble that was the delayed roar of their passage through the atmosphere, as the sound of their exhausts caught up and arrived after the first, violent detonation. If you heard a V2, you knew that at least you were still alive to hear it. But the flying bombs — buzz-bombs, V1s, chase-me-Charlies, doodle-bugs: there was no shortage of nicknames for them — were a terror long-drawn out, entering the tissue of your nightmares. The sharper your hearing, the greater the strain on your nerves, as they chugged across the sky, trailing a flame and seeming barely to skim the treetops.

'Listen!' he shouted, but 'No... No, I can't hear anything. Dorothy, can you?' his father would go on saying; 'No, you're imagining it.'

'O, *listen!*'

His nerves screamed inside his skull.

When the fuel ran out, the motor cut and the contraption tilted and fell, gliding down in a silence measured only by your heartbeats and ending in a crash of flame. Most nerve-wracking of all were those few times when the thing passed by, leaving you safe, it seemed. The motor cut. After a second or so the throaty snarl began again as a last cupful or two of fuel swished out of the tilting tank. Then sometimes the doodle-bug swung round and back the way it had come, seeming to hunt you down. When the motor cut a second time, there was no reprieve.

*

September 1944 found the members of 5A — but for the few who might pass on into the Sixth form — in their final year. Time to settle down to serious study and put away childish things. In a few month's space their futures, as PC Druce never tired of reminding his son, would be at stake once more.

'And never mind how that Slaney spends his time. I've seen him hanging around with girls—'

'*A* girl. *One* girl. Pauline.'

'Don't argue the toss with me, my son. I'm not having *you* hanging around street corners with a gang of tarts. Just think of *my* position. If I ever hear that you've been wasting your time with girls — and if you do, I'll get to hear of it, you can assure yourself of that — you'll have your mother and me to answer to. Time enough for girls when you're at University. Until then, you've got your work cut out to pass your exams. One day you'll thank me for keeping your nose to the grindstone.'

But all work and no play makes Jack a dull boy, he muttered to himself, alone again. And Pauline had a younger sister, Madeline. Once or twice the four of them met up, skylarking together in the meadows along by the river, and his father never got to hear of it.

But his mother did, by heaven knew what secret grapevine of her own. She hung around outside the Girls' School in the Village every afternoon until she managed to confront Madeline and warn her off. Her son, she snapped, had better things to do with his time than chase after girls. Now, out of the blue, whenever he encountered Madeline in the Village, she tossed her head and walked away in a fit of giggles. Not until thirty years later, meeting Madeline by chance, did he learn the reason why.

But the Lois affair was more shameful and more shaming.

He was strolling with Bren one Friday evening along Hawkswood Road when they ran into Pauline and a group of friends from her class. Lois was one of them. Dusk fell as they chattered together and told silly jokes, and jigged from foot to foot. Lois seemed to single him out, shrieking the loudest whenever he ventured a witty remark, and stretching her eyes wide at him. 'Now we've met each other, we must meet again,' she told him, before they all waved goodbye to one another and scattered off home.

On Sunday he was moving down a side-aisle at All Saints, taking the collection, when suddenly there was Lois at a pew-end, smiling at him.

'Hallo,' she said, 'I've never been to All Saints before. But I think I'm going to come every week now.'

He felt himself go scarlet. People must have heard her four or five pews away. He motioned her to pass the collecting-bag on along the row, and moved down the aisle to wait for it to come back to him. After the service, he loitered in the vestry, only emerging when his fellow-server reported that the coast was clear.

On Tuesday, the bombshell burst.

He came in from school to a tight-lipped mother, stalking around the kitchen and at her old trick of blowing out invisible matches, Phhh!

'Your tea is on the table. Just eat it up before your father gets in. He's got something to say to you, my lad.'

Minutes later his father slammed in and sat down at the table.

'So who is this Lois?' he said.

O God.

'No one. A girl. I don't even know her.'

'I see,' said his father. 'I see. You don't know her.' He flung an envelope across the table, addressed in green ink to 'Mr Robert Druce'.

'Just oblige me by reading *that*. And then try telling me you don't know her.'

My darling Robert,

Why the sudden change in temperature? I am trembling all over. I must see you, there is something I must tell you.

Your loving Lois

*

The cross-examination and the speeches for the prosecution went on for more than half an hour before he was released, trembling with rage, to thump through his piano practice, and try to settle to his school homework. What a stupid girl that Lois was with her cow eyes and clichés! What a stupid letter to write to anybody. Couldn't his parents see that for themselves? Why did he have to defend himself against such girlish rubbish? What did they think he *was?*

'I've a good mind to go and see the girl's mother,' said his father, half-rising from the table.

'No, no!' He pleaded. With a grim smile, his father heard him out. Then informed him that he had already spoken to the woman.

Putting on his Police Constable's uniform for the occasion, he had gone to Lois's house. No small part of the rage he turned upon his son was accountable to the cool, half-amused reception her mother had given him.

'Where does this leave *me*, when you get yourself mixed up with these kind of people?' he said.

'You might have the decency to think of your father's position, once in a while,' his mother put in antiphonally.

Only much later did the truth dawn on him. Yes, yes: that he had stood around and flirted with a girl — could he deny *that?* No — No, that was insubordination enough. But not for the avalanche of fury that had thundered down upon his head. No, there had been more violent undercurrents lurking in the atmosphere that afternoon.

Lois had addressed the envelope to 'Mr Robert Druce'. His parents opened one another's letters. There was the answer.

Whatever the fifteen-year-old Lois thought she meant, it wasn't that she was going to have a baby. With a sudden swoop, his heart went out to his father, coming in off duty in all innocence to a wife who had read an unknown female's letter over and over, thinking it was addressed to her husband. What thoughts had gone through *her* mind? How long had she made his father sweat it out, before she had flung the letter in his face?

That was his parents' affair, not for him to pry into. But he had a good mind to throttle that stupid Lois, and not only on his own behalf.

*

In fact the older you grew the less impressive, and the more vulnerable, so many adults seemed to be. You observed their idiosyncrasies, their fallibility, in a brighter light: the Bishop turning over two pages of the missal and not realising what he'd done, the new Chemistry master smashing test-tubes in a rage, his own father and mother, Mr Moon. All along the line, the cardboard psychologies of childhood were giving way to a shrewder view.

Ever since the first form at Monkswood, Druce had admired Walter Mason's knack of raising one eyebrow. Walter, as he dared to think of him now, used that eyebrow as an adjunct to his voice. Raised, it cast an equivocal light on what he said, hinting that he might not be entirely serious, and that he certainly wasn't taken in by the tale you were telling him.

Now his pupil laboured to acquire the same knack, prodding his eyebrow muscles into place while he watched in the mirror and willed them to move of their own accord. When he had mastered the trick and tried it out, it seemed to work. People looked disconcerted, without seeming to know why.

One afternoon in 1944 Alwyn Black, patrolling the gangways during an English composition class, reached down and drew *Man, Microbe and Malady* from Druce's blazer pocket. He flipped the pages back and forth, while the eyes that swam behind his glasses opened wider; having fallen, no doubt, on the chapters devoted to venereal disease.

'Druce, does your *father* know you read this sort of thing?'

But Black, thin-lipped and sardonic as he always was when faced with Druce, was no longer a bugaboo.

'Yes, sir. Yes, he does,' Druce answered, raising his eyebrow. *And so what?* he hoped it implied.

Black's 'Hmph!', like the elaborate sigh which followed it, had lost its force. How could a grammar-school master be so narrow-minded? And endeavour to make a virtue of it?

He would never warm to Alwyn Black. But now his former contempt was transforming itself into a recognition of Black's meticulous knowledge of his subject, and a weary tolerance of the man as man.

His acceptance of Miss April, as 1944 passed into 1945, was more compassionate, although he disliked her subject and in the dining-hall daily found her opinions intrusive. During that school year she took her place at the head of his table at lunch, and wanted to know why he held his knife and fork in the wrong hands.

That's how he had been taught to eat by his left-handed mother, he explained. She had stood behind him, holding her hands over his. Miss April found the habit gauche, a social stigma. She set out to cure him, compelling him to swap his knife and fork over. But he fought back against her implicit criticism of his mother, cack-handedly shovelling his food back and forth across the plate and asking when might he be allowed to eat it?

'He is thoughtful and well-mannered but a little resentful of criticism,' Miss April's Geography report concluded.

Miss April moved house to the Riverside estate that year. When the weather was clement, as she put it, she walked to school across the meadows. Druce and Slaney would join her sometimes, pushing their bikes along at her side, sometimes even daring to tease her a little, as one might tease an elderly aunt. On frosty mornings a drop of moisture would glitter, like a tear, at the end of her nose, and for Bren's benefit he quietly hummed the tune of 'Bonny Mary of Argyle', thinking of the words. 'O, to see the dew-drop clinging,/To the rose just newly born…'

But no, you couldn't dislike Miss April, red-haired spitfire though she at times became.

Not the least of his regrets, after the mock-election that loomed ahead across the months, would be the thought of having betrayed her.

*

After a last bitter winter of starvation, the war in occupied Europe swept to an end, and so did the fifth-year's school lives along with it, but for the score or so who would move on into the Sixth. Suddenly they all were ranged behind desks in the assembly hall, fretting their way through mock school-cert exams. When the air-raid warning sounded in the middle of a session, they fled across the playground to the shelters, seeing a doodle-bug snarling over the treetops as they ran. It was the last intrusion of the war into their school timetable.

The blackout had long become less stringent, almost a thing of the past. Barbed wire and tank traps were beginning to vanish from the landscape, although it would be a very long time yet before the beaches were cleared of mines. In the yard at the back of the Council offices in the Village, workmen were hauling out the signposts and giving them a new lick of paint.

On May 1st the news came that Hitler had killed himself. The following evening there was word of the surrender of the German troops in Italy and, only hours later, of the fall of Berlin. On May 4th it was announced that the German troops in Denmark had surrendered. Then days passed without further news, while people throughout the Village planned street-parties, and ransacked their lofts for Union Jacks, and fretted to know what was going on. At last, on Monday 7th, came the announcement. Tuesday 8th would be Victory in Europe Day and, along with Wednesday, a national holiday.

'Which doesn't mean you're let off homework, in case that's what you're thinking,' said PC Druce.

And, a final reminder: for the rest of the month, no clothing coupons would be needed for cheap red, white, or blue cotton bunting.

The weather was warm on V.E. Day. People took to the streets, shopkeepers sold out of bunting, and pubs in the Village ran dry. All afternoon the Fire Station bell tolled for Adolf. For a penny you could view him in his underclothes, in a coffin donated by the local undertaker. At dusk the Firemen cremated him.

Bob wandered around the River estate with Bren until late that night. Red, white and blue, the flags and pennants fluttered from house to house across the streets. Everywhere lights blazed behind undrawn curtains, and in River Parade a man in an Air Raid Warden's helmet was bawling, 'Put that Light ON! Don't you know there's a War over?' The wood and tarred paper of blackout screens flared on street bonfires, and people were capering round them, some of them hurling their Identity Cards — Britons never never never shall be slaves! — into the flames. Couples clung in one another's arms, mouth to mouth.

Here and there, people had wrestled pianos out onto the pavement. Knots of people swooped and circled nearby, dancing: 'O, Knees Up, Knees Up, Don't get the Breeze Up, Knees Up, Mother Brown,' women throwing their skirts up to reveal their underclothes. Bob could have sworn he glimpsed a pair of thighs innocent of knickers, but no, she wouldn't have, *would* she? — it must have been a trick of the light.

In Nelson Avenue they were fêting a returned Prisoner of War, and a sprawl of men was trying to hoist him onto their shoulders. In Christchurch Gardens they were dancing the Palais Glide. A little girl with russet curls was lifted onto a table in her pyjamas, and she danced and sang, 'O, animal cwackers in my soop...' At the corner of Christchurch Gardens and Auckland Drive, some handyman had set up a stand. For a penny you could throw chunks of wood at a plywood Adolf, and knock his head off.

Bob fell into bed that night with a raging headache. He felt depressed and alienated.

People went on organizing street parties every weekend until early June. A line of trestle-tables down the centre of the roadway; a mid-afternoon scramble for seats; sandwiches, jellies, and a clergyman to say Grace; a conjurer, a dancing display, a sing-song; the local funny-man keeping the party going: 'Are we down-hearted? No, let 'em all come!'; squeaks and booms from loudspeakers too close to the microphone; the children packed off home to bed at 10 o'clock; piano and gramophone music until 2.30 a.m. when the adults called it a day.

The war in the far East was a million miles away. Here in the London suburbs it was suddenly all over.

*

For a week or more the Monkswood fifth-formers sat in the gym, scribbling for dear life in their answer books, and knotting them together with string, just as they had done five years before. Once again it was the real thing.

They poured out into the corridor at break and lunch-times, cross-questioning one another: 'What did you make of Question 3? What did *you* put?' One of the questions in Geography had been: *Illustrate three methods of showing relief.* 'Just watch me when I walk out of this exam-room...' he had been minded to write. 'Hey, Drucy, you never wrote that *down*, did you?' 'No, of course not!' But he'd been sorely tempted.

And then it was all at an end, and they were free to lounge about in the classroom, playing chess or Monopoly. Free to lounge on the playing-field around a wind-up gramophone, listening to Swing in the sunshine. Athletes hurled javelins and discoi, and pounded round the track. Bookworms read themselves into other worlds. Slaney and Druce got leave to take part in a chess tournament, and spent every evening and two afternoons that week in a sequence of London theatres, sitting up in the gods for a shilling, and losing their matches by default.

When enough of them felt energetic, they played softball. American soldiers at a nearby camp had been made free of Monkswood's playing field at weekends and, when the last man was out, scrambled their kit among the Monkswood boys who dropped by to watch. 'Ball one, strike one. C'mon Sidney, slap that kidney!' Marsh's parody of a Yankee accent would echo across the school drive until Alwyn Black heard it in the staffroom, and ran out to halt the appalling vulgarity.

There were other excitements. With the end of the war and a General Election in sight, party politics became an issue once again. A School Mock Election was planned to take place at Monkswood towards the end of July. Factions divided 5A. To the great surprise of many, it was John Robbins, quiet-voiced and unobtrusive, who emerged as a fervent candidate for Labour. With the official announcement of a general School Mock Election, Miss April's proposal of a small-scale mock election within the Geography Society almost fell into abeyance. But Druce R.C.L. had other ideas in mind.

As early as June 2nd, Winston Churchill had toured within eight miles of Monkswood, beating the bounds of his new Woodford constituency. No-one, it was taken for granted, would stand to oppose him. But within weeks, Alexander Hancock, a forty-seven year-old farmer and retired shoe-manufacturer from Northamptonshire, announced his candidature. He was 'The Man with The Plan'; his master-scheme requiring that nobody should work for more than a few hours a day on essential goods or services — what people did with the rest of their free time was up to them.

Few people expected the Conservative party not to sweep to victory. Nobody doubted that Churchill would win the seat. But there were hecklers at the Woodford election meetings, and a group of songsters, many of them senior Monkswood boys, regularly greeted the Prime Minister with a revised version of 'Clementine' (the tune itself, perhaps, a delicate allusion to Mrs Churchill's Christian name):

Vote for Hancock,
If you can, cock;
He's the Man, who's got the Plan.
Fire and brimstone,
Down with Winston;
Vote for Hancock, if you can!

Alexander
Doesn't pander
To the Tory Beaverbrook.
Against the Tories
His strength the more is;
He will bring them all to book!

When it came to Election Day, 26th July and the first day of the school holidays, Hancock more than saved his deposit, winning 10,488 votes against Churchill's 27,688. Over the country as a whole, there was a landslide victory for Labour, with a pattern of voting that had been remarkably foreshadowed by John Robbins' triumph in the Monkswood Mock Election.

*

With the war at an end and a Victory Fair and a week of festivity being daily planned in the Village, he had somehow assumed that death, too, might take a holiday.

But in the first week of July, Angus Moon's own seventy-three year saga came to an end. The Druces drew their front curtains as a mark of respect, and Mrs Washington arrived next door to lay out the corpse. It was then that she confided to Mrs Druce her belief that Mr Moon's toenails had not been cut for a decade. Bob overheard his mother whispering the story to his father and in his mind's eye saw rafts of horn creaking under Mr Moon's naked footsoles as he hobbled to the back-door steps or out to the front gate. He thought about Angus Moon as he had once known him, and felt sad.

A fortnight later he read in the *Advertizer* of a man fifteen years younger than Angus Moon who survived the war, only to end his own life. PC Robert Druce had arrived to cut down the corpse of John Sydney Farmer, aged 58, who had laid a plank across the open ceiling trap-door at the top of his stairs, and hanged himself in a piece of webbing.

Off and on for a week Bren and Bob and their friends wandered around the Fairground that had settled near the railway station. They rolled pennies down little plywood ramps and prayed that one would land on a sixpence. They flung quoits. They shied wooden balls at coconuts — where on earth did *they* come from? but there they were — and if, O whoops! — accidentally on purpose a ball flew high and over the back-sheet and out of the ground, never mind. They'd track it down later in the hedge and use it for rough cricket: you couldn't get your hands on a decent cricket ball for love or money. They stood up in the swingboats and swung them so high that the iron rods clouted the safety-stop on the cross-bar, and the proprietor shouted and threatened to call the police. They swooped overhead in the chair-o-planes, rhythmically tugging the chains of the empty seat at their side so that they would fly out not only sideways but up and down in a looping ellipse, defying death and the man who owned the chairoplanes.

Every night that week and just before the entrance gates were due to close, a man set fire to a layer of petrol on a canvas water-tank, then clambered to the top of a tower of scaffolding in the flickering, smoky light. Up there he waved and called out to the crowd, dousing himself with paraffin, and setting it alight. Then he dived out of the sky, an incendiary star. The impact as he landed in the tank sent gallons of water gushing across the grass and extinguished all the flames. The crowd released their caught breaths and applauded out of the sudden darkness.

But suppose he had missed the tank? or broken his neck on the steel frame that supported it? or inhaled a lungful of flame as he fell? Walking home to Auckland Drive each night through the dark and the chattering voices, Bob couldn't rid himself of the vision of a burning man falling to his death, clay slumping over Mr Moon's coffin, a webbing noose swinging above a stairwell.

*

And then it was the last day of school in E.J. Greenleigh's history room, 5A's form-room. Druce, along with Slaney and Humby and Verity who were in the know, arrived in time to sow the room with tiny ammonium-iodide crystals before their form-master's arrival. On the edges of the drawers in Greenleigh's desk, in the light switches, under the chalk-box and the blackboard pointer, in the cupboard lock and across the floor and along the hinge of every desk, the crystals that had come to school wet, in a screw-capped bottle, were now drying to a fulminating sensitivity.

Earlier that week Miss April had accepted Druce's kind offer to tidy up the cabinet in the Geography room and make a new set of labels. And so he had.

But when he put the key of the cabinet back into her hand, the little bottle labelled 'Iodine' was more than three-quarters filled with anthracite. Broken small and rinsed under the tap, it was indistinguishable to the eye from the layer of iodine crystals that lay at the very top of the bottle, an insurance against anyone who cared to make a perfunctory test of the contents.

By mid-morning break, Greenleigh was seething. 'Well, well. Aha,' he had said, as the first explosions began to crackle around the room and under his own feet, sharp as the snap of Christmas crackers. 'Most amusing. But I think that's enough.'

But there was no way of stopping it. All through the morning and the afternoon the crystals snapped at a touch into a tiny cloud of violet vapour. Greenleigh snatched up his coffee at morning break and confronted Fitz Fitzroy with the tale; so Druce heard from Walter Mason years later. Fitz glanced up from his armchair for an instant. 'Ah,' he said. 'Ammonium iodide.' He went back to reading his paper and puffing his pipe, and left E.J. to his unhappy incomprehension.

Two days later, Bob and Bren got rid of the rest of the stuff: it was far too dangerous to have around. They saved the last saltspoonful for a grand finale at the bottom of the garden, pouring the little heap of damp crystals into an old iron ladle and propping the ladle with a couple of bricks over a candle-end. Then Bob lit the candle and they fled to the back doorway. There was a crash and a clang as the ladle leapt across the concrete path. They went back and gazed in awe at the hole in the metal, as big as an eye, that had been blasted through it.

*

While the ammonium iodide was an unmitigated success, Druce's suggestions for the Geography Society's mock election, innocent in intention — witty, even — touched off a disaster.

'It would be stupid to cancel the Geography Society election,' he said, 'just because there's going to be an official mock election. Look: what always strikes me is how politicians never convince one another. You never hear a Conservative listening to a Labour speaker, and saying "My God! Of course you're right, and all along I've been wrong." Well, do you? And vice-versa. So why don't we do just that?'

'How?' said Marsh.

'Well, we would put up candidates, Tory, Labour, Liberal, Communist—'

'Old Ma April would never accept a Communist,' someone said.

'I'll be the Communist,' said Dogger Bone.

'She would if we all said of course he had no chance of getting a single vote, but in all fairness she ought to let him stand.'

'And then?' said Marsh, 'No, wait. I think I can guess what's coming next.'

'So we all cheer the Conservative, and groan at the Labour candidate, and boo the Communist. And then the Liberal—'

'Me,' said Marsh.

'Yes. You'd be marvellous. Then *you* say, "All this time I've been wrong! But after hearing my friend here — nay, my comrade!"—'

'Comrade Bone,' said Dogger.

' — "After hearing Comrade Bone, I realize that only Communism will save this country!" And so on, blah, blah, blah. Well?'

'And we can all dress up with blue or yellow ties and carry sheets of blue paper to wave,' said Marsh, 'and then when I make my speech, we can take off our blue ties and put on red ones, and rip up the blue paper and unroll sheets of red paper instead. Agreed?'

It was out of Druce's hands. The candidates arrived next day with their eight-minute speeches prepared, and Marsh rehearsed his audience in responding to his gestures, training them to cheer when he threw both arms up to the heavens, and boo when he waved a clenched fist.

The Geography room was packed with boys from every year in the school, when Miss April, looking worried, opened the meeting at five o'clock. By half-past five she was worried enough to dispatch Kingsley of 4A, a toady, to fetch the Duty Master. Ensconced and all oblivious in his room in the farthest wing of the school, the Duty Master was unaware of any trouble. He stayed aloof, and Kingsley never reached him.

The Tory speaker was greeted with a cheer and a great waving of blue paper at the end of every phrase. The Labour candidate spoke into a groaning silence. Bone made his ranting speech to a chorus of boos and catcalls. Then Marsh, Liberal, stood up, splendid in the part.

'My friends! (Groans) Do I say friends? Nay, Comrades! (A cheer) For after hearing Comrade Bone's arguments (Louder cheers), I realise what a fool I have been for so long (Laughter). I came before you as the Liberal candidate (Groans). But now I speak to you as a committed Communist. Comrade Bone has convinced me! (Prolonged cheers)...'

And so on, Marsh surpassing himself in eloquence and all going hilariously according to plan, until it came to the planned tearing up of 5A's sheets of blue paper. The sight of the ripped-up blue paper, and the brandished sheets of red, seemed to inflame the spectators. Druce watched in amazement at what his intended joke had unleashed, as an audience turned into a gleeful mob, and destruction escalated.

He was among those invited by Dusty the following morning to survey the damage, and arrange that it was paid for. The mob had rampaged around the room, ignoring Miss April, until at last members of the fifth year and a couple of sixth-formers had joined forces to shoulder them out, close on seven o'clock. The piano had been damaged, wall-maps gashed, chairs broken. Ink and broken glass littered a corner of the room where someone had been throwning inkwells against the heating-pipes.

Fearing further damage, Miss April had not dared to leave the room in search of the Duty Master. In his fastness, the Duty Master had heard nothing of the racket and had not come to the rescue, because Kingsley had been waylaid, and gagged and tied up in the locker-room. There he had remained until the Duty Master overheard his groans at eight o'clock.

If the events of V.E. night had offered a view of social restraints loosened, for 5A — for them all — the Geography Room election was an object-lesson in mob violence.

17

MR PRITCHARD

'No more Latin, No more French; No more sitting on a hard old bench…'

On their last afternoon at Monkswood, a dozen members of 5A capered around a playground waste-paper basket, ripping pages out of no-longer-needed exercise books and sending them fluttering down to feed the flames. Druce was among them, and his ancient labours in mathematics and geography — the thickets of royal blue ink, the scarlet ticks and crosses of Miss April and Miss Rook, and his own elaborate north arrows — crumbled into smoke.

Nevertheless for Druce and Slaney, as for Mike Grace and Charlie Farmer, the chant was inappropriate. Over in the bike sheds the satchels strapped to their cross-bars already bulged with the texts of Higher Certificate Latin, French, English and History. *Hamlet, Much Ado about Nothing*, Chaucer's *Prologue, The Nun's Priest's Tale;* Auden, MacNeice, Eliot, Caesar, Catullus, Racine, Corneille. At home that evening, Druce flitted from one volume to another, cracking their spines and smoothing the pages flat, savouring the scent and texture of new print and binding, wanting to devour everything all at once. The summer stretched ahead, filled with anticipated pleasure.

Within a month, the war in the East blazed to a sudden end at Hiroshima and Nagasaki. The Empire of the Rising Sun collapsed and surrendered. In Britain there was another round of bonfires and street parties and victory parades. They were tamer now this second time around, an anti-climax.

But let there be rejoicing amid the austerity and the shortages and the continued rationing of food and clothing! The world had witnessed the dawn of the Atomic Age, and a new freedom. Atomic! — the word flaunted itself on post-war shopfronts — Atomic Cleaners; Atomic Radio Supplies;

an Atomic Café, even. Not for months would the horror be fully revealed which would come to haunt their lives.

But other horrors had broken into the daylight. From across the globe, prisoners of war were bringing home their nightmare memories. In Nuremburg the War Crimes Tribunal began to sift through a catalogue of evil, military and civilian.

Auschwitz-Birkenau, Buchenwald, Majdanek, Bergen-Belsen, Treblinka, Theresienstadt, Dachau, Sachsenhausen… In a London where great stretches of rubble were alight with willow-herb, Bren Slaney and he were encouraged to walk one afternoon — despite the school uniforms which should have denied them entrance — into a photographic exhibition of the Nazi extermination camps.

Cinders. Smoking chimney-stacks. Images in soot and ash.

Stacked firewood that at a closer look resolved itself into bone and dead flesh, jutting pelvises, taut bellies trailing corruption. Knots of survivors, rags and bones and bright-eyed skulls, staring through wire. An undead skeleton in a barrack-room, naked and clinging with outstretched arms between rows of beds, staring at the rescuers who had arrived too late to save her.

At dusk in Wardour Street, where American GIs strolled up and down and the pavement was lined with whores, a woman accosted the pair of them, holding her fur coat open for a moment, revealing her nakedness beneath it but for her high-heeled shoes and stockings. Gazing at her silky and inviting flesh, he saw it eclipsed by an image of a dying woman.

*

Moving on into a place in the Lower Sixth was a privilege which, freer-swimming fish though they now were in a small scholastic pool, only confirmed their dependent role in society at large.

Look at John Robbins. There he was, from Monday to Saturday, off to the City in his pinstripe suit, tapping a cigarette on his bright new cigarette-case as the train drew away from the platform, opening a newspaper, answerable to himself, a man of means, earning his keep, putting money away each week. And here were Druce and Slaney, like all the others in the Monkswood Sixth, trailing to school with satchels slung on their shoulders or strapped over the cross-bar of their bikes, still aliens in an adult world.

Bob's school cap was hunched on uncombed hair, and his wrists dangled out of the too-short sleeves of his weekday blazer. If there were gaspers lodged along the bottom of his or Bren's pockets, they had been paid for from a dole of pocket-money. Within the gates of Monkswood, and on journeys to and from it, they were contraband.

In a Europe still licking its wounds and burying its dead, where — so his brother in the British Army of Occupation told Don Betts — you could buy a woman for a bar of chocolate, it was privilege enough to be alive and uninjured. To walk unchallenged through the streets, to cross open fields, to come home to food on the table. To wear warm clothing on your back and not lice-infested rags.

But on Sundays, strolling to and from All Saints with John Robbins, he went on envying Robbins his status as a wage-earner. And took for granted the bookish freedoms and that access to learning which it seemed Robbins so much envied him.

One evening after school, Lou Marsh turned up at Monkswood School, confronting head-on no doubt, since that was his way, his own envy of what he too had been compelled to give up. Raincoated, trilby-hatted, passing his cigarette case around after first slipping into his trouser pocket the contraceptive nestled in a corner, he told them anecdotes of his life as a cub reporter. 'These,' he said, brandishing an imaginary pair of panties in imitation of the co-respondent he had watched in the witness box, 'I have covered with a thousand kisses.'

Within a month of Bob Druce's moving on into the sixth form — the way God, like the bottled demons of his childhood thoughts, always seemed to give you what you asked for when it was least convenient — the prospect of a month in an adult role arrived out of the blue. At the end of the school year, every prospective sixth-former had received a circular letter from the local education committee asking if he had would consider a career in teaching. 'Yes,' Bob had muttered, putting a tick on the tear-off slip; 'Yes, I might consider it.'

Now, in the last days of September, the seven members of the Lower Sixth Arts were ordered to report on 1 October to their allotted schools. They would spend the month as student teachers. Druce, raging at the intrusion, found himself directed to Cavendish Street Junior School, four miles away from Monkswood and the Village.

*

The sight of Mr Pritchard, jerking open the door marked 'Headmaster' and peering out through a cloud of smoke, swept his visitor back across half his sixteen-year lifetime, to Consort Road and Moggy Jenkins. For a tingling instant, Welsh Mr Pritchard *was* Moggy, exhumed from memory, *redivivus*. Druce-the-trainee-teacher stared at the headmaster's ash-and-dandruff-sprinkled shoulders, and felt the bones of his hands shiver in recollected agony.

'Yes? Who? Drrr-yoose?' As Mr Pritchard pronounced it, Druce's name seemed to belong to him no more. 'Ah. Sit there, Drrr-yoose, will you?'

Mr Pritchard gestured towards a cane-bottomed chair in the middle of the room and then settled himself behind his desk.

'One moment, now.'

Drrr-yoose watched for a long minute while, cigarette in mouth and left eye closed against the smoke, Mr Pritchard hunted through his desk drawers, tore a page from an exercise book, and began to jot something down.

'Drrr-yoose. Er... Yes. Now. I received a telephone call about you last Friday from the Reverend Cranwell-Pugh. You will be with us until the end of the month, he informed me. Very well, then. Pull your weight, make yourself useful, and we'll see if we can't lick you into shape...

'Er. Made yourself known to the staff already, have you? That's right, then—'

Mr Pritchard slowly crushed his cigarette into the ashtray, shook another from the Woodbine packet on his table, lit it, and inhaled. Mister Drrr-yoose-the-trainee-teacher watched and waited, and in his mind's eye riffled through his impressions of the four women he had encountered twenty minutes earlier.

Well, now... Mrs Bullace. Easy to remember her name, she's got a face like a bull. Fortyish. Fairish. Fattish. Squeezed into a chintzy dress too tight for her. Face powder. A limp wet handshake. Like shaking a cod fillet... Miss Hatton. Scrawny, round-shouldered. Horn-rimmed glasses. Pimples. Gave me a sour stare. Thirty? Forty? I don't know... Miss O'Leary. Irish. Getting on in years. Red hair. And smudgy orange lipstick, off-centre. Out of register, like a badly printed comic... Miss Greenaway. Blonde. Freckled. Young. A friendly smile...

'You're paying attention to me, are you?' said Mr Pritchard. 'Right, then…

'Today and tomorrow you can sit at the back making notes. On Wednesday morning, you can start taking lessons yourself.'

He peered down at his notes.

'Now then. This morning you'll be with Mrs Bullace, Room One, right? After dinner, you can sit in Miss O'Leary's class, Room Four, other end of the school. Tomorrow morning I've put you down for Miss Hatton's class, Room Three. Then back to Mrs Bullace for the afternoon. Got that, have you?'

Mr Pritchard shoved his piece of paper across the table.

'Well, there you are then. It's all down there…

'Next business. Dinner. Brought sandwiches, have you? No. Well, you can get your dinner at the British Restaurant, cheap and cheerful, three streets away, know it, do you?…

'Look here then, turn left out of the gate, down Cavendish Street, first left into Russell Terrace, turn right when you get to the Six Bells. You'll find the British Restaurant in what used to be the Baptist Hall. You'll see the notice, you'd have to be blind to miss it.'

Mr Pritchard suddenly prodded the air with a nicotine-stained forefinger.

'Hold on, wait a sec now. You might as well go along with Miss Greenaway, give her a hand escorting the pupils. Relieve Mrs Bullace, that would, she's got her hands full. Well, er. Right then, be in the hall at twelve sharp…

'Got any questions for me, have you? Yes? *Staff* lavatory?'

Mr Pritchard sighed deeply. 'Over there, isn't it?'

He nodded to a door set at angle in a boarded-off corner of his room. '*If* it's strictly necessary. People marching in and out every five minutes, it's a disturbance to me. Well, fair play: there's no alternative for my lady staff. *You*, though: well, I've no objection to you making use of the boys' lavatories across the school yard.'

He lit another Woodbine from the dog-end of the last, and glanced at the alarm-clock on his desk.

'I expect you to take full notes of everything. Only way to learn. Brought an exercise book with you, have you? Right. Rap on my door tomorrow before you have your dinner, hand me the fruits of your labours.'

Mr Pritchard stood up and bustled to the door.

'Get off to Mrs Bullace now. She won't be overjoyed, you coming in late and interrupting her lesson. Outstanding teacher, my Mrs Bullace. Hang on her lips. Cast-iron disciplinarian. Model yourself on her and you won't go far wrong in your teaching career.'

*

Mrs Bullace was writing on the blackboard as he knocked and pushed open the glass-panelled door of Room One. She grinned briefly in his direction — whether in welcome or distaste, he couldn't decide — and jerked her head towards the corner of the room. Eyes swivelled to watch him, as he wormed himself into the iron frame of an empty desk at the back. Mrs Bullace lifted the lid of her own high desk and slammed it down with a crash.

'Eyes front. Hands on your heads. Listen to me, Standard Four. When strangers come into this room, you will pay no attention to them and get on with your work in silence. Got that, Ringworm — Oh, I *do* beg your pardon, Ring*rose*? And you can sit up straight, Peacock, if you don't want more trouble. How many times did I give you the slipper yesterday? Three times, was it? Next time it's the cane, my lad. Right, hands on your desks, all of you, and get on with it. If you're not finished by playtime, you'll come back as soon as you've drunk your milk and sit here till you *have* finished.'

Mrs Bullace dusted her hands, perched herself on her stool, glared round the class, and began to tot up the register. With tongues writhing between their lips and a great scratching and spluttering of pens in the inkwells and across the pages of their exercise books, Standard four laboured, while Cavendish Street's new student-teacher bent over his exercise book, fountain-pen in hand, gazing around the room from time to time, and noting down what random thoughts crossed his mind.

Cavendish Street School. Monday 1st October, 1945: Room 1: Standard 4: Mrs I. Bullace: English… Old building, access to classrooms through adjoining classrooms. Outer doors to school kept locked: why? Musty-smelling, draughty, shivery. Heating (too early for it yet) by mixture of radiators, gas-heaters, coal-fires. Mrs B's room, like remainder, tall church-windowed barn: bad echoes. Floors worn, knots standing ¼ inch above softer wood. Bare walls. Cream-painted at top; milk-chocolate brown at bottom. Nothing to look at. English composition lesson. Blackboard (hard to read): 'Why I would/wouldn't like to live in China'. Mrs B: 'The subject's on the blackboard. Get on with it. I don't want to hear a peep out of anyone. Understood? When you've finished your scribbling, Mr Druce-is-it? stroll round & see how they're getting on.' Boy walks in: Mrs B: 'You're late! Any excuse? No? Bend over!' Whacks him with slipper. 'Now apologise to our Visitor there, for disturbing him.' (Psychologically speaking, won't this set him & class against me, the intruder?)...Asked Mrs B about locked doors during milk-break. (Mrs B: 'Why? Because!').

*

After his midday lunch, eaten in a dusty mission-hall that smelled of boiled cabbage and ginger pudding, Miss O'Leary came over to him in the staffroom. 'No, no, sit where y'are,' she said, smiling at him through her freshly off-centred orange lipstick. 'We'll not be startin' for another ten minuts. N' where are ye from? What school?'

He told her, 'Monkswood.'

'Monkswood, is ut? N' before that?'

'Consort Road School. It's over in — '

'I *knew* ut! Gob, haven't I the second sight? Did ye go to the Infants there? Quick now, what's the name of the Headmistress of the Infants, will ye tell me that?'

'Miss O'Flynn.' Ten years of his sixteen fled away, and he was standing in Miss O'Flynn's room, explaining the mysteries of a plasticine radio set...

'Sure n' isn't Mary O'Flynn me oldest friend on this earth?' Miss O'Leary clapped him on the shoulder in triumph. 'Come on wit' ye now,' she said, 'Tell me about yerself on the way to me classroom...'

Mouths grinned and eyes gaped up at him as Miss O'Leary led him through a cluster of children and flung back the door of her room. She clutched his elbow while her class settled into place, then pushed him into an empty desk in the back row, and clapped her hands.

'Children, this is Mister Druce, and Mister Druce has come in to look at yez. He'd like to hear you sing the Our Father, isn't that right, Mister Druce? Eyes down now, and hands together, and we'll sing ut for him.'

As Miss O'Leary clumped back to the front, he dropped his own eyes in reverence.

'Aow-er — FA!'

He jerked his head up and stared around, galvanized by the sudden wail that broke from the lips of the class.

'Ver-witch — AH! Tin hevv-n — HA!'

Miss O'Leary was leading the clamour in a wild contralto and beating time on her desk with a ruler:

'Low-ed — BEE! Thine-AIM!...'

on and on, the tuneless melody swooping up and down like the wailing at a wake.

Once they had done with the Lord's Prayer, and Miss O'Leary had settled at her desk to read the class a story, he opened his exercise book. But what was there to write about so far? Not much. So he counted the rows of double-desks, and the numbers of children, and noted it all down, and half-listened to Miss O'Leary's voice, and gazed out at the October sky, remembering Consort Road and Gulliver among the Lilliputians.

A view of life from the far side of the fence. *Vice-versa*. Topsy-turvy.

A chiel is come amang us taking notes.

Then he noticed a pair of boys, two desks away from his own, squeaking with laughter. They were grinning and craning their necks to stare in his direction, past a white-haired boy who sat on his own in the adjacent double-desk, and whose back was turned.

'Pssst!' he said, and the white-haired eight-year-old swivelled round. In one hand he was holding his penis, the worm-sized very tip of his foreskin dripping blue-black. In the other was the china inkwell into which he had just dipped it.

The white-haired boy's pale skin blushed red with shock. Engrossed in his pantomime, he had become oblivious of the visitor close by.

'Go on, then,' whispered Mister Druce the would-be teacher, as Miss O'Leary's voice droned on ten yards and a world away. 'Write your name with it.'

But again the incident was hardly a matter to greet the eyes of the headmaster. When the long afternoon wound to an end, Druce had a bare half-line of jottings about what he had seen and heard in Miss O'Leary's classroom.

Cavendish Street, Day 2. Tuesday, 2nd October 1945.
First Period: Room 3: Standard 3: Miss G. Hatton: Arithmetic.
Miss H: 'Mental arithmetic: Class, Arms fold! If you know the answer, put your hand up. 6 × 8: Webb? 9 X 9: Bell? etc. I buy 3 pounds of nails at 18 pence a pound. How much change will I get from a 10-shilling note: Salmon?' etc. She only asks those 3 & 2 others. Piano in the corner: Miss H is music teacher. Class looks bored. Written answers now, sums copied off blackboard. E.g. £4..13s..5½d minus £1..19s..11¼d. At Miss H's suggestion, I walked round checking answers. Davis came in 9 mins late. Miss H: 'There's no excuse. I'm not interested.' D told to kneel in the corner for 3 mins, to show he's sorry. D catches up fast: copies down sums & does them faster than I can. Miss H: 'He's a trouble-maker. Aren't you, Master Davis? Too big for his boots. Always asking some clever-clever question.' D finished long before the others, every answer correct. Asked for more sums to do. Oughtn't D to be in a higher class? Miss H: 'Sit with your hands on your head till the end of the lesson.' 38 in class, only D got 10/10; next best, 5 with 7/10. 6 got 0/10. They have to stay in & do them again...

Midday: Sandwiches for lunch. Mrs B said she'd been expecting me to take her class to the British Restaurant again. Oh, dear.

*

He ruled a line under his day and a half of notes, knocked on Mr Pritchard's door, and handed him the book.

He was biting into a second corned-beef sandwich when the Headmaster threw open the staffroom door and glared at him: 'Finish your dinner, will you, boyo? And step over to my office. Miss Hatton, see no-one disturbs us, will you?'

He was still swallowing the last mouthful when Mr Pritchard jerked the door of his office open in a shower of cigarette ash. 'Yes, you,' he said. 'Drrr-yoose... In yere.'

Mr Pritchard closed the door, and seated himself. He glared across the desk, and prodded his forefinger on a page of his student trainee's exercise book, open in front of him. He made as if to speak, and shut his mouth again.

Then he began an elaborate pantomime, pausing between each act to stare Druce R.C.L. in the eye for a long moment.

He fumbled in a pocket for a Woodbine packet, shook out a cigarette, and laid it down on the desk. He reached across the desk for a brass lighter and stood it beside the cigarette. He fished in his top pocket and drew out a gelatine capsule of lighter fuel. He slid the bottom half of the lighter open, and soaked the cotton wool with petrol, squirting the capsule empty. He threw the capsule into the wastepaper basket. He flipped the wheel of the lighter with his thumb, and blew across the wick when it failed to ignite. He flipped the wheel again. He blew again. He went on doing this until at last the fumes caught in a puff of flame.

Then Mr Pritchard lit his cigarette, and snapped the lighter shut.

He smoked more than an inch of his woodbine, tapping it against the ashtray every few seconds, but still not uttering a word and all the time staring his aspiring student in the eye. He seemed to be trembling with rage, and trying to calm himself.

Suddenly he clutched the open exercise book and flapped the written pages back and forth.

'Now what, exactly, does this mean, eh? *Bare walls... Doors kept locked... Why, because?* Now, what sort of comment is that? What's that supposed to mean? *Blackboard hard to read...* A judge of writing on the blackboard, are you? Well, we'll see about that when *you* try... *Whacks him with a slipper...*

'What's the point of writing this kind of slander down? Libel, this is: Mrs Bullace could have you up before the courts for this kind of remark, boy, you realise that?...

'Mrs Bullace: a teacher of thirty years' experience, and you have the audacity to write down this kind of impudence...'

'*Psychologically speaking...* Studied psychology then, have you? An educational expert, are you? One of His Majesty's Inspectors of Schools, perhaps?'

'Just who do you think you are, boyo? I'd like to know. You come marching into my school like Lord Muck...'

'What's your game, Drrr-yoose, eh? What are you up to?'

'Miss Hatton now: *She only asks those three boys and two others... Class looks bored... Oughtn't D to be in a higher class...* Well, *well?*'

'I'm sorry,' he answered, blushing with shame. 'I've never had to write lesson notes before. I thought this was what was meant.'

'Now don't you come waltzing in here, boyo, telling me the tale. Thought, did you, *thought*? Damn, you know very well what lesson notes are. Easy as falling off a log. I don't have to teach you, do I? And it's not this, this—'

Mr Pritchard suddenly grasped the offending pages, ripped them away from the staples, tore them into shreds and cast them into the wastepaper-bin, among the ash and cigarette butts.

He threw the exercise book across the desk. 'Now listen here, Drrr-yoose. I'll give you one more day to buck up your ideas. The Reverend Cranwell-Pugh can't accuse me of not having given you a fair crack of the whip. A *more* than fair crack of the whip. Which is a hell of a sight more than you deserve, boyo, on the strength of this...

'Now, listen. I'm making a change of plan. This afternoon you can sit with Miss Greenaway, give Mrs Bullace a respite from you. Miss Greenaway will be taking Standard Two for Art. Make notes. Proper, professional, teaching notes. Got that clear in your head, have you?

'After that you can take yourself off home. And get back here tomorrow morning for Mrs Bullace's class with an apology and a bit more respect.'

*

It was Miss Greenaway, only a couple of years out of training college herself, who put him wise to the kind of notes that the Headmaster of Cavendish Street School could be expected to require. *Teacher, Class, Subject. What The Class Knows So Far. The Object Of The Lesson. Getting It Across. Checking How Much They Have Understood.* Anything else you might notice, keep it to yourself. Nobody would thank you for it. Except, of course, when you were making notes on your own lesson, when modestly adverse comments on your own performance wouldn't come amiss.

Miss Greenaway's strategy paid off. Not that Mrs Bullace or Miss Hatton would ever welcome his appearance in their classrooms. And meanwhile Mr Pritchard had devised a subtle revenge.

'First lesson tomorrow, after assembly, you'll be taking Standard Four,' he announced at the end of Druce's third day in his school.

'What subject?'

'All in good time,' said Mr Pritchard. 'All in good time. It won't be any problem for you, will it? No, not for you, what with your educational expertise, and your knowledge of psychology. The fact is, perhaps you'll be able to give Mrs Bullace and me a tip or two, who knows? Eh?'

He caught an earlier bus the following morning, and was waiting outside Mr Pritchard's door when Mr Pritchard arrived.

'Subject?' said Mr Pritchard. 'A born teacher can teach anything. Off the cuff. Any time of the day or night. Well, what am I telling you *that* for? You'd *know* that, wouldn't you? Being the educational expert you are. I shouldn't try to teach my grandmother to suck eggs, should I?' And he stubbed his woodbine out and strode off to take assembly.

It wasn't until they both paused outside Mrs Bullace's classroom door with seconds to go before the start of the lesson, that Mr Pritchard vouchsafed the topic he was to take. 'The Post Office, Mister Drrr-yoose. Give them a lesson on the Post Office.' Mr Pritchard settled at the back of the room alongside Mrs Bullace, to witness the debacle.

Day 4, Room 1. Thursday, 4th October 1945. First Period: Room 1: Standard 4. Teacher: R. Druce. Topic: The Post Office. This lesson was a shambles. This shambles was observed by the Class Teacher and the Headmaster.

*

His note was not enough to appease Mr Pritchard. On four further occasions during the ensuing weeks of October, the headmaster pulled the same trick. It was effective, no doubt of that, in putting a cocky sixteen-year-old in his place. But could you justify sacrificing pupils to periods of needless boredom and time wasted in the same cause? he wondered.

Slowly the month wore away as he fumbled through the routines of the school day, marshalling the children indoors after playtime, and supervising the morning milk-break: 'Can you be trusted to do that?' Mr Pritchard asked him. Mrs Bullace and Miss Hatton daily permitted him to take their classes for English and Arithmetic and History, while they sat enthroned in the high desk at the front of the class. They broke in on his lesson from time to time, snapping their fingers or slamming down their desklid to glare at the children or quibble about what he had just said. Once Miss Hatton sent Davis to kneel in the corner, for talking to his neighbour. Told to get on with his lesson, Druce was powerless to intervene.

Three times — each an unalloyed pleasure — he took an Art lesson with Miss Greenaway, bringing in branches of copper-coloured leaves, crab-apples, rose-hips and horse-chestnuts for the boys to draw and paint.

Miss Hatton, who took Music throughout the school and played the piano for assembly with two fingers of each hand, allowed him just once to take a singing lesson. He chose 'O, No John, No, John, No' because it had an elaborate and showy introduction, and a running background tune which varied between each verse and culminated in octaves that echoed the ringing of wedding-bells. He practised it every night for a week and, when he let it rip on the piano in Miss Hatton's room, watched with satisfaction as the fury sparkled in her eyes.

He spent as little time in the staffroom as he could, loitering in the classroom to check his notes and clean the blackboard, or write up something new upon it. At midday, on the Thursday of his first week in the school, the day of his disastrous 'Post Office' lesson, Mrs Bullace had cajoled him into buying the fish she was too busy to fetch for herself. He spent the remainder of his lunch-hour queueing outside a fishmongers' shop two streets away, and had to run to be back on time. After that, unless it was pelting with rain, he walked out of the school at midday, and sat in the nearby park to read a book and eat his sandwiches.

When he *did* sit in the staffroom for any length of time, Miss O'Leary's effusive attention was more embarrassing than the inimical glances of Miss Hatton and Mrs Bullace. Coming to sit in an armchair beside his own, and puffing a cigarette in the exact middle of her pursed and eccentrically-lipsticked lips, she regularly told him that Miss O'Flynn wanted to be remembered to him. Her own remembrance, just as regularly recounted, was of how as a girl in Ireland she had won a pig at a fair by climbing the greasy pole. Leaning towards him and gripping his knee or his arm, she retailed the story as if it was her most precious memory, the pinnacle of a lifetime's achievements.

But Miss O'Leary's most memorable performance was when, coming into her room one morning, he found her standing at the front of her class, pointing with an outflung arm at the eight-year-old who stood snivelling six feet away, facing the class.

'Look ut him, boys, look ut him,' she cried, Sarah Bernhardt in the role of Phèdre, *toute entière à sa proie attachée*. 'He's a durrty little divvle, that's fwhat he is. Look ut him!'

Tears were streaming down the child's face, and a turd was sliding at a snail's pace down the back of his left leg and on behind his knee. At last it met the rumpled top of his sock, and there it lingered.

18

ROGUES' GALLERY

It had not been a satisfactory first teaching practice. Mr Pritchard, sitting at his own desk once more and tossing Drrr-yoose's teaching practice-notebook back across the table for the last time, was at pains to make that clear. Miss Hatton had complained about his arrogant conduct — not least in his having walked out of the final assembly while she was playing the hymn, without a word of explanation or apology later. Mrs Bullace had found him uncooperative. Well, there it was.

A week later and back at Monkswood — a trainee employee no more, but taking his ease among the Shakespeare texts, Catullus, Eliot, and La Bruyère — he was irritated to receive a summons to the local education office.

One by one his fellow sixth-formers who had spent the previous month in teaching practice were received by the Reverend Cranwell-Pugh. Each emerged with the offer of a training grant. Druce was left to cool his heels until five o'clock, the last in line.

'Not satisfactory,' said the Reverend Cranwell-Pugh, looking up from the letter on his table. 'Not satisfactory at all: "My staff complained about his high-handed manner ... mnh, mnh ... his critical attitude..." I'm quoting the report on you written by the headmaster of the school: you realise?... Mnh, mnh... "less interested in what my staff had to teach him than in taking the pupils' part".

— a ten-year-old in short trousers kneeling on the floorboards — Mrs Bullace flipping a desklid over to crash on a pupil's head: 'Now will you stop talking?' — shit sliding down a child's leg, as he stood in front of the class and sobbed —

'Are you attending to me, er Druce?'

'O yes. O, of course I am. Sir.'

'However,' the Reverend Cranwell-Pugh cast his eyes up towards the ceiling, and cleared his throat. 'However, I — in my function as Chairman of the Education Committee, that is — am prepared to offer you a chance to redeem yourself...

'Well? You make no comment. I should have expected gratitude.' Druce made no sign and the Reverend Cranwell-Pugh sighed. 'However, as I say, I am prepared put down your name for an Honorary Teaching Grant.'

Druce stood up and moved round behind his chair. 'Honorary? I can't quite see how an Honorary grant would help me pay my way through teacher training. Sir. Nor how, if Mr Pritchard finds me unsatisfactory, I can be worthy of any such honour at all... I never asked to be sent on teaching practice. I do not want a grant. I have no intention whatsoever of ever becoming a teacher. I can only apologise for having wasted your time this afternoon, Sir. But a month at Cavendish Street has been a waste of mine. Thank you.'

He walked to the door, and clicked it shut behind him.

He'd had a chance to think his words out earlier, kicking his heels in the corridor and waiting upon the Reverend Cranwell-Pugh's summons. As for his faint thoughts of a career in education, he wiped them from his mind.

And as for Miss Hatton, before the turn of the year her name, coupled with that of Davis, caught his eye by chance in a local newspaper. She had sent Davis to kneel in the corner once too often, and his parents had taken her to court. She had been publicly criticised, and made to pay damages.

*

There were seven of them in the Lower Sixth Arts: less than half the number of fifth-formers who had gone on into the Science Sixth to sit at the feet of Fitz Fitzroy. But here they were, thrown into closer acquaintance than they had so far known.

Bren Slaney. David Price. Charlie Farmer, who was a head taller than the others and already shaving on Saturday mornings. Charlie had returned from his month at Woodlands Secondary Modern with a report full of superlatives. Bob Druce. Mike Grace, who had tittuped around with him in silk stockings and high heels in their third-form days — *Ah! Bonjour Denise — Bonjour Marthe!* — and who was soon to be made Captain of Football and

Cricket. Chaffinch and Sherriff, still unknown quantities, newcomers from the B-stream. They shared Walter Mason as form-master with the Upper Sixth Arts, and home was a room on the top corridor, close to the library. The sacred stair, alighting opposite the Headmaster's office and forbidden territory to the Lower School, was the thickness of a wall away.

After a month at Cavendish Street, and glimpses of life from the teacher's desk and the far side of the staffroom door, Druce cast a more critical eye around him at his fellows. He was not the first, and the back wall of the room was embellished with a Rogues' Gallery of cartoons of their fellow-students and the staff, made by members of the Upper Sixth. Soon his own lampoons took their place in the Gallery. Until the day he went too far.

It was Fitz Fitzroy who challenged them to think anew about the world around them and to cast earlier judgements back into the melting pot. Once a week Fitz met the Lower Sixth Arts and wrestled them through whatever science topic they might care to choose. At the start of the year he asked them to think about the shifts of scale that came with adolescence.

*

Not just the upward climb of the horizon from the level of a child's-eye view, but the changing reports of your own body. Heavy becoming childishly light, immoveable objects yielding, the lids of jars which once had seemed welded into place now sliding round at your grasp, rigid steel now bendable. What's more, said Fitz, wasn't their coming to grips with physical things matched by new insights into what made people tick? Were adults still the people they had once seemed to be?

Yes, it was. And no, they weren't; thought Druce, listening to Fitz and struggling to meet his thought on its own ground. Take Miss Hatton and Mrs Bullace, and Pritchard and the Reverend Cranwell Pugh — figures who once would have been huge enough to stalk his nightmares — today they were puppets, smugly posturing, shrunken to human size. Almost to be pitied.

And members of the Monkswood staff, so recently his mentors, in whose hands key-subjects had lain. His old, unquestioned attitudes towards them were worth scrutiny.

Mrs Churchyard, who'd replaced the red-bearded Kavanagh as head of

Art the previous year. 'Brassieres? Where the devil would mermaids buy brassieres?' Kavanagh had once roared, patrolling a lesson in which he'd set 4A to compose an underwater scene. Oh well, in *that* case! 4A needed no second bidding, and reached for their erasers.

Mrs Churchyard issued no such invitations and was happiest when her students finicked over detail, like drawing every brick in a wall and shading them one by one, with a sharp hard pencil. Druce was 'far too heavy-handed' for Old Ma Churchyard's liking, so now he kept his painting to himself, at home.

Mrs Constable, who had taken over their Latin lessons from Dusty in their third year, and who taught, so she informed them, as her contribution to the war effort. In her grip Latin became, for Druce at least, a deadly and deadening chore. Fragmented phrases, paralysed, gutted. With the war's end Old Ma Constable retreated once more into retirement and a Cambridge Classical-Tripos man took her place. Slick as Druce was at guessing his way through translation into English, Mr Shalford arrived too late to teach him to handle Latin with facility. But Shalford led them all into Virgil, Horace, Ovid and Catullus: amazing landscapes never hinted at by Old Ma Constable.

With matriculation maths behind them, members of the Sixth Form Arts no longer encountered Miss Rook, except in the corridors; before long she would get engaged, marry and leave. She was younger than the other women on the staff. When she appeared in their classroom in the spring of 1944, the members of 4A had held a meeting after school to vote on a first name for her. They couldn't call her 'Old Ma Rook'. It was out of the question to classify her alongside Mrs Constable, Miss April, and the rest. Something lovelier, they felt, was needed, and the only clue they had was her initial 'C.' 'Christine?' No. 'Cynthia?' Possibly. 'Clara?' Yuk! Finally, they agreed on 'Claire'. It was a name which spoke of moonlight and things French, and which, when you whispered it, lingered along your tongue.

If Claire had evoked their calf-love, Old Ma Walker, who took over from Fitz for two pedestrian years of General Science, had proved to be a different proposition, tight-skirted and roundly attractive as she was. When Collins dropped a pencil in the third year and she caught him gazing up at her from the level of the floor, she handed him a detention slip and announced: 'I've written "Insolence" here for your parents' sake. But *you* know, and *I* know, that you were looking up my skirt.' The members of 3A blushed and shuddered to a man.

She had pinned Druce too, like an etherized moth, to her display board.

'The trouble with you is that you try to turn every woman teacher into your mother,' she told him one day. 'Snap out of it.'

She was right: with adolescence, women teachers unnerved him. But he could not forgive such hateful perceptiveness.

*

Fitz himself too, who had not taught them in class since the first year, had palpably changed. What was striking as he questioned the Arts sixth, was the way Fitz seemed to think of thought itself as a muscular struggle: 'Do you follow?' he would ask; 'Try to get a grip on the facts.'

It was all of a piece with Fitz's inventiveness, his love of gadgets, his happiness among formulae. In 1940, when batteries were in short supply and wartime cycle lamps had to be hooded, and dimmed by a layer of paper under the glass, Fitz demonstrated how to solve both problems at a stroke. Prise the battery open, snip the connecting wires and, where the individual cells had been joined in series, resolder them in parallel. Half the power, twice the life. QED.

The science store-cupboards were full of contraptions that Fitz had rigged up out of bent and blown glass tubing, discarded alarm-clocks and ancient clockwork motors; devices that made distillations, or demonstrated the force of gravity on sprouting seeds, and the acceleration of falling objects. 'Every boy should have a junk box,' Fitz had told 1A. 'When you come across a washer or a screw, or a likely scrap of metal, store it away in your junk box. Sooner or later you'll discover it's *exactly* what you want for a given job. Druce: have you grasped what I've been saying?'

O, he had: today he can't leave a nail or a screw to glitter in a crack in the pavement, but must carry it home in his pocket.

Fitz's muscular imagery was nothing like Bob's father's mode of thought. PC Druce's world was a world of visual images. He thought with a pencil in his fingers, getting ideas down in black and white. 'Now look here,' he'd say, gazing around for a scrap of paper and sketching a diagram. 'Can you see what I mean? No? Use your eyes!' When he searched his memory for a fact, he stared upward, frowning. As if he were turning the pages of a notebook in his head, and reading aloud what he saw written there.

Then there were people who asked you to use your ears and listen, and got ratty when you interrupted. Alwyn Black was like that. 'And where did you hear *that?*' he wanted to know, if you came up with a notion of your own. 'Listen to what I say,' he would tell you, and cocked his head if you asked him a question, as if he were listening for a spoken answer somewhere in his brain.

There were others who didn't favour any single way of keeping in touch with and tasting the world; but seemed to reach out and look and listen with all their senses brimming over and interlocking. MacNeice's poetry, when Druce first stumbled onto it, was like that. Synaesthetic. A door flung open wide into a welter of sensations.

There tastes chimed, sounds glittered, and rainbowing colours tingled along the listening pulse. He recognized in that hot brilliance of sensation a habit of imagery familiar enough, but as yet still sicklied o'er, in his own pale cast of thought — and, God, there it was again in *Hamlet*; just as he had found and fingered it a year before in *Macbeth*, in a witch's cauldron of clotting light and ambient air clinging and gelatinous, roping like blood.

*

Every aspect of French now was a joy: literature, and translation-classes in and out of French. They'd made a start on textual commentary in the French manner, *explication de texte*. An unravelling–image by image, and structure by structure–of a writer's thought. An explanation, and an unfolding.

By and large, English too was a pleasure; and Alwyn Black's custom of dictating textual comments, hour by hour and line by line, was a training in scholarship. Nor, for Druce at least, did it desiccate the text or strip it of its magic. Shakespeare and Chaucer could hold their own against that.

Less bearable was Black's impassioned involvement with the Romantics, Wordsworth (and at his prosiest) above all other. The member of the Upper Sixth who cobbled together a Wordsworthian pastiche in 1946 —

While reading through that poem by Rupert Brooke
In which he tells, for all posterity

To know, of many simple 'Loves' that give
Him joy, methought that I must also write
To honour simple things that I should love
Because my inner being so dictates —

was rewarded with its publication in the school magazine.

'Methought', forsooth! But Black's approval seemed to be all of a piece with the man, just as was his habit of referring to Jane Austen as 'Miss Austen', and the quaver in his voice when he told 2A of Virginia Woolf's death by water in 1941.

And all the while in their school anthology of modern verse, waiting only for a reader's senses to light the fuse, was an explosion of revelations:

Smoke from the train-gulf hid by hoardings blunders upward,
    the brakes of cars
Pipe as the policeman pivoting round raises his flat hand, bars
With his figure of a monolith Pharaoh the queue of fidgety machines
(Chromium dogs on the bonnet, faces behind the triplex screens) —

MacNeice's *Birmingham* stunned him. As did Yeats, glimpsed through anthologised fragments. And Auden. And, in a second explosion, Eliot's *Waste Land*.

He scoured Eliot's text again and again, then took himself off to the County Library and ordered Jessie L. Weston's *From Ritual to Romance*, and Frazer's *The Golden Bough,* both referred to in Eliot's notes to the poem. When he arrived a fortnight later to collect the books, the Librarian asked, 'How are you going to carry them?' and led him into the store-room. Fourteen bulky volumes were stacked on a table. He hurried back home and fetched his bike, the Librarian hunted out a cardboard box, and told him he could keep the books for a month. Tingling with anticipated joy, he wheeled the books home, balancing the box on his saddle; and devoured every page.

Compared with French or English, Latin was a grind. But purposeful; and once fairly launched on Book IV of Virgil's *Georgics*, he embarked on his own blank verse translation. It was always a worthwhile plan to translate French or Latin verse into English verse of a sort, especially in an unseen: you could lose among your own metrics any phrases you weren't sure of and, what's more, retain all the poetic inversions which so bedevilled a translation into prose.

With Fitz once a week on the philosophy of science, and Dusty once a week to carry them through the Dean of St Paul's commentaries on the *Sermon on the Mount*, the remainder of their time in the classroom was spent on History. American History and English Social History with E.J. Greenleigh; European History with Philip Court, straight out of University.

English Social History began promisingly enough, with Greenleigh dictating lines from Shelley's *Masque of Anarchy*: 'I met Murder on the way — — /He had a mask like Castlereagh — — /Very smooth he looked, yet grim;/Seven blood-hounds followed him… /Next came Fraud, and he had on,/Like Eldon, an ermined gown;/His big tears, for he wept well,/Turned to mill-stones as they fell…' But Druce and Slaney's involvement rapidly faded, as it did in Greenleigh's account of American History, when they were faced with a slish of dates and politics.

Philip Court's approach was diametrically opposite. Lesson after lesson he dictated notes without pause for interruption, leaving the reading of the textbook to his students. His notes were machine-like, inexorable, progressing through a sequence of sections, sub-sections, and sub-sub-sections: I,II,III…; A,B,C…; 1,2,3…; a,b,c…; i,ii,iii…; a),b),c)…; α, β, γ. When he needed a level lower than Greek, he went on to dashes and blobs. 'Big fleas have little fleas, upon their backs to bite 'em,' muttered Druce, who had just become acquainted with the rhyme, 'And little fleas have lesser fleas, and so on *ad infinitum*.' His own first contribution to the Rogues' Gallery was a clerihew:

> If E.J. Greenleigh's History
> Is an unfathomable mystery,
> There's always P. Court;
> As a last resort.

*

The underlying trouble was that so much was blue-pencilled out of existence, decreed unfit for the eyes of minors, even although they were members of the Sixth Form. Two years earlier, 4A's school edition of *A Midsummer*

Night's Dream had been bowdlerized, as comparison with the copy in the bookcase at home revealed. Puck's account of disguising himself as a joint-stool and tipping an old lady onto the floor was mutilated: 'Then slip I from her — , and down goes she!' What was so shocking about, 'Then slip I from her *bum*'? As a nine-year old he'd scrawled 'bum' often enough, and with relish, on Fatty Pemberton's front path.

A month or so into the Sixth, he bought a copy of Chaucer in a second-bookshop, wanting to read beyond the officially-required *Prologue* and *Nun's Priest's Tale*, only to find baffling gaps in its continuity: 'At this point the Miller tells his tale … Here the Reeve tells his tale.' It made no sense. If Chaucer was the father of English poetry the books said he was, what was going on? Given the language of the playground, and the contraband texts you sometimes caught a sight of, it looked like a conspiracy. And a mealy-mouthed one at that. What are they hoping to hide? Or hide from? But Walter Moon was dead, and PC Druce, endorsing the Vice Squad's view of the corruptive power of words, was no help.

In the final week of the summer term of 1945, the five future Lower-Sixth-Form Latinists of 5A had been invited, along with the Monkswood Upper-Sixth-Arts, to a reading of part of Virgil's *Aeneid*. It took place at the Girl's Grammar School in the Village. As they filed in and along the row, a gang of seventeen-year-old males were already mopping and mowing and gawping around with cow-eyes in the presence of a roomful of gymslip-clad womanhood.

The reading began.

What amazed Druce R.C.L, peering back and forth from the Latin-spouters on the platform to the open text on his lap, was how so many of his fellows could not only follow Virgil's lines, but were chuckling at the jokes. Jokes in Virgil: he'd never known such subtleties existed, but there was the merriment. His own ineptness in face of the text depressed him; how could he ever aspire to such mastery?

A member of the Upper Sixth nudged him awake and handed him a typescript, muttering, 'Keep it out of sight. When you've read it, pass it on.' He unfolded it between the pages of his book, and found himself making his acquaintance with the *Ballad of Eskimo Nell*. 'When Dead-Eyed Dick and Mexico Pete go out in search of fun;/'Tis Dead-Eyed Dick who swings the prick and Mexico Pete the gun...'

So *that* was why there were twitching lips and chuckles along the rows of Monkswood boys.

'If you've seen the mighty piston strokes of a giant C.P.R. — *Canadian Pacific Railway: he knew that one* — With a pulling force of a thousand horse, then you know what pistons are…'

All this while on stage, Dido was instructing her maid to prepare a funeral pyre, and the two principal speakers were taking turns to rise and rave at one another. At the edge of the platform a pigtailed girl was hunched over her book like a clenched spring. She kept her place with her forefinger as she waited to insert the '*said she*'s of Virgil's text. Every few seconds, she sprang up and cried '*Ait!*' and sat down again. 'I come from the land of the frozen north,/Where the nights are six months long,' Eskimo Nell announced from the typescript on Druce's lap. *Ait!* cried the pigtailed girl with almost perfect timing.

*

Smoking in school uniform was a flagrant breach of the Monkswood rules. Dare to light up on the way to or from school, and you could be sure that some busybody would spot you and pass the news on to Dusty. He would suspend you for a week for a second offence. It was galling to watch former classmates like John Robbins fishing out their cigarettes in public.

The restriction was too much for Druce and Slaney, who carried their rebellion into enemy terrain. From previous explorations of the roof they knew a way up which bypassed the official route through the solarium and up a six-foot iron ladder to the higher level. If you straddled out through a certain window at the end of the top corridor, you could crouch on an outside wall, and haul yourself up by your arms over a parapet. Thereafter a twenty-five-yard journey took you past the clerestory windows of the Library — it was wise to crawl that stretch on hands and knees — to another iron ladder.

Once up that, you were on the flat roof of the assembly hall where you could smoke in peace, secure from view behind its waist-high walls. The only danger of being spotted came in the vital minute or two of getting in or out of the window and balancing on the wall.

But climbing *inside* the roof had been a Sixth-Form tradition long before

Druce and Slaney took it up. There was a ceiling-trap directly over Walter Mason's desk. If you put his chair on the desk and stood on it, it was child's-play to push the trap open and haul yourself up into the roof. One evening after school, when Walter had safely left for the staffroom and home, Druce and Slaney were initiated by Blake and Byron, the leading rebels of the Upper Sixth.

A catwalk of planks ran the length of a wing in one direction, giving access to watertanks. Nothing remarkable there. Progress in the opposite direction, towards the upper, central level of the roof above the Library, was barred by a head-high brick wall. The way forward was to climb onto the wall and cross from side to side along the top of it as best you could. You could crawl, or inch painfully along astride it; or standing up, release your grip on a rafter and launch out like a tight-rope walker through what felt like acres of airy twilight before you could grasp another.

To your left, ten feet below the level of your eyes, was the open trap. Daylight glared up from the room below, and Walter's desk and the chair upon it seemed far away. To your right there was darkness and the knowledge of a drop to a frail plaster ceiling below which the imitation marble of the sacred stair was waiting to break your neck.

The wall successfully traversed, you set foot on another catwalk which led you over the Library ceiling to your goal: the foot of the tower.

Topped with a turret and a weathervane, the eight white columns of the tower rose above the central roof. They were not made of stone, as from ground-level they appeared to be, but of painted wooden cladding around a steel girder. The cage of girders ran down to an anchorage above the Library ceiling. Clamber up it, get a shoulder below the lead-covered circular lid and you could dislodge it, tipping it sideways into the daylight. You could breathe deep and survey the landscapes beyond the circle of mock stone columns.

Then all that was left to do was to pencil your name and the date on a convenient column, and find your way back again to the chair on Walter's desk without putting a foot, or worse, through the ceiling plaster at any point, or arriving in the Sixth-Form room to an audience of cleaners.

To Druce and Slaney, mere pencil-lead did not seem enough: what was needed was perdurable bronze. Well, a copper label at least, screwed to the wooden surface of the column. And they had a suitable copper sheet to hand. They planned the exploit for so long and in such graphic detail that years later they were ready to swear that they had carried it out.

*

Inevitably, it was Walter Mason who put a stop to the Stalky & Co. adventures inside the roof. At lunchtime on their last day as members of the school, Blake and Byron of the Upper Sixth made a farewell tour of the twilight world under the tiles, and Druce joined them briefly. His legs were dangling through the trap above Walter's desk when its owner returned.

'Is there anyone up there with you?'

Druce looked around at everything but the motionless Blake and Byron.

'I can't *see* anyone, sir.'

'Get down out of there.'

Then Walter sent for the caretaker to nail the trap shut.

Druce and Slaney extricated themselves from the merry crowd who had gathered to watch, and fled to the Chemistry lab. There, beyond the far end of the Library, was a ceiling-trap and a wall and an upper catwalk, the mirror-image of their own. Slaney kept *cave* while Druce scrambled up and through to warn Blake and Byron to take the escape route. He found them in the loft above Walter's room, aware that the way down was blocked, and about to tackle the balancing act along the wall. He whispered to them to get a move on and hastened back. He was preparing to descend, when Walter arrived with the caretaker in tow, prompted by the treacherous Price, to nail *that* trap-door shut. The sight of Druce R.C.L.'s legs once again dangling from the ceiling made such an impression on Walter, it seemed, that his rage was swept away in amazement: the boy was clearly unhinged, a subject for psychological enquiry rather than punishment.

There for Druce the story ended. But not for Blake and Byron who, with the second trap-door nailed in place, had only one way out: back to the Library ceiling, up the girders, and out through the lead-covered lid between the columns. There they faced a hazardous slide down to the ridge tiles of the roof, a lengthy journey astride the ridge, and a final slither to the solarium roof and safety.

None of this might have come to light, had chance not taken Dusty out to lunch that day. He drove through the school gates to see two senior members of the school astride the roof. They — *morituri te salutant* — cheered and waved to him, too far gone in misbehaviour to care. At the final assembly that afternoon, Dusty reported their desperate act of impudence to the school. Only the fact that it was their last afternoon had saved Blake and Byron from instant expulsion.

From then on, with the upward routes barred, there was no further challenge to any Monkswoodian to test his nerve as an indoor steeplejack. But the window and parapet route to the exterior of the roof was not cut off. Nor had it ever been except once, and then by treachery.

Late in their first term in the Lower Sixth, Druce and Slaney were smoking somewhere on the roof, when Price went to the window they had left not quite closed, and slammed it shut. They, returning with barely a minute to spare, found Price capering on the corridor side of the window, refusing to slip the catch and rubbing his hands with glee at what would happen to them. There was nothing for it. Druce wrapped his fist in his blazer, punched it through the glass, then reached through to open the catch. Slaney and he flung up the window and leapt down into the corridor like avenging angels. Price fled. But Druce and Slaney would have a score to settle.

However, first things first; there was Dusty to see, and another tale of a broken window to smooth over.

Such was the term in which, as Walter Mason pointed out, his French blazed like an orb while all around was Stygian gloom, and he hid in the coalshed from his father's wrath.

19

JACQUES

Sunday, July 21st, 1946. The summer term was almost at an end, and Bob and Bren were sauntering along the tow-path at Richmond with their Belgian friends Jacques and Jean-Luc. All four were licking watery post-war ice-creams. It was a warm afternoon.

A knot of people had gathered at the embankment rail close to the foot of Richmond Bridge. Curious to see what was going on, Bob and the others hurried towards them. They were standing in a circle, laughing and joking. A large bellows lay on the ground at the centre of the circle. Alongside it stood what looked like a tea-urn. It was open at one end, and a perspex window had been puttied into its side. A gas-tap was screwed to the top.

'Et alors?' said Jacques.

A small, bird-faced man in a raincoat thrust his way into the ring, with a sprawl of garden hose in his arms. He spilled it down onto the ground, and made a performance of coupling one end of it to the bellows and the other to the gas-tap on the tea-urn.

Then he peeled off his raincoat. Underneath it he was naked but for a bathing-slip, galoshes, and a belt weighted with lead blocks.

'Do me a favour, mate,' he said to an onlooker who was standing close to the bellows. 'When I give you the thumbs up, start pumping. It'll only be for a second or two. I'm relying on you, mind.' He picked up the urn and walked down the embankment steps, across the muddy foreshore and into the water, dragging the hose behind him.

When the water was up to his waist, he turned and shouted, 'Pump!' and put the tea-urn over his head. His assistant, looking less than willing, began treading on the bellows, pumping air along the hose. The man waded further out, and the river closed over him.

Six feet or so from where it was screwed to the tea-urn, what looked like a red-rubber football-bladder was connected into the air-line. It had swelled a little, and floated on the water, pulsing to the rate of a man's breathing.

Bobbing and pulsing, the bladder slowly jerked itself further away from the river-bank. Lungfuls of air burst at the surface in its wake.

'Qu'est-ce qu'il fait là-bas? What ees he doing down there?' said Jacques.

'Search me, son,' someone said.

At the end of a minute, the man working the bellows was red in the face and out of breath. 'Give us a hand, somebody, for Chrissake,' he said. The bystanders edged away from him, staring out across the water.

'Hallo! There's something going on,' said someone.

The bladder was rapidly swelling, its bright redness dulling as the rubber stretched. Soon it had doubled in size.

'Gawd blimey, now what?' gasped the man with the bellows. Bob glanced at him. The man looked as if at any second he'd take to his heels.

'You can't jack it in now, mate,' somebody said.

Yards away across the water, the bladder rapidly shrank to its earlier size.

'Panic over,' said a woman at Bob's elbow. She sighed noisily, and giggled.

'I wish to God he'd get a bloody move on, and come back out,' said the man pumping the bellows.

Again the bladder began to swell.

This time it did not shrink, but went on swelling and stretching until it had become a taut bubble of pink rubber more than two feet in diameter, barely resting on the surface of the Thames.

The group fell quiet. Bob looked at the man with the bellows. He was still pumping, not knowing what else to do. He looked ready to weep.

Then the huge bubble burst.

'Christ Almighty,' somebody said. Two or three bystanders edged away sideways, but still gazed out across the water.

Suddenly a voice spoke behind them, and coins rattled in a tin. 'Thank you very much, ladies and gents,' said the voice. 'Don't forget the diver.'

The bird-faced man, bare-headed and streaming with river-water, set his tea-urn helmet on the ground and moved round the group, rattling a tin under their noses. The weighted belt was still buckled round his waist, and mud squelched out of his galoshes at every step. 'Many thanks, friend. Much obliged,' he said to the man at the bellows.

For a moment the man stared back at him, clenching his fist. Then, 'Sod you,' he said, and shouldered his way out of the ring of onlookers.

'Are all the English mad?' said Jacques. 'And what is, "Sod you"?'

*

Jacques had been staying with him for a week, one of more than a hundred Belgian lycéens, male and female, who had arrived on an exchange-scheme with schools in Southern England.

The plan had been to match social like with like; rural pupils with rural, city-dwellers with city-dwellers, young people from well-heeled backgrounds with their wealthy counterparts. Jacques, whose father owned and directed a private lending-library, and Jean-Luc, the son of an army General, were students at a college in Brussels. They and their fellows had been destined to exchange with sixth-formers at a school in the Kentish stockbroker belt.

But at Victoria the organization was a shambles, as it was to be again a few weeks later at the Gare du Midi in Brussels. Off went the wrong set of Belgian students to Kent, while two hours after the appointed time, the waiting sixth-formers at Monkswood faced a party of tired and hungry Bruxellois from family circumstances altogether different from their own.

In the event, the mismatch didn't matter at all. Mrs Druce fussed over Jacques as if he were a long-lost son, while Robert Druce Senior hustled him into the front room to teach him a dozen Ju-Jitsu holds, and couldn't wait take him on at chess. At the Slaneys', Jean-Luc mucked in with Bren and his brothers like a good comrade. And so on down the line. It was agreed all round that when the Monkswooders got to Brussels, their present partners would return their hospitality.

But for two participants. The single blot on the *entente cordiale* was the loutish son of a Belgian newspaper-proprietor who tried to swing a punch at Croker, his host. He found himself pinned to the floorboards, while Croker brandished a pair of scissors and hacked off most of his guest's hair.

'Très bien. Bonne idée,' said the Belgians when they got to hear of it. 'Don't worry, we will find a nice family in Bruxelles for Croker to stay with.'

*

Falling as it did in the final weeks of their first year of Sixth-form life, it was an irresponsible fortnight for both sides. Past anxieties and assumptions went by the board.

The Belgians had arrived expecting to find the English reserved and distant in manner, concerned to preserve a *sangfroid* tantamount, in Belgian eyes, to cold-bloodedness. For their part the Monkswooders had been prepared for humourless pomposity: Hercule Poirot at his worst. In the event, both groups were charmed with one another.

Twice they made official visits to London, and racketted around Westminster Abbey, the Science Museum and the National Gallery. At the British Museum Bob carried Jacques off to meet Old Ginger. Together they leaned over the Embankment wall and spat into the Thames. They picked their way among boarded-off bomb-sites in the City, and he and Bren and Jacques and Jean-Luc raced one another to the top of the Monument and the Whispering Gallery at St Paul's, where they sent their French and English ribaldry echoing around the wall's perimeter. By arrangement with Price's father, who had something to do with the Docks, the whole group spent one muggy afternoon sniffing their way through warehouses redolent of fruit and oil and spice and leather, and rounded off the day in the underground cold-store with a snowball fight among the carcasses.

The Belgians spent the remaining weekdays sitting-in on lessons with the Lower Sixth. Dismissing any need for himself or anyone else to translate his pearls of wisdom, Alwyn Black held forth in a loud voice, stretching his lips and baring his teeth in his endeavours to enunciate his mother tongue as carefully as possible for the benefit of the visitors. They, when they failed to understand, were too over-awed to raise a hand and question him.

In Court's and Greenleigh's History classes, it fell to Druce to act as official interpreter whenever anything cropped up that the Belgians mightn't get the hang of. Not until half-way through a session of ill-suppressed merriment, did it dawn on Phil Court that his text was being laced with a ribald commentary, and that Druce's services would be better dispensed with.

In the long summer evenings and at weekends, Bob and Bren carried their guests off into the meadows along the river, and into the forest. On the slopes above Consort Road they recited for them the ancient names of their climbing trees. They led them behind a curtain of water where the overflow at Gregories spilled down into a tunnel, and showed them where to leap back and forth across the sluggish summer brook. With Pat lurking at Bob's side, stockstill as any poacher's dog, at dusk they lay low and watched for deer and nightingales.

While Jacques and he sat chattering in French over their supper late one evening, Bob heard his father speaking to his wife in the kitchen.

'Just listen to them, Dorothy,' he said. 'Doesn't that make all our sacrifices worthwhile?'

*

Three weeks later, the Monkswood sixth arrived at the Gare du Midi into a crowd more than a hundred strong. On one side of the locked barriers to the platform were the English, and on the other their Belgian hosts, shouting and waving. On both sides, officials pushed their way through the throng, brandishing lists and bawling mis-pronounced names through megaphones. It was late at night.

Bren and Bob stood together and peered across the barriers, hoping to catch a glimpse of Jacques or Jean-Luc, who had promised to meet them. Nearby a voice was shouting: 'Englisch shoolers, here are your instructions, pliss pay attention to your instructions… Monkesswoot shoolers!' Bren nudged Bob: 'Hey, look. Over there on the other side of the barrier: isn't that Jacques? I think he's seen us.'

An instant later, out of the chaos, Jean-Luc materialised at Bren's side. 'Vous voilà,' he said. 'Okay. Follow me.'

He led them to a dark corner of the platform, clambered to the top of a locked gate and sat astride it while they handed their cases up and Jean-Luc passed them down to Jacques. 'Alors,' Jean-Luc said, when Bren and Bob had dropped to the ground at the far side, 'The English are not the only ones who like climbing the walls. Soyez les bienvenus à Bruxelles! Welcome to Brussel. So, we go home now, Bren. A demain, Jacques.' With a formal handshake all round, Jean-Luc carried Bren off into the city. 'Attends. One instant,' said Jacques and vanished, to return wheeling a bike. He strapped Bob's case to the carrier. 'Et maintenant,' he said, 'you will ride and I will run beside you and tell you where to go. Tu comprends?'

Brussels was a dazzle of neon signs, like the West End of London before the years of blackout. Cars raced past, hooting, and the granite-cobbled roadway was treacherous with tram-tracks. Jacques pounded along the pavement, gasping instructions, and yelling, 'Tiens la droite! Tiens la droite!' at each intersection, as Bob veered away over the cobbles towards the left-hand side of the road, and his suitcase lurched across the carrier with him.

Falling into a clash of dreams that night, in a bed that folded down out of the wall, he relived the day. Kissing his anxious mother goodbye. Swapping sandwiches with Bren on the train to Dover. The ferry, and Price and Grace hanging over the rail being sick. Escaping from the Gare du Midi. Swerving across granite cobble-stones, fighting to keep his front wheel from locking into the gleaming tram-tracks. At last sitting with Jacques and his mother over plates of soup, downstairs in the warm kitchen.

And the bread! After years of grey wartime loaves that gritted against your teeth, he had forgotten that bread could be creamy white. In England now, with the war won, the National Loaf had just been put on the ration.

'Robert: you will be my second son,' Mme Frédérick told him, hugging and kissing him, and leading him upstairs to this room that was to be his for the next fortnight.

After the Great War, she had been awarded an MBE for her work as a nurse on the staff of Edith Cavell's hospital. And now she stood blushing while Jacques showed him the illuminated parchment and the bow of grey-edged rose-pink ribbon and the gold cross pinned up in a glass case in the entrance hall.

In the night-time twilight of the city, shadows clung in the walled garden below his bedroom window, and he could hear the murmuring voices of Jacques' parents somewhere nearby.

'I'm abroad!' he said aloud. 'Me voici à l'étranger. Enfin.'

*

There were official excursions in which all the Monkswood scholars and their Belgian hosts took part. An express-tram ride to Tervuren, and ornamental gardens which were a provincial replica of Versailles. A railway journey to Antwerp and a day of migraine and blinding sunlight. A coach-ride to Waterloo, where again they mingled with busloads of Englisch shoolers and were herded about by a Belgian teacher with a megaphone. Bren and Jean-Luc, Jacques and Bob clambered up the memorial mound, stood under a Dutch lion cast from the captured French cannon and took windblown snaps of one another. In a pavilion nearby there was a panorama of the battlefield, its painted landscapes and tiny figures fading and flaking. Thirty or so at a time, the visitors were prodded into an adjacent room to watch a film.

June 17th 1815. The sound-track cleared its throat and blared into the sounds of revelry by night. Through a rainstorm of scratched emulsion, Wellington's staff and their ladies waltzed to the National Anthem, while Napoleon slid his finger over a lamplit map. The scene cut to a battlefield where black-and-white mannikins staggered through billows of gunsmoke.

The only clue as to who-was-who was the bar or two of the Marseillaise or 'God Save the King' squealing from the soundtrack at that instant. The Belgian students, so recently liberated from the occupying German troops, seemed surprised by the dismissive laughter of their British guests.

For the greater part of his stay in Brussels, le petit Robert went native and, except for Bren, shunned the company of his fellow-countrymen. On his first Sunday in Brussels, he walked to High Mass with Jacques and his mother. Not knowing what to expect, he was swept away by the orchestral and choral music.

But the sounds were inextricably entwined with earlier visions of that same morning. A drunk, veering across the pavement, gashing his forehead against a wall, and gazing down at the blood on his hand. An old woman who stared this blazered English schoolboy in the eye, then straddled a drain and released an unbroken stream of piss.

At the Théâtre de la Monnaie a few evenings later, he was aware of Jacques' mother side-spying him to see if he laughed at the jokes. Chamber-pots, fleas in the bed, henpecked husbands, red-nosed drunks, honeymoon couples: it was the world of Breughel's peasantry, the world of Collins' music-hall, of smutty jokes and seaside postcards, vulgar and familiar.

But there were sudden and inexplicable cultural conflicts. Jacques and his fellow-students and their girl-friends smoked casually in public, as of right, and were amazed to learn that smoking in school uniform was an indictable offence at Monkswood, even for eighteen-year-olds. Then one afternoon in the Bois de la Cambre, Bren, who had tagged along with Jean-Luc, spotted an open-air dance-hall; what more natural than to invite the girls to dance? Their, and Jacques' and Jean-Luc's outrage was amazing:

quelle vergogne! one might have been asking them to strip themselves naked. Yet then, in Antwerp, hadn't a waitress burst into the men's lavatory to answer the telephone at length, while a row of English schoolboys blushed and wished the floor might swallow them? During their visit to the law-courts, an advocate suddenly snatched up an ink-well and hurled it across the chamber. Robert waited for a chaos of retribution to break loose; yet Jacques brushed the incident aside as nothing out of the ordinary. Most disturbing of all for PC Druce's son, was the pistol that jounced in a holster on every policeman's hip.

Recollected in tranquillity, the evening with Jacques' uncle was crazier yet than anything Belgium had had to offer.

The sitting-room of his flat was five metres wide and more than twenty metres long. The pelts of zebras clung intermittently along its walls like marbled butterflies. The floor was booby-trapped with the skins of tigers whose claws rattled on the parquet when you jarred your foot against them. The huge skulls snarled, dripping invisible and bloody saliva from sabre-teeth, and stared you out with their yellow glass eyeballs. Assegais and tribal drums stood in groves along the walls. Between the zebra-skins, the walls were cluttered with tribal masks, gourds, arrows, and framed photographs.

One photograph was instantly familiar from a fourth-year geography text-book.

A fourteen-foot python, its gut monstrously distended by the pig it had swallowed whole. An intrepid and mustachioed white hunter in a solar topee, flanked by Congolese bearers. He stood with his right foot on the earth and his left foot on the swallowed pig whose death he had avenged with his express rifle, as composedly as if he were posed in front of a painted jungle in a photographer's *cabinet*.

Jacques' uncle, that same great white hunter — his skull now topee-less and balding, his weeping walrus moustaches snow-white and no longer waxed — advanced down the room with outstretched hand. 'Dîtes-moi: vous la reconnaissez, ma photo-là?'

Recognize it? Indeed he did, and hastened to say so.

'Si. Il y a longtemps que je l'ai recontreé à l'école, dans un livre de géographie. Mais que je suis enchanté de faire votre connaissance, monsieur.'

'Ah, qu'il est gentil, ce jeune homme Anglais,' murmured Jacques' uncle's *compagnonne*: wife? helpmeet? mistress? it never became clear.

'I will 'ave a treat for you, after dinner,' said Jacques' uncle. Pink-faced and twinkling with benevolence, he took his guest's arm and led him to the table.

If the great white hunter was, with hindsight, more than a little comic as he posed with his pomaded whiskers curved in a smile, and his pig-in-a-python, the promised treat was an agony of suppressed laughter. Robert stood, perforce, to attention for minutes at a stretch and fought to fill his mind with sober images.

As soon as the dessert had been cleared away and the coffee drunk, 'Venez, venez, je vous en prie,' said Jacques' uncle. As his guests drew up their chairs around him, he opened the lid and front doors of a piano, threaded in a cardboard roll, seated himself, and trundled on the pedals underfoot. He folded his arms, while the piano keys rattled up and down as if impelled by invisible fingers. You could tell when a showy passage was coming, from the sudden rainstorm of holes punched in the pianola roll. There was discreet applause when the cardboard roll had slid out of sight.

'Mesdames, messieurs,' said Jacques' uncle, drawing a fresh roll from its cardboard tube, 'vous me permettez de rendre hommage à notre visiteur. I would honour our visitor. God Save the King! Vive l'Angleterre!'

The company rose to their feet, while Jacques' red-faced uncle pedalled away in their midst. Major, minor. March-time, gallop, Viennese waltz, military two-step, polka. The British National Anthem clanged and tinkled through a never-ending sequence of variations. Entirely conscious of the figure he must cut in his brass-buttoned blazer, the English guest stood to attention, staring at the patterns on the pianola roll and trying to match them with the changing rhythms. He found himself brimming over with a sudden huge affection for Belgium and Brussels and Jacques and his family and friends, as he tried desperately not to giggle.

*

At midnight on Sunday August 11th, Robert Kitchener Druce's twenty-five years in the Metropolitan Police Force came to an end. He had long been disenchanted, and eagerly awaited early retirement. He was forty-four years old, anxious to make a clean break. But now, in a world in which returning ex-servicemen were flooding the labour market and claiming their right to employment, he found himself one of a host seeking work.

The skills that he had acquired had prepared him for little more than a job as a 'security guard', prospective employers informed him. The title was an exaggeration: the positions that he was offered — and for a month or two at a stretch persevered in — were as gateman, door-opener, patrolling snooper, uniformed night-watchman.

He spent a month or so as a water-bailiff with the Metropolitan Water Board, patrolling the reservoirs and inspecting fishing-licences, and from time to time marching home with a fish. Once he brought with him a bream too fat for the oven. On another evening he arrived with a jack-pike. Tipped out of the swaddling newspaper, and already hours away from the water, the pike snapped its hook-toothed jaws at Mrs Druce's fingers.

'Well, Dorothy, you can't ask for fish fresher than that,' said her husband, and brained it with the coke-hammer before chopping off its head.

Then one day a fisherman remarked in his presence that all policemen were bastards, and he gave the man a crack on the jaw that landed him in the reservoir, and that was the end of that job.

For a month he guarded the gate at a fragrance and flavour factory. The day-long sweet effluvium turned his stomach, and the cigarettes he rolled and smoked at every break tasted like nothing on earth. His family could nose his homecomings: his skin and clothing reeked of synthetic scent. When he walked away from that job, he burned a pair of good shoes in the kitchen boiler. The sickly stink had become indelibly trapped in the leather.

Daily he grew more morose and inconsolable as money grew tighter; and his wife went back to the plastics factory where emergency regulations had drafted her during the last years of the war. There, too, the easier times had passed, and now she spent the long hours on piecework, smoothing the rough edges of plastic mouldings with a file. Before she learned to protect her fingers beforehand with sticking-plaster, she sighed over her broken fingernails, and skin rasped and bloodied by the edges of the file.

With Bob at school, they needed the money. Nor would his parents for an instant countenance his involving himself in the family finances. He nagged them to let him take on a paper-round, or work at weekends in a nearby nursery whose owner was always on the lookout for cheap labour.

'Certainly not! Your education is paramount,' his father told him. 'All you have to do is to get yourself into the university. It's *our* business, not yours, the sacrifices we choose to make for you.'

Other troubles were looming. With the war safely over, the landlord wanted his house back. Thousands of returning servicemen, many just married, and many with long-postponed babies on the way, were demanding homes of their own, too. Seven hundred acres of meadow and ploughland close to Woodlands Green were requisitioned by the London County Council and quickly splattered with prefabricated concrete boxes. But these were exclusively for East-Enders whose homes had been bombed into rubble. There was no private rentable property available in the Village.

As an ex-member of the Force, Mr Druce no longer had any entitlement to Police housing. As a resident of more than twelve years' standing in the Village, he had a claim upon Council accommodation, but the waiting list was choked by ex-servicemen with young families. And who should now be Chairman of the Housing Committee but the Reverend Cranwell-Pugh, whose name was scattered across the pages of the *Clarion & Weekly Advertizer* week by week as he thrust his gleeful, busybody fingers into every pie?

When Robert Druce Senior arrived to present his case for a council house, 'Out of the question, my dear man,' said the Reverend Cranwell-Pugh. 'Unless there is a Court Order against you requiring you to vacate your present accommodation. In which case, your name will be added to the waiting list.'

The landlord's civil action was heard in November, and the court gave Mr Druce six months to vacate the house in Auckland Drive. He returned to the Reverend Cranwell-Pugh, who advised him to look for a place to rent. Failing that, the most that he could hope for was temporary accommodation in a hostel.

'Patronising, sanctimonious, dog-collared little toe-rag,' snarled Bob's father, home again from the interview, belching and wincing with pain from his duodenal ulcer. 'Calls himself "Reverend"? He doesn't know the meaning of the bloody word. I know his type. Expecting you to be beholden to him. "Yes sir, no sir, three bags full, sir." In his glory when people go crawling to him on their knees. Well, I told him *his* history.'

Which, like his son's earlier outbreak of anger at the reverend gentleman, may have relieved Robert Kitchener Druce's feelings, but was of no help at all.

*

Watching his father swirling stomach-powder around in a glass and gulping it down, and listening to his admonitions — 'Be guided by me. Don't make the mistakes I made. Get to university. Get security behind you, my son. Be beholden to no-one,' — Bob shared his resentment of jacks-in-office, and of people who patronised him.

Even of those, like the Vicar and churchwardens at All Saints, who were moved by friendship. Mr Turkentine, the Vicar's Warden, who was a member of the Monkswood board of Governors, more than once clapped him on the shoulder in the vestry after Holy Communion, and told that he'd be welcome among the Young Conservatives. Mr Knightly, the People's Warden, whose Sunday morning Young Men's Guild he had joined along with John Robbins, invited him to tea. He played a piano duet with Mr Knightly's daughter Janet, and Mrs Knightly invited him to do the stage-lighting for the Church Players.

'Sultanas and walnuts? In a lettuce salad? Humph!' his mother said, when he reported back to number 66, 'Funny old sort of a salad if you ask me.'

More than once Mr Knightly, who was in insurance, asked him if he'd ever considered a career in the City. And the Reverend Eric Stanford began to be a burden, with his long and searching looks deep into Bob's eyes, and his habit of remarking, 'There is a place waiting for you in the Church, you know. Promise me that you'll listen for the Call.'

Very well. He would be civil to them all, but not beholden. His choice of path, whatever it turned out to be, lay elsewhere.

Of that he was sure.

His parent's devotion was difficult to accept and acknowledge with good grace. His father's rehearsal of the sacrifices made for his sake blackmailed him into tongue-tied irritation. In face of such love, how could he argue a conflicting point of view on any topic in the world? When he was safely alone, the sight of his mother's cramped fingers moved him to tears. But they were tears torn between tenderness for her, and rage that she should insist on sacrificing herself for his sake.

His sense of being possessed by the too-condescending goodwill of Mr Turkentine, the Reverend Stanford and the Knightlys, and by his parents'

love, found some release in the lampoons he composed for the Rogue's
Gallery at the back of the Monkswood sixth-form room.

*

The winter of 1946 was harsh and unrelenting. From December until early
March, rutted ice, steel-hard and impacted with grit, was piled in the gutters
and alongside paths and pavements, the levels rising higher with each
snowfall. In mid-March, the floods which followed the thaw were to be the
worst on record.

On Saturdays and Sundays as long as the daylight held, toboggans
skimmed down Maze Hill, careering down the river of ice that fell steeply
from the hill crest to the edge of the forest brook. With the brook itself only
yards away, the trick was to veer to the right, and bounce to a standstill amid
the snowy ant-hills and the gorse. Only the suicidally-minded attempted a
wrenching left-hand swerve. It carried them another thirty yards or more
on a wavering track between the trunks of beeches and a plunge to the yard-
deep bed of the brook, the fantastical combs of ice, and the pebbles. You
might have guessed that Tom Oliver, a fellow server at All Saints', would be
idiot enough to try. He broke his leg and cracked his skull and was prayed
for in church for two Sundays running.

Bren and his younger brother rummaged in their loft for the ancient
skating-boots that had belonged to their parents. 'Don't come asking us for
skates for you to go and break your neck on; we're not made of money,' Bob's
parents told him. But Bren dug out a pair of makeshift skates for his friend.
Each skate was a shallow, boat-shaped piece of wood with a metal strip let in
as a keel. You had to screw it to the sole of your shoe with wood screws. Bob
found an old pair of shoes in his cupboard, and took them round to Bren's
one Saturday.

That afternoon Bren and he trudged through the forest to Grimston's
Lake. In June they'd creaked around it in a boat, and lingered after dark to
listen to nightingales. Now, in the bitter wind, they launched themselves
across the ice.

Weeks went by, the frost showed no signs of abating, and skating began
to lose its attraction. Young men drove their cars across the lake for a bet,
and at dusk one day a group of them lit a fire of branches close to the centre.

In the morning, the three or four inch depth of melted ice was frozen fast once more. Roughened with ash and charcoal, the fire-circle remained, a trap for the unwary, plucking at the blade of your skate and throwing you over.

At Monkswood the playground coke-pile shrank alarmingly, and in classrooms furthest from the boiler-room, boys and staff alike put their scarves and gloves and overcoats on again. In the library, under-equipped with heating pipes, the members of the Upper Sixth Arts were granted an electric fire, but every week their fingers were numb for a double period as they copied down notes on European History from Philip Court's dictation. Garibaldi, Bismarck, Metternich, Cavour. Ever since then they have been figures posturing in Druce's memory in a frozen landscape, stretching bloodless fingers out to a feeble electric heater and stamping their boots to coax the feeling back into their toes.

At 66 Auckland Drive the Druce's stores of coal and coke were soon consumed. So was the heap of dust from the coal-shed floor, mixed by his father with watery cement, and compressed in flowerpots into coal-black parodies of sandcastles.

Once again the house was impregnated with a stench. It overmastered every other household smell and clung in your throat and seemed to coat your lungs with soot. This time it was a stink of burning asphalt as the wooden setts that had been cleared away from East-End streets along with the tramlines, now smouldered in the fireplace. They were the only fuel available. Impacted gravel detonated as they burned, scattering fragments across the room out of the smoke-cloud and sending Pat yelping upstairs.

Twice that winter the water froze in the loft and they had to wait their turn with the plumber. The second time was disastrous. The feeble warmth of a hurricane lamp left burning in the loft had no effect, and thickening ice stretched its muscles and split the rusty metal of the water-tank.

Swaddled in three woolly jumpers, an overcoat, a balaclava helmet and mittens, Dorothy Druce perched on a kitchen chair below the ceiling-trap at the head of the stairs, reaching up to take each brimming pailful of water and ice as her husband baled out the tank. In the roof above her, straddling the rafters, he cursed the luck that had chosen to burst the tank with a bare two months of their tenancy to run. It was the task of his son, as clumsily swaddled as his mother, to take the pail from her, trudge downstairs with it and shoot the contents across the lawn. In the roof above, his father raged about the time each journey took.

'Dorothy? Dorothy! Put a toe behind that boy. He's like a little frozen turd.'

Without warning, the pail, too hastily handled, caught on the edge of the trap as his father swung it downward. Mrs Druce and her son, braced to receive it, were deluged with water and blades of ice.

'That's it, then,' said his mother. 'That's all I needed. Come and get into some dry clothes. Your father can sort it out on his own.'

'I say, you can sort it out on your own,' she said, raising her voice, as she marched her son first to the bedroom and then downstairs.

Up in the freezing air of the roof her husband's babbled excuses transformed themselves into shouted commands. Mother and son listened with half an ear to the distant raving as they cradled their hands around mugs of cocoa in the kitchen.

'Shouldn't we—?' said Bob. But 'frozen *turd*', huh? The insult rankled, and he was too cold to care about abandoning his father.

'It won't hurt him to stew in his own juice for a bit. It's high time that man had a little consideration for his family,' said his mother.

Moments later there was a clang. It was followed by a rattle and a volley of curses. His father, missing his step from rafter to rafter, had plunged his foot through the lath and plaster ceiling.

'You can put a stop to that sort of talk if you want any help from *me*,' said Mrs Druce, condescending at last to clamber back onto the chair under the trap-door. 'From now on just *watch* what you're doing with that pail. When this little lot's done, I've got a bedroom to clean up, thanks to you…

'Poking your foot through the ceiling,' Bob heard her mutter as he carted another pailful of ice downstairs. 'You're like a great child at times…

'Poked it through deliberately, I shouldn't wonder…'

'O yes. With you, it's anything to get attention. You don't have to tell me.'

20

EXILE

In June Bren and he had listened, darkling, to nightingales, reciting 'thou wast not born for death' in a whisper. Despite which, and despite the alarms of war, they had never yet watched the sun rise.

'Awake! For Morning in the Bowl of Night/Hath flung the Stone that puts the Stars to Flight...'

Their heads were awash with the *Rubáiyát of Omar Khayyám* and with the *Wind in the Willows* vision of the god Pan piping at the Gates of Dawn. It was high time, they agreed, that they kept vigil and watched rosy-fingered Aurora, child of the morning, climb the eastern sky.

They agreed to sneak out at night and walk till daybreak. They fixed a date. Whatever the weather — rain, hail, sleet, snow — Bob would creep down and let himself out of the house, and meet Bren in Hawkswood Road.

It was drizzling as he reached Bren's gate soon after midnight, looking forward to pitching handfuls of gravel at the bedroom window. He was disappointed to find the front-door ajar, and Bren's face peering round it.

There was a bottle of water in the pocket of Bob's mac. In another there was a brown-paper bagful of cocoa, powdered milk, and sugar, stuffed into an enamel mug. Bren was bringing a picnic stove, methylated spirits, and a kettle. They whispered together by Bren's front gate, agreeing not to be deterred, and set off, hatless, through the thickening rain.

An hour later they reached Woodlands Green and sheltered in a telephone-box while sleet thrashed against the panes. They were drenched through, and condensation streamed down the glass around them. They fumbled under their shirts and dried their hands as best they could on their vests before lighting the cigarettes that Bob carried in an empty tobacco tin. Bren, remembering his Boy Scout days, had brought red matches in a screw-capped bottle. Only underneath the coin-box was there a surface dry enough to strike them on.

Two cigarettes apiece later, the air in the box was thick with smoke. They pushed the door ajar to see how the weather was getting along. The sleet had given way to snow.

Melting snow streamed through the roots of their hair as they set off, with more than seven miles left to complete the circle back to the Village. 'Now, let's see,' Bren said. They were almost at the end of March, and the sun was due to rise, according to the newspaper, a few minutes after six. Say five o'clock, then, for the first streaks in the sky.

There was a wartime bunker in the corner of a field about five miles distant, just outside Shalford. They ought to get there, and be safely ensconced, soon after four o'clock. Right? Then they could dry off a bit, smoke another cigarette and brew their cocoa.

After which they would step outside and watch the dawn come up like thunder. Or creep with silver-sandalled feet, like a frightened girl. Either way. They didn't care which.

When they reached the concrete bunker, straddling over brambles, they found it a foot deep in water, but they stumbled upon a pile of bricks and a empty petrol-can outside the doorway that they could perch on. Below the firing-slit there was a horizontal shelf: they could brew up there.

Bren filled his picnic kettle and lit the stove. Bob clawed the sodden mess of cocoa-mixture and brown paper bag out of the mug, tipped half of it back into the mug and set the rest on the concrete shelf. When the water was hot they poured it in on top, and stirred the mixture with a pencil. They made it last, taking turns to clasp their hands round the mug and drink. When they'd finished the second cupful, they lit their cigarettes. By the time they stepped outside again it was a quarter to six.

The wind was rising and the rain had died down a little. The sky was still black. So where was rosy-fingered Aurora? She must have arrived and made off again, behind a black arras of thunder-clouds. So much for the promised joy.

It was still almost as dark half an hour later, when they reached the bridge over the river, beyond the far side of which lay Hawkswood Road and Auckland Drive. For ten months of the year you could cross dry-shod over the stepping-stones a hundred yards downstream from the bridge. That way you cut half a mile off your journey, quitting the road and taking to the meadow-paths.

But in the half-light, they could see the river swirling noisily against the river-bank and the piers of the bridge. The slippery stepping-stones would be under a foot or more of water.

So what? They couldn't get any wetter than they were. They trudged downstream and plunged across the gravelly river-bed, ignoring the stepping-stones and leaning their weight against the water as it surged thigh-high, lapping their groins.

They reached their separate homes with scarcely time to towel themselves dry and hide their sodden clothes. All day they yawned through classes. Before the afternoon ended they were sneezing.

Well, there you were. So much for the Romantic vision. What's more by now their mothers would have found their wet things and there'd be a court of enquiry to explain themselves to.

*

April 7th, 1947. Easter Monday. His head swam and his skin smouldered and stung as he wrenched himself from side to side in the spare-room double bed. Above the door, a newly-plastered patch of ceiling gleamed whiter than the rest.

'Never mind that, it's the only room fit for Doctor Bürstner to see you in,' said his mother. 'She wouldn't have space to turn around amidst all the junk you fill your bedroom with. Heaven knows what she'd think.'

Alone again after Dr Bürstner's visit, with a dusting of penicillin on the weeping blisters on his face — the stuff was still far too precious to use on scars less likely to be seen — he sobbed with fury and frustration. Bren and Mike Grace and the other four were in Paris, just as *he* should have been.

Notre Dame, Versailles, the Louvre, the *Comédie Française*: Walter Mason had planned it weeks earlier, even taking time to warn them against the *filles de joie* infesting the streets of Paris. In spite of the impending move and all the uncertainty that hung over him and his family, Mr Druce had insisted that his son should go. Then a smallpox epidemic in the French capital and a prophylactic vaccination which for Robert flared into an attack of vaccine fever, conspired to make mockery of every plan.

And here he was.

The door was pushed open, and his father came into the room.

'Ah, you're awake. Good,' said his father. 'Listen, I know it must be a disappointment, but these might cheer you up a bit.'

A box of Swan Vestas and two green-and-yellow packets of twenty cigarettes dropped on the coverlet: Player's Sun Valley.

'Dad?'

'All right, all right, my son. I know you smoke on the quiet. You can't kid me. Hang on, I'll fetch you an ashtray...

'Now, what else I can get you?'

*

Three weeks later the Druces left Auckland Drive and the apple trees and the shedful of ironmongery and books.

For weeks on end his father had brooded over a nightmare vision of his family and property being ejected onto the street. But at last, six days before the eviction order was due to take effect, a letter arrived to inform Mr R.K. Druce that temporary accommodation could be found for him and his family in a Council hostel. The letter was undersigned *per pro* the Reverend Cranwell-Pugh.

The downstairs rooms at number 66 were stacked with a clutter of tea-chests and borrowed packing cases, as his parents wrapped their belongings in newspaper and packed them away. Bob piled into cardboard boxes those school-books that he couldn't do without.

'*All* that lot?' sighed his mother. 'Heaven alone knows where we'll find room for them at the hostel. Are you sure you can't make do without them? Can't you weed a few out — for *my* sake?'

A pantechnicon drove the larger furniture away to a depository, and returned to take the Druces and their day-to-day belongings to a pair of adjoining rooms in the hostel. There'd be no more piano-practice until the council rehoused them, and who knew when *that* day might dawn? Still, look on the bright side, that would give young Bob more time to get on with revising. Isn't that right, Dorothy?

The hostel was a former office building in Monkswood High Road, its lofty Edwardian rooms divided by plaster-board partitions. Three families were already ensconced there. Mrs Druce was appalled and depressed when she heard that she would be sharing the single gas-stove in the ground-floor kitchen, and a sink and a table in the scullery for her washing and ironing.

The front door opened into a narrow hall. Bikes were propped against the right-hand wall, and the Druces had to squeeze with their cardboard boxes past Freddy Harker's tricycle and the Grice's pram. The door at the end of the passage opened into a communal dining-room. Someone had pinned a rota to the the wall, allocating responsibility for sweeping and dusting the public areas day by day: Mrs Grice, Mrs Sparks, Mrs Harker. 'Mrs Bruce!' had been pencilled at the bottom.

There were six bedrooms on the first floor. One was occupied by John and Mary Grice and their five-month old son. Two rooms belonged to the Harkers: nine-year old Freddy, and his mother. Sly-eyed Mr Sparks not long demobbed from the navy, and his white-fleshed and sultry-looking wife, lived in a room at the end of the row. The Druces settled into the two rooms still unoccupied, with Freddy and the Sparks as neighbours on either side.

John Grice, home from the Army, worked for the BBC. He and his wife were a friendly couple, both in their late twenties. When Bob trailed in from school, Mrs Grice would always offer him a cup of tea, ask him what sort of day he'd had and tell him about hers, while she gave a breast to the baby. 'Call me Mary,' she told him.

'She's *Mrs Grice* to you,' Bob's mother hissed after she had heard him do so. 'I don't know what's got into him,' she added, smiling at Mary Grice. 'He's not normally so rude.'

When he went upstairs later, she followed him into his room. 'I don't want you getting familiar with these people,' she said. 'I don't want strangers knowing all our business. Keep yourself to yourself. That's not too much to ask, is it?'

But to her son, the Grices — John, ambitious and in no doubt about his future career, happy with peace-time and his marriage; Mary, cuddling and singing to her baby, making the best of the hostel — were refreshing company, glamorous in their youthfulness and their free-speaking, free-thinking ways.

Not so was draggletail Mrs Harker, with her perpetual whining diatribes against the husband who had left her high and dry. Nine-year-old Freddy he felt sorry for, but that didn't make any more bearable the messes Freddy left behind him, his constant attempts to pull Pat's tail or poke her with his sticky fingers, his foul mouth, his unending string of questions. Impossible to read a book if Freddy caught sight of you.

But the weather stayed mainly dry and sunny, and most evenings Bob darted across the High Road and into the forest, clambering into an oak-tree with a book or two in his pocket. It seemed to be a peculiarly appropriate spot to work his way through Virgil's *Georgics*. With his back against the trunk, his legs dangling through a net of leaves, and Pat curled up at the foot of the tree, he stayed there until it was too dark to distinguish the words.

*

The nightly antics of the Sparks kept his imagination at a stretch. Albert Sparks was a greasy-faced, surly little man, who caught the bus each morning to his job as a hospital porter at St Katharine's, nine miles away. He never looked you in the eye. If you chanced to catch his glance, he jerked his cropped head away, and stared in another direction. An instant later he would be side-spying you, while he flickered the out-thrust tip of his tongue from side to side within the O of his half-pursed lips. In company, Bert Sparks said little, hardly raising his voice above a whisper. But at night behind the locked door of his bedroom, his voice was a throaty growl that cut across his wife's whimpering as he beat her up.

On his first night in the hostel, Bob heard the noises from the adjacent room, thrust a bookmark into *Northanger Abbey*, and set his ear to the plasterboard wall.

What was going on? Murder?

He wondered if he should knock on his parents' door and ask for help. But they had miseries enough of their own.

He went on listening, as the noises modulated into the grunts and squeals of pigs slobbering at a trough. There was a rhythmic crunch of bedsprings. Then it dawned on him that the Sparks were *doing* it. Shagging. Having a go.

Minutes before, he'd been punching and slapping her. And now just hear them. *Honeying and making love over the nasty sty.*

If Jane Austen was a genteel world away, Shakespeare's bloat king was not. Nor was Maupassant. Nor the peasants — *animaux farouches:* wild animals, male and female — which La Bruyère saw labouring in the fields of France.

Human-faced, communicating with one another in what might have passed for articulate speech. The subhuman cries of the Sparks and the scroinch of the bedsprings accelerated to a climax, and died away to a sobbing silence. Nightly they repeated their performance while, a plasterboard wall away, he tried to put his mind to Catullus or English Social History.

Encountering Bert Sparks at breakfast times, he would stare him in the eye, and watch the man look away. Then he would turn his gaze upon sultry Mrs Sparks, on the freshly-powdered bruise on her cheek, her lips split and swollen under the lipstick, or her blackened eye.

*

Chatty and welcoming, in those moments he snatched with her over a cup of tea and cigarettes, Mary Grice was like a breath from another world. She talked to him about Rupert Brooke: 'He must have been so like my John, so young, and fighting for England,' she said. One afternoon she was waiting for Bob with the present of a paper-covered copy of *1914 and Other Poems*. Here it lies now, under my hand, the flyleaf dated and signed by its new owner in a backward-looping scrawl that looks like a bunch of crushed wires.

He began to hasten home from school, standing up on the pedals of his bike, craving the pleasure of Mary Grice's company. Before his mother came home from the plastics-factory, with her torn fingers, her sour glances and her muttering, and broke the spell.

His mother put a brave face on things in public, saying little and holding herself aloof. He wished that she would relax with his new companions, accept their friendship once in a while, and not be so continually upon her guard. But he recognized how it was that she could not. She was too deeply shamed by the turn of events that had uprooted the family from their home and made them dependent on the whim of the Reverend Cranwell-Pugh and the Housing Committee. For twenty years, in London and Sparrowfield Lane and Auckland Drive, her kitchen had been the centre of her life, a place where her husband and son could relax around her — or try to — and be themselves. Now her right even to light the gas under a saucepan had to be validated by the time-table pinned up on the wall beside the stove. She forced herself to smile at the other women, and did not complain in front of them. But she took it badly.

Her husband felt his own loss of status just as bitterly. There was work of sorts to be had; but he hated it, and felt himself looked down on. He had no-one but himself to blame: it had been *his* decision to retire from the police at the earliest opportunity. Through the partition opposite the wall that divided him from the Sparks, Bob caught snatches of his parent's muttered recriminations. The only thing that seemed to unite them was their anxiety that *he* should have a better start in life. Should never have to swallow his pride. Never have to beg for favours, cap in hand.

*

Every Friday after tea, he stowed a book or two in his satchel and biked to Walter Mason's for an evening of conversation in French. Walter had first issued his weekly invitation several months earlier, refusing to accept any kind of reward or payment other than that of helping a favoured pupil. Weekly, his breathless downhill ride carried him along the forest paths from Monkswood High Road to Thornbrake Way. Like his slow return through the dark, the journey intensified the joy of release from the hostel with its cold lino-covered floors and cream-painted plasterboard partitions.

His hours of freedom framed themselves in another language, in sprawling discussions neither invoked nor cut short by a bell. Once the politenesses were over and Mrs Mason had carried away the tea-cups and the plates, their talk ranged wide, wider than French literature and culture alone. And then — like Mary Grice when she tickled her baby's tummy changing his nappy, and pouted an unlit cigarette towards Robert's match — Walter, explaining Henri Bergson, fetching a book to illustrate a point, asking Robert his opinion of a painting or a text or a crucial theory, for a while opened a door into a relaxed and saner world.

Back in the weekday classroom, his skills began to exfoliate into textual explication. More and more was becoming grist to the word-mill as the months passed, trash and the valid alike. *Hamlet* and Tommy Handley's *ITMA* on the radio; *Much Ado About Nothing* and Max Miller; Jane Austen's finely-poised irony, and Mr Hackett's innuendos in the *Clarion and Weekly Advertizer* — 'That a Black Maria was seen in Monkswood High Road yesterday. That the name of the occupant is not at present known'; Dickens' *Pickwick Papers*, and the yiddish jokes of Maxie Bacon who, like Sam Weller, couldn't tell his 'wees' from his 'vubble-yous'. He began to devour the shelf-long row of novels in the school library, more than twenty of them so far and still not yet complete, that made up Jules Romains' *Les Hommes de bonne volonté*. With Eliot's *Waste Land* still ringing in his memory, he stumbled upon John Dos Passos's *USA*, and was lost in it, finding confirmation of richness in its collage of texts, *things being various*.

The sepia photographs of the work of Otto Dix and Kokoscha and Lehmbruck and Kandinsky and George Grosz on the shelf above his bed in *Modern German Art*, taking off from where Dr Foote's gaudy illustrations came to a halt. The colour-bright reproductions of Cézanne and Van Gogh on the classroom walls at Monkswood. The memory of his father's oleograph prints of Millais and Holman Hunt now gathering dust in Chisholm's Repository in Consort Road. The Corot landscapes Walter discussed with him all one evening. All, all of it came now as grist to the mill.

But where Walter threw doors open into wonder, Alwyn Black seemed happier to slam them shut. Or, rather, to bar all the doors except those behind which the answer that Black required might lie. To every text there was a proper response: Alwyn Black knew what it was. It was the task of his students diligently to seek it out. Black's questions were never quite as spurious as what Druce R.C.L. would one day hear in another grammar-school English classroom: 'Now I wonder who can tell me what this verse makes *me* think of?' But at times they were not very far removed from that.

Rebelling against Black's literary directives, Druce answered curtly, perversely dismissing a text as often as praising it. 'Shallow,' Black told him one afternoon. 'Your answer is too shallow.'

'Sir, Wordsworth's poem is not *that* thick,' he replied. 'If we go any deeper, we'll poke our fingers out through the other side.'

It was nonsense, as well he knew, but it relieved his feelings. And irritated Alwyn Black.

The trouble was that Romantic sensibility got under his guard, exposing his tears, his quivering inability to cope. Lamartine — yes, you could dismiss the haughty posturings without difficulty. But not Victor Hugo at his most sentimental. Not Dickens. Reading on, he dreaded their almost casual skill in brimming his eyes with tears.

With La Rochefoucauld and Oscar Wilde as touchstones, he honed aphorisms of his own, getting them by heart. When week by week Dusty Rhodes discussed Christ's Sermon on the Mount as explicated by the Dean of St Paul's, Druce conjured them on cue like rabbits out of a hat.

'Druce, I sometimes wonder whether you know what morality *is*.'

'Sir, it seems to me that morality is the peculiar concern of the bourgeois class: the aristocracy have little use for it, and the proletariat barely understand it...'

'As always, Druce, you take everything too far.'

'But, sir, how can you know where the limits are until you have contemplated them from the far side?'

It was a measure of Dusty's patience and sincerity, that he could take this adolescent arrogance in his stride. Perhaps, from Walter Mason, he had heard of and understood the sudden turmoil in his pupil's life that occasioned it.

*

Morality, sex, sexuality: exile to the hostel had thrown everything out of frame.

'We do earnestly repent, And are heartily sorry for these our misdoings; The remembrance of them is grievous unto us; The burden of them is intolerable. Have mercy upon us, Have mercy upon us, most merciful Father...'

But, leading the general Confession, cassocked and kneeling on the altar-steps of All Saints', pitching his voice up at the east window to be reflected back into the chancel and the nave, the firmness of his speech belied the sudden hollowness of his belief.

He struggled to make sense of those emotions he so anxiously wanted to know and feel, but could not comprehend. Love and sex, *l'amour et l'amitié*, pestered him with a incessant clash of viewpoints. Rupert Brooke's yearnings at one extreme. At the other, Hamlet's paranoid disgust. Only a tissue of words, it seemed, could ever reconcile them, bed them together.

'Love and friendship are mutually exclusive': so claimed La Bruyère.

Or again, 'Love evaporates when there is no occasion left for hope or fear.' That was La Rochefoucauld, sardonic, alluring. There was no room for scrumptious sentimentality there, no room for 'moon' and 'June', and lovers

243

reflected in one another's eyes as the screen faded from sunset to dark and the cinema audience shuffled towards the exits.

No room for love, certainly, in the doggerel 'Eskimo Nell', where flesh metamorphosed itself into pistons, combination locks, cisterns, mechanically coupling. Nevertheless that imagery, far distant from lovesick yearnings of the flesh and anguish of the mind, was easier to be comfortable with than the Sparks' nightly rutting. How could the sounds that reached him through the wall be allied with gentleness, or love?

'Stewed in corruption, in the rank sweat of an enseamèd bed...' The phrase-making helped. There was a breathing-space and a distancing in Shakespeare's vision: these gibbering puppets are not such as we; our withers are unwrung. But the Sparks were reality, not creatures in a play. Not puppets, but flesh and sweat and his nightly neighbours. An eavesdropper, willing and unwilling, he was caught in a no-man's-land of prurience and revulsion.

Where and how did it all — the courtly cynicism, the cartoon capers, the morning bruises on Mrs Spark's face — chime with Rupert Brooke's, 'When Beauty and Beauty meet/All naked, fair to fair,/The earth is crying-sweet,/And scattering-bright the air...'?

Within a year or two he would recognize the mawkishness of Brooke's verses, the dishonesty of images spooned out of John Donne and diluted with honey and lukewarm water. But here and now, for a while they seemed admirable. He wished there was someone he could feel and think and write like that about.

*

Bren Slaney sensed his friend's wayward moods, and read his essays and his fumbling verse and heard out his diatribes in patience. At school they were seldom if ever apart, though their bike-rides home now carried them in opposite directions.

Bren's younger brothers were both at Monkswood — Don in the Lower Sixth, Frank in 4A. In the Slaneys' three-bedroomed house in Hawkswood Road, all three jostled for space and quiet to get on with increasing quantities of homework. So each Saturday Bren and Bob escaped together, sitting side by side all morning in an East-End civic library, glowered at and shushed by other inmates, researching their weekly essays for Alwyn Black.

At midday they walked to a nearby café and stood in a queue for canned spaghetti or roes on toast. They washed it down with a cup of coffee concocted from hot water and black fluid from a bottle, and smoked a twopenny cigarette from a tumbler by the cashier's desk. Minutes afterwards, Bren was plunging ahead of him through the cold shower and the chlorinated footbath and into the indoor swimming-pool which stood next door to the library.

*

Somehow, in this new mental space of peacetime, you had to put it all together — birth, copulation and death: religion, politics, and art — and try to make sense of the addition. Capturing it in a network of words.

All Saints' and the stained glass images which gazed down at a weekly ceremony of blood: 'Blood of Our Lord Jesus Christ, which was shed for thee, Preserve thy body and soul unto everlasting life...' And the remembered snow of glass along the gutters of Silver Hill, where a sea-mine commandeered by Herman Goering from the naval munitions of Admiral Doenitz had floated down on a parachute and comminuted a woman and two children.

Goering himself climbing into the dock at Nuremberg and now already six months dead, like Eva Braun and Heinrich Himmler, of a cyanide capsule while Albert Pierpoint dropped his hangman's trap from under the feet of other Nazis. Violence for violence. Justified revenge, and a counterpoint of self-sacrifice. 'If I should die, think only this of me...'

Trying to make sense of it. With only borrowed words, second-hand images, and a clash of politics to start from.

It began to seem to him that only in created art, in words and images, was there a place where stability might lie: the brushstrokes and paradigms and sub-texts were holdfasts and footholds. Cling to them and perhaps you could ride the wave in that insane sea of adult self-seeking and self-delusion in the midst of which his parents seemed to be capsized and drowning.

21

HIGH CEDARS

O, if only! Scents at nightfall in springtime, a girl's face framed by cyclamen, the shudder of shared kisses making havoc in his heart.

> Le cyclamen du soir
> Encadre ton visage;
> Le cyclamen du soir,
> Pâle sous le ciel noir,
> Dans mon coeur fait outrage.
> Le cyclamen du soir
> Encadre ton visage.

But like the antique rondeau form with its recursions, its rhyme-scheme, and scansion, his images were an exercise in invention. An invocation of imagined visions. Sensation and emotion craved for, but unfelt and never known.

If only, if only.

The French verses he wrote had never been otherwise, for the language, alien and whimsical, imposed its capricious discipline. He wrestled with patterns of sound and rhythm, and technique took precedence.

His models were outdated. Ronsard. Verlaine. Alfred de Musset — and that love-sick sonnet by Francis Jammes which he had done into English, with its valediction: 'And I taste on your lips the taste of red roses and wasps.' Melting, sensuous stuff: second-hand envisionings of blood racing in the veins, air *scattering-bright*, earth *crying-sweet*. Yearnings whose emptiness was masked by the magic of a foreign language.

The verses he attempted in English were rarely like that: in your mother-tongue it was not so easy to hide threadbare emotions behind a glamour of words. At least, not for long. The shimmering visions soon faded and wore thin.

'Along the margent of the glinting stream,/He strode…' The fragment had hovered in his mind for months now. Cresses, and the fall of the light on tinkling water. That was easy enough. Pure scenario. But *who?*, and *why?*, and *to what end?*, eluded him. Time to call it quits for a while. Better stick to satire in his present mood:

> With January tread M. takes his walk —
> With fervent prayers for prey to fit his ire;
> Walter Mason, inoffensively pilloried in the gallery; and Philip Court,
>   a safer target, to round off the quatrain —
> While C. trots sadly in his book-strewn mire,
> Piglike and solemn, sentimental, portly, pompous pork.

Yes, stick to satire. Aspire to a harsh manliness. Fire your darts, but keep your own soft underbelly covered. O, by all means go on frothing up his romantic falsehoods in French verse. 'But surely you realise it's a *pastiche*,' he could retort to any critic. 'A five-finger exercise. I had hoped *that much* was obvious!'

Trifling verses in French, then, to feed his yearnings. Satire, for the rogues' gallery; Fantasy or caricature. Flight or fight.

His eye fell on Miss Ellis, a temporary replacement for Alwyn Black, off from school with his sinusitis again:

> Miss E. lows like a melancholy cow. Her bovine gaze
> Suits calves of Chippendale.
> She ruminates her words to every male,
> Cudwise. And minutes wind in solemn funeral
> Behind her brow of bone,
> Where horn-rimmed eyes dimly obtrude…

Vicious stuff. Unjustified. But let the record stand. It was another species of lampoon that stopped him in his tracks. Mike Grace drew a set of cartoons of the Monkswood staff, while Druce footnoted each with a citation from *Hamlet*.

Philip Court, who much resembled Charles Laughton in looks and physique, was easy enough to pinpoint: 'He's fat, and scant of breath…' And so, tongue deliciously not quite in cheek, was Walter Mason:

See what a grace was seated on this brow,
Hyperion's curls, the front of Jove himself,
An eye like Mars to threaten and command,
A station like the herald Mercury
New-lighted on a heaven-kissing hill…

E.C. Greenleigh seemed to offer almost as easy a target. Confirmed bachelor that he was, sharing a house with his unmarried sisters, he blushed and raised his trilby hat whenever he came face to face with a Monkswood senior in the company of a girl. When a visiting American teacher talked to the combined Sixth about her students' courting rituals, Greenleigh excused himself, and hurried away. It was the Sixth form's cherished theory that Greenleigh had been crossed in love in his youth. Yet Hamlet's 'the pangs of dispriz'd love' was a little *too* pointed, Druce and Grace agreed, even for the Rogues' Gallery. So Druce sought to soften the allusion by extending the quotation:

The pangs of dispriz'd love, the law's delay,
The insolence of office, and the spurns
That patient merit of the unworthy takes…

'Aha! More victims in the Rogue's Gallery,' said Greenleigh, arriving to take a history lesson, and strolling to the back of the room. He grinned as he read, until he came to his own lampoon. 'Aha. This must be me,' he said, nodding at Grace's drawing, then bent to peer at the words beneath it. He blushed and suddenly went pale.

'Patient merit of the unworthy,' he said, seeming almost close to tears. 'Patient merit. O, dear. O, dear.'

No more misapplied quotations, Druce told himself. No more lampoons. Never again.

Trêve de discours.

But poetry — as opposed to mere verse, — Druce was persuaded, was a place of truth. The serious poems he struggled to write in English were his private affair, not for the Senior Master's eye. Nothing would induce him to lay them open to Alwyn Black's tinkering.

Since the school's foundation, Black had edited *The Monkswoodian*, altering submitted text as the fancy took him. In 1946, Byron of the Upper Sixth submitted a sonnet, and Black chose to improve Byron's, 'light bled from the sky' into 'light fled from the sky'. Byron raged against the mutilation when he discovered it in print, ripped his copy of *The Monkswoodian* in two, hurled the fragments across the room, and strode out to demand an apology from Black. Black did not give him one.

Now, a year later, here was Black asking Druce whether he wished to submit anything for consideration: preferably in English. Druce handed over a set of five-finger exercises in French, take them or leave them. All or none. As they stood. The Senior Master made a *moue* and sniffed, but took them.

*

As suddenly as it had happened two years earlier, schoolwork was all over and done with. The revision, the ploughing through old notes, the getting dates by heart, the frenzy of pouring it all back out again in the examination room, were things of the past. So, too, was the recurrent nightmare out of which he so often fell awake. Examination Day. Oversleeping, leaving his ink-bottle and pen at home, limping into the exam room hours late, begging the invigilator to restore his name to the list and loan him a pen. The pen breaking in his fingers, his answer book sodden with ink and beyond redemption. Fully awake, he could grin at imagery so obviously sexual, but the terror was real.

Now, for the length of two or three years, they could all be quit of such fantasies. For the rest of the summer — before university entrance or national service put salt on their tails and plucked their feathers — the Upper Sixth were the cocks of the walk.

Elsewhere, too, things at last seemed to be changing.

His father still searched despairingly for a job that suited him, but the Druces were quit of the hostel. They were still a long way down the list for a council house. But at last his father was — for some of the time, at least — more like his old self.

In mid-July they were moved to a flat in the Village, the attic floor of High Cedars, a Victorian house that stood in its own grounds close to the forest. Their flat was draughty and rambling, contrived out of what had been the servants' bedrooms, but there they could close the door on the world and, in public, hold their heads up higher. A tiny room in an angle of the roof, reached by a final stair, was Bob's. There he found space for books and a bed, Pat's basket, a table and chair. Directly overhead, as he sat to read or write, was a skylight glazed with wired glass. The first moment he found himself alone in the room, he perched the chair on the table, shoved the skylight open, and climbed out onto the roof.

*

'Very well,' said his father, 'I suppose you've earned it. All work and no play makes Jack a dull boy. But don't abuse the privilege. I'm not having you coming home at all hours, is that clearly understood? What time does the place close? Ten o'clock? Very well, you can be indoors by ten-thirty. All right, Dorothy? No, listen to me, my son. That gives you all the time in the world to walk back here from Joslin Road.'

'I don't see why you want to hang around a youth club all evening and half the night in the first place,' said his mother. 'Isn't your home good enough for you?'

'You got them to agree?' said Bren the next morning. 'We'll join the ballroom-dancing class, eh? Slow foxtrot, quickstep, waltz. You know, it's a social asset, being able to dance. I can stagger around the floor a bit already, but I need a lot more practice.'

'Social asset? You should hear my old man on the subject! According to him, dance-halls are hotbeds of licentiousness: "licensed licentiousness, that's what it is, my son: the first step on the slimy path towards adultery." He can't forget his years on the Vice Squad, that's his trouble. Raiding night-clubs and brothels.'

'This is a youth club, not a night-club,' Bren said. 'Ah well, don't tell him we'll soon be foxtrotting the night away, once we get the hang of the steps.'

But getting the hang of the steps was misery. Seventeen-year-old Dawn Anderson, giggling in the corner with frizzy-haired Barbara, didn't make things any easier. Bren grabbed up his Pauline but Bob lurked in the doorway, eyeing lads like Ted Meggle and Jim Wade whom he'd first met in the infant class at Consort Road. Since then, Ted and Jim had mixed with girls every day in the Senior School and at work, and now treated their womenfolk with aplomb. They were men of the world, with their own cash in their pockets. They spun their partners around like professionals, tacking and weaving and never clouting into other couples or the legs of people sitting around the dance-floor. They'd all had a good two years of practice already.

Bob bought a book for beginners by Victor Silvester, and kept it in his desk at school, safe from his parents' prying eyes. Bren and he pored over the diagrams, trying to get them by heart. SLOW, *quick-quick*, SLOW. Hieroglyphics, with explanatory arrows. Left shoe: right shoe. *His* feet: *her* feet. Patterns of tracks across the page, like the spoor of a pair of punch-drunk animals printed in soot on a snowy landscape.

So that's the quickstep, is it? Better start on something simpler, eh? Yeah, let's look at the waltz.

ONE, *two, three.* ONE, *two, three.* LEFT, *together,* forward. RIGHT, *together,* forward. Swing round into the turn, carrying the lady with you. Hell!

That was the point, when you struggled to put it into practice, twisting the remembered page of diagrams around in your mind's eye, where you kicked her ankle or trod on her toes, and backed away, despairing. Victor Silvester's helpful trigonometrics seemed to have no connection with the flesh and blood and bones a breath away or the damp palm clutched in his own, as he swivelled his shoes across the borax-slippery floor.

After he'd *found* a partner, that was, peering shortsightedly at unaccompanied girls. 'Girls never want passes,/From boys who wear glasses,' he told himself, adapting Dorothy Parker's maxim, and tucked his spectacles into an inside pocket a street away from the club. He held the girl at arm's length, and only spoke across her shoulder, fearful that despite the scrubbing of his teeth and the medicated toothpaste his breath might smell.

He persevered for a month or two, for Bren's sake as much as his own.

O God, who would ever *want* to circle round the floor with him? Why not abandon the whole idea, as from now on?

'No, I don't dance... No, I'm sorry, but it's never interested me... Dancing? Licensed licentiousness; isn't that what dancing is, when you come down to it?...'

Emily, when they met and got engaged, had won a gold medal for ballroom dancing. But he never danced with her.

*

In any case, you could meet girls at the youth centre without being forced into dancing with them. There was an art club and a drama group and Mrs Smith, the club warden, had started up a quarterly magazine. Bob put a poem in her pigeon-hole: 'Slum Vista'. It leaned heavily upon MacNeice for its tone and title and was over-egged with epithets. 'Curved shards of glass wink salaciously under the bleary hiccups of the gas,/Steam drifts from a doorway, lounging along the gutter,/Lingering upon drains, and damply absorbing the mutter/Of traffic amok in the rain-daubed streets… Framed lines of tenements frame the unwelcome, treacherous sky,/Shearing away the light, snatching the air, wilting a fern set high/In a warped and blistered window-box…' But he hoped he might one day see the thing in print and here, accepted or not, at least it would sidestep Alwyn Black's defilement.

Not every girl was ballroom-dancing mad. After a play reading or a magazine committee, or nothing more than a cheese-sandwich and a coffee in the canteen, they might even let you walk them home. If you were lucky, they'd allow you to kiss them goodnight at the gate. Then it was back to High Cedars before you turned into a pumpkin, grinning at the thought, and not forgetting to scrub the lipstick off with your handkerchief when you'd turned the corner into your road. As he hastened through the streets, 'gaslamps click prim, deprecatory, metallic tongues,' he told himself, as he passed from one pool of light into another, and listened to the ticking time-clocks.

The first time he walked a girl home, he forgot about lipstick on his handkerchief. His mother was lying in ambush when he got in from school the following afternoon.

'So whose is *this*, then? I demand to know,' she hissed, thrusting his discarded handkerchief under his nose. 'Decent girls don't let themselves be messed about by boys.'

After that he searched his hankie for traces of lipstick, and scrubbed them out before he cleaned his teeth and went to bed with a book.

*

The roof at High Cedars was like a raft swimming on a green heave of foliage at the top of the world. Flanked on all four sides by a chimney-stack, its steep, red-tiled slopes seen from the ground looked like any other roof. But when he shouldered up the skylight and clambered out, he found himself on a lead-covered platform, yards across.

For a while, at every visit the barely ankle-deep parapet of ridge-tiles at each side, and the huge sky, took his breath away. His clothes and hair were plucked at by the wind, and he clung to the propped-up skylight for support. Ahead, across a swoop of valley, he could make out the landmark tower of Claybury asylum, and southwards beyond it a bluish mist of outlines that was London. At his back the flanks of the forest rose a little and fell away and rose again to a distant rim of sky.

Ribbons of copper ran up each chimney stack, to three-fingered spikes thrust out above a cluster of chimney-pots. Seen from so close at hand, the pots were never less than monstrous, each shoulder-high to a man. When he thought he had found his sea-legs and ventured towards the edge, the raft rocked underfoot, for its individual stretches of lead tilted towards a central gutter.

He took to clambering up at twilight, with cushions and a book. In foul weather and nights of storm, he pushed his table against the wall, and dragged his bed beneath the skylight. Gazing up into the dark, he listened to high seas of rain flooding across the deck and roaring away through the scuppers. One night as he stared upward through the glass, lightning struck the copper spikes and leaden roof, and his retina was swamped with mauve light for a quarter of an hour.

It was a place to be shared with Bren, a place to sit in talk as sunset stained the chimney-pots blood-red and deepened the green of the forest beeches, before the lights of the Village began to twinkle below them… It was not for nothing that Chesterton's *Manalive* had joined the row of paper-bound books on the shelf by his bed in the room below. He clambered down one evening and fetched the book and read it aloud to Bren until it was too dark to see.

Throughout that summer, Bren and he would climb onto the roof at twilight to watch the moon rise and the stars revolve above them. Chesterton's Michael Moon had carried a bottle of cheap claret up to his landlady's roof at the top of a high hill in north London and, having drained it, had sent the bottle whizzing like a wheel of glass to break upon the stones below. The best he and Bren ever managed, was to scrounge the remnants of a vile South African sherry left over from Christmas. Yet, swallowed in tiny gulps among the stars, like Moon's vintage it put on a kind of perfection.

Wiser not to send the bottle whirling between the chimney-stacks, alas.

'Bob? Where have you got to? Bob? O my God, they're on the roof. They'll fall and kill themselves!' Mrs Druce wailed, on first coming into an empty room with a skylight gaping open. But she seemed to accept the allure of the world beyond the ceiling.

'Well, all right,' she said, after very little pleading. 'Just you make sure you both keep well away from the edge. Promise me that. And come straight back down if the wind gets up.'

He couldn't persuade her to join him on the leads although, sensing her suppressed desire, he tried.

'Phhh! Now what would people think if they saw me cavorting about on the roof? Your father would have forty fits.'

But she condescended to perch on the chair below, and thrust her head out into daylight. She peered around into the blue distances through the spaces between the chimney stacks.

'Isn't that Claybury over there? Well! That can't be the spire of All Saints, can it? Well, I never. The top of it's lower down than we are.'

Unasked, and despite the continued rationing, she made them sandwiches from time to time: bacon still sizzling or sausages slit lengthwise, clapped between slices of bread. She called up into the twilight and he lowered an old satchel on a string.

*

On his eighteenth birthday, he stood on the roof for a while, staring out across bronze tides of forest beeches scudding in the wind and sprinkled here and there with the gold of birch and thorn. John Robbins had been called up in the spring. Now he was in the Royal Army Educational Corps and stationed at Buchanan Castle, hard by Loch Lomond, two hundred and thirty miles away north-westwards, beyond the forest slopes and across the shires. Beyond the blue distances and the village mapped below his own feet, Bren was twenty miles away at another point of the compass.

Bren had travelled the forty miles to Suffolk and basic infantry training a bare fortnight previously. It would be another week before the rookies in his intake were allowed home on a twenty-four hour pass. 'Centurion noster dixit mihi in castram manendum erat ut pomis terrulis scindendum': Bren's hasty dog-Latin note was a tale of confinement to barracks and potato-peeling.

Bob hoped to be in uniform himself before the turn of the year. He had asked for an early call-up: Navy, Air-force, Army in order of choice. He was bored with kicking his heels.

'The time can't come too soon as far as I'm concerned, for you to get out from under our feet.' His father had been saying it again and again, as soon as the holidays began. 'Up reading half the night, and then lolling about in bed till past midday. I blame your mother. She's letting you turn into a namby-pamby. You'd better get in some practice at rising early, my son. Once they get you into uniform you won't know what's hit you. I'll give you a shout in the morning, shall I, when I get up myself?'

*

All his life a manic-depressive, Bob's father had spent the months in the hostel in a mood of suicidal despair that rarely lifted. Now for a while at High Cedars he became more like his old endlessly-changing self, and plunged and soared from elation to gloom and back again within the space of an hour. When a wave of euphoria took hold of him, he flung the door of Bob's room back on its hinges and struck a pose and recited verse by heart and by the yard:

AWAKE! For Morning in the Bowl of Night
Has flung the Stone that puts the Stars to Flight:
And Lo! the Hunter of the East has caught
The Sultan's Turret in a Noose of Light!

You could *hear* the capital letters, as he went on declaiming, unstoppable, quatrain after quatrain, until he reached the end of the piece and cast around in his mind for fresh territory to conquer.

HO, TRUMPETS, sound a war-note!
Ho, lictors! Clear the way!

The knights will ride, in all their pride
Along the streets today…

That first version of the *Rubáiyát of Omar Khayyám*, seventy-five quatrains long, and Macaulay's *Lays of Ancient Rome*, were not the only verses he had by heart.

Back from an interview at the end of which he had been appointed Superintendent of the Casual Ward at St Katharine's Hospital, he was full of himself. Before many months were out, the job would come to sicken him, but at that moment he was jubilant. It was late July. The sun was shining.

'Tell me, Dorothy, would there be any Guinness in this house? I fancy a glass.'

'Now?'

'This minute. Things are looking up.'

St Katharine's, a sizeable hospital, was a day's march from London. It had grown up around the nucleus of a Workhouse for the paupers of a union of parishes. There was still a Casual Ward, 'the Spike', where tramps and wanderers with no visible means of support could get a bed for the night. It tickled Robert Kitchener Druce's fancy to assume the role of Workhouse Master and, as always when he was elated, he had verses for the occasion. In his high, Micawberish mood, he struck an attitude:

'Twas Christmas Day in the Workhouse,
The Master of those stately halls,
Wished the paupers a Merry Christmas
And the paupers answered —

'Bob!' said his mother warningly.

'Bob?' said his father, 'The paupers answered "Bob"? A curious thing for them to say. Given the circumstances. However. To resume.'
He cleared his throat and struck an attitude once more.

At last the Christmas pudding
Came steaming into view.
The raisins: they were scanty;
The currants: they were few.

Up leapt one brave old warrior,
Like a comrade stout and true.
He stood up there before them
With a face as bold as brass:
'We don't want yer Chrissimass pudden —

He paused dramatically.

'You can stick it up — ' his son cut in swiftly.

'No, NO! Dorothy! Good God, what do you teach the boy when I leave the pair of you on your own?' he said.

We do not *want* your Chrissimass pudden;
Kindly give it to the Bible Class.

'Ha!'

It was good to have him back in high spirits for a while.

*

Towards the end of July, Mrs Smith, Warden of the Youth Centre in Joslin Road, handed Bob Druce a note. It was from her friend and former tutor, now co-Warden and wife of the Warden of a residential youth centre at Pargetting. Kate Smith had sent her a copy of the magazine.

'Slum Vista': *there was much in it to be admired,* she wrote. *It would be nice to chat with the poet. Why didn't he pay a visit to Pargetting? Three six-day holiday courses were planned for August. Could they expect him? He would be very welcome. Sincerely, Jean Somerville.*

The blood was hot in his cheeks, as he read and re-read the note.

Now here he was a day later, on other business, sprawling on a bench on Chelmsford railway-station platform, his mouth still cloyed with the sweetness of grossly over-sugared coffee. He frowned into the sunshine, trying to anchor in his memory every detail of that morning's interview. He had to be ready for his father's and mother's cross-examination.

A large conference room at County Hall. Tables — not *desks*? well, no; tables really — ranged in an arc with, at its focal point, a single upright chair.

As though the tables were the reflector of an electric fire and you, perched on the chair, hot and blushing, were the element.

'Ah, Mr Druce. Monkswood School, isn't it? Please sit down.'

The chair had no arms. Fold your hands in your lap. Take a deep breath and try to relax. At gaze in a committeeful of faces.

Questions coming from different angles, so that he had to swivel his glance to answer the questioner. What did he hope to do, if she might ask? Tell me, did he have a career in mind? No, no, if he had no clear idea as yet, that was of no consequence. Please forgive a somewhat personal question: did he have his parent's full support? Were they prepared to help with finance? What was his idea of a university? Could he enlarge on that, perhaps?

Questions — even a couple in French — about the books he read and how he spent his leisure-time. *Très bien.* The chairman, directly ahead of him, looking around the room and gathering eyes. Any further questions for Mr Druce? No? All done?

Faces smiling.

'Well, you will be pleased to know, that on the strength of your Higher Certificate examination and the present interview, this committee is delighted to award you a County Major Scholarship…

'Now, if you'd care to come along with me…'

Getting to his feet, his thoughts whirling, tears prickling behind his eyelids, ready to brim over.

The chairman putting a hand on his shoulder and leading him to an office where they'd see to his travelling expenses.

'If you should choose teaching as a career, let me know and there'll be a post waiting for you in Essex. We like to look after our own.'

*

And now, after drinking coffee in a nearby café, killing time before his train, here he sat on the platform. He'd telephoned Dusty already, hearing his congratulations. Tonight he'd write to Walter, on holiday in Wales, giving him the news. He drew a magazine out of his pocket, his own reward to himself.

Lilliput. He'd often glanced through copies on railway bookstalls, skipping through the pages to find the invariable nude, but had never bought a copy of his own. But today: well, why not? And this time he wouldn't scamper through to find the nude. There was no hurry. Man of the world, he would read the magazine from end to end and page by page. Then when he came across the nude, she would be a nice surprise, well earned.

He settled down to read.

A shadow fell across the pages, and he looked up to see two nuns smiling down at him. They joined him on the bench. And now the nearer of the two seemed to be looking to see what he was reading. What now? Supposing the wicked image was lying in wait, perhaps only a page away, to accuse him? Should he slip the magazine back into his pocket? That would look furtive. That would convict him out of his own act.

Clergymen, policemen, nuns: why did the mere proximity of one fill him with a sense of guilt?

He looked down at the pages and tried to forget the nude, and focus on the story he'd arrived at. Bill Naughton, a name unknown to him. 'Late Night on Watling Street.' The sinewy prose swept him along, and he was lost. When the train pulled into the platform, the nun tapped his arm.

'Come along,' she said. 'If you don't want to miss your train.'

He came to the end of the tale, with the nude still lurking somewhere further on, unseen and forgotten, and turned to the list of contributors. He wanted to learn what sort of man he was who could write like this. Bill Naughton had grown up in Bolton, the magazine told him. Drove a coal lorry for a living. When his wife had cleared the plates away, Bill sat at the kitchen table, writing out his stories in pen and ink in a twopenny exercise book.

His own triumphant morning faded from his mind. In face of Bill Naughton's narrative, his own hollow trifling with words, his lack of anything to say, the forced images of 'Slum Vista', suddenly seemed futile, a petty waste of time, his bright new scholarship unearned and undeserved.

22

ELLEN GREEN

He was sitting in the drawing-room of the Old Vicarage at Pargetting, one of a crowd of youth club members being welcomed by the Warden. Ex-Major Somerville lounged against the mantlepiece, going through the bluff routine that Bob would hear again, word for word, a week later. Mrs Somerville loitered in the doorway, keeping an eye lifting for late arrivals.

'I hope you've brought some poems for me to see,' she had announced to Bob when he arrived, along with George Harris and Ernie Parsons, after striking up an acquaintance with them on the bus. 'No, no, later will do,' she said, as he dropped to one knee and sprang the locks of his case. Now she stood watching her husband. The muscles of her face — her mouth twitching into a smile, eyebrows flickering up, eyes stretching wider for an instant — added an irreverent commentary to what he had to say.

'You're here', the Major was saying, 'to enjoy yourselves, get about, see the countryside, swim, mess about in boats. Ping-pong and snooker tables in the old coach-house across the yard. You're eighteen, some of you, but none of you are twenty-one as yet. Which means that my wife and I are responsible for you. *In loco parentis.* Standing-in for your parents, that is, for all practical purposes. For as long as you're under this roof. So behave yourselves. Keep out of scrapes. My wife's got a few fancy activities lined up for you. Leave it to her to tell you about them. Jean?'

'Apart from the billiards and the table-tennis — darling, I wish you wouldn't call it ping-pong — there's a croquet set and you can play on the lawn. Every Tuesday evening there's country dancing: it's great fun, I hope you all give it a try. On Fridays, there's a standing invitation for eight or nine of you to listen to a concert at Malmesey Green: Leo Brant's music school. If you have any idea of classical music at all, you'll have heard of Leo Brant, of course...'

'Washing up,' said the Major. 'Tell them about the washing up.'

'Thank you, darling, I was coming to that. Pargetting Vicarage is not a private hotel, I hope you all realise, and I expect you all to take your turn to clear away the dishes and wash them up. I don't think that is too much to ask...'

Bob found himself on washing-up detail after dinner that first evening with Ellen Green, who lived in the nearby village and helped in the kitchen. She handed him a tea-towel. 'No. Wait till I've put four or five plates in the drainer, then dry them all at once,' she said. 'That's the way, shuffle them like a pack of cards...

'Have you ever read James Joyce's *Ulysses*?' she said, after they'd been working and talking together for a while. 'No? You ought to. I'm nearly at the end of it for the second time round.'

'Well, I've heard of it,' he said. 'But I've never seen a copy.'

'Don't stop drying while you're talking. I heard her ladyship — whoops, sorry, Mrs Somerville — talking to some literature group about it one afternoon. Thought I'd give it a try. So I snitched her copy for a bit. Leaves books trailing all over the place, she does. She'd just think she'd left it lying somewhere...

'It's hard going, mind you. I couldn't make heads or tails of some of it at times. Took me a fortnight to get to the end. Then I started at the beginning all over again. A day in Dublin. My dad's a Dublin man.'

But her own speech was a slow Essex drawl.

'My father's mother came from Skibbereen,' he said.

'County Cork,' she said. 'Well, there you are then. That black hair and blue eyes. I said to meself when you came in there's more than a drop of Irish blood in *that* one most like...

'How old are you?' she said.

'Seventeen. Eighteen in two month's time. Why?'

'Just wondered.'

'And you?'

'Me? You shouldn't ask a young lady her age... Twenty-four, if you must know. Hardened old sinner.'

She pulled the plugs out of the sinks, and let the washing-up water gurgle away.

'That's the lot then, till next time. Don't forget to have a look at *Ulysses*, eh? It'll knock your socks off.'

Well, well.

'I heard Leo Brant play at the Wigmore Hall last month,' he told Ernie and George later that night, as they sprawled on their beds in a top-floor room. 'I went along with my piano-teacher. Hey, I wish we weren't forbidden to smoke in the bedrooms.'

'We can shove up the window, and blow the smoke outside,' said Ernie, 'He'll be none the wiser.'

With the sash open, they could hear girls' voices giggling on the floor below.

'Forbidden fruit,' said Ernie, cupping a lighted match in his fingers. 'I don't suppose we could…'

'You heard the man,' said George. 'It's monks and nuns.'

'That's what he said,' said Bob. He'd been observing the phenomenon of the Major and was treasuring up mental notes of his telegraphic speech.

Bedtime, ten-thirty. Lights Out, eleven sharp. Gentlemen on the top floor, females on the first floor. No smoking. No fraternising. No midnight wandering. Understood? Slightest hint of any hanky panky, you'll find yourself catching the milk train to Colchester tomorrow morning. Don't care WHO you are. No point in asking you not to talk after Lights Out. But keep your voices down. Other people in the world besides you. Once you're upstairs, you're monks and nuns. That perfectly clear? Right.

He joined his new-found friends in the twilight by the window, and lit his own cigarette from Ernie's.

When the church clock chimed two, he was still lying awake, staring across at the grey rectangle of sky. *Ulysses*. He'd order it from the Library the day he got home.

*

When his mother rang from a call-box on Tuesday evening, 'Listen,' he said, 'Can I stay on for another week? Mrs Somerville suggested it. What d'you think? I don't need any money, I've got plenty left. O, please.'

Before her third lot of pennies had run out, she said yes.

George and Ernie wanted to stay on for a second week, too. On Friday evening the trio tapped on the Warden's door.

'Want to come back next week? All three of you?' said the Major. 'Can't see any objection from my end. There's *space* enough for you...

'But get this straight. Course ends tomorrow morning, Saturday. Breakfast at eight. Quickish final meeting nine-thirty. I want you out by midday sharp. Pack your bags. Goodbye. No hanging around. Finito. We've enough headaches of our own. Rooms to clean. Bed-linen. Fodder. Accounts to make up. Staff to pay. Don't want to see hair or hide of you after that till Sunday tea-time, when next week's mob arrives...

'Up to *you* what you do with yourselves tomorrow night. Shouldn't have any trouble finding somewhere to get your beauty sleep. Poacher's Arms usually has a bed or two. Or try Jim Harker at the Rose. One or two village ladies do bed and breakfast.'

They counted out the money they had left. It was tight. You couldn't get bed and breakfast at either pub for less than ten bob. It might be a bit less if you stayed privately.

'Listen,' George said. 'It's fine weather. Not cold. Practically a heat-wave. Why don't we sleep rough?'

'That'd be a lark,' said Ernie.

'Yes, why not?' said Bob. 'We could watch the dawn come up.'

'Why not doss down in that empty boat-house down by the estuary?' asked Ernie. 'We can walk there from here in a quarter of an hour.'

'Yeah. Then if it *should* come on to rain we'll be in the dry.'

'So that's agreed?'

'What about dinner?'

'Sausage rolls, or cheese sandwiches, or something; at the Three Colts, or the Rose?'

*

When they got to the Three Colts the following evening, 'I'll have a black and tan,' he said, man of the world. 'Guinness and bitter.' He'd heard his father mention the drink. Now he was a safe thirty miles from the Village, he'd find out for himself what it tasted like.

'I'll have the same,' said George. 'Me too, then,' said Ernie.

As he waited to catch the landlord's eye, he became aware of Ellen Green, standing at his elbow.

'You know what they say about black and tan?' she said. 'Makes you randy, that does.' She nudged him in the ribs.

'Hey, listen, where are you going to sleep tonight?' she said a moment later. 'They do beds at the Poacher's Arms.'

'We're roughing it,' Ernie said. 'We're going to doss down in that old boat-shed by the estuary. We took a look around there this afternoon. It seems to be deserted.'

'It's a warm night,' said George. 'We'll be all right. It does you good to rough it sometimes. Bit of a lark.'

'Boat-shed? What, a bit along from the wharf? Riggs's boat-shed, that used to be,' Ellen said. 'Here, you'll have to watch out for courting couples down there.' She nudged Bob in the ribs again.

'O, I'm sorry — can I offer you a drink?' said Bob, remembering his manners, and hoping she wouldn't ask for something expensive.

'Ooh, that's nice,' she said. 'I'll have what you're having, eh?' She nudged him again. 'Black and tan will do me nicely.'

He turned away and leaned on the bar, while she chatted to Ernie and George.

'I was just saying, my boyfriend's over to Braintree with his darts team tonight,' she said as he handed her the glass. 'Well, then. Cheers. Good luck...'

'No,' she said, 'they'll not be back till well past midnight. Drunk as bloody lords, the lot of them, like as not.'

She glanced around and dropped her voice. 'I might pay you a visit later on, see you're tucked in nicely for the night, what do you reckon? —

'Listen,' she muttered, a little later. 'Why don't you go on ahead. I don't want people to see me leaving along with you. Too many old bitches round here watching your every move.'

The church clock struck ten close by as they crossed the meadow and came to the stile and the old bridle-way. They went on downhill towards the estuary, their cigarettes glowing in the deepening twilight. Nobody seemed to be around when they reached the boat-shed.

There was a loft up under the tiles and they clambered up the ladder to reach it, feeling for a place to lie down where the floor-boards had the fewest cracks between them, and brushing away the dirt as best they could. There were sea-birds crying along the estuary.

*

'That was all talk. She'll never come,' said Ernie. 'I'll bet you anything you like.' He stubbed out his cigarette and struck a match to light another.

'Didn't expect her to, did you?' said George.

There was a scuffling down below, and a whisper. 'Hoy! Are you up there in the sail loft?' Then a shadow darker than the blackness around them was hovering above the topmost rungs of the ladder. Ernie struck another match.

'We're over here,' he said.

Bob was lost in amazement as Ellen crept past him and snuggled down between George and Ernie. Now what? he asked himself. Ernie's match went out.

There were more scufflings in the simmering darkness. Ellen giggled. 'Don't you be so bold,' Bob heard her whisper. He felt his senses reeling.

He lingered over his own cigarette, and for a long moment ground out the butt-end, back and forth, back and forth, in the grit on the floor. He crawled through the darkness, over to the others, feeling for Ellen's shoes.

He crouched at her feet.

He took a deep breath, then leaned forward and began to trace the curves of her ankle bones with the amazed and anxious fingertips of both hands. Under her shoes, her feet were innocent of socks or stockings.

He could hear the muffled sounds of kissing.

He inched his fingertips higher, as the blood pounded in his head. Along the contours of her calves, and over and between the cool skin of her knees.

She hitched herself into an easier position, dark against the darkness, parting her legs as he reached her thighs, silently inviting. The palms of his hands caressed the changing landscapes of her flesh, smooth and cool, then warm. Suddenly his fingertips encountered —

O! but she isn't wearing any —

a brittleness of hair, then heat. Then slid into wetness.

Ellen Green.

*

That was the curse of diagrams.

They were useless when you came down to it. As futile as those patterns meant to teach you how to dance, showing you foot-soles twisting across a blank page. O, he knew about the mechanics of sex as well as he knew about meccano. Cut-away drawings in an anatomy book. The diagram in Rennie Macandrew's *Red Light*, the manual of married love that Lou Marsh read out to 5A behind the bike-sheds. He could draw you a rough map from memory. But it would be light-years distant from this warm and terrifying flesh.

So.

When Beauty and Beauty meet. The clitoris is erectile tissue. His heart pounding. *Dans mon coeur fait outrage.* Making havoc in his heart.

The dizzying in his head did not help.

Never, ever, before had he —

Under his touch Ellen quivered, and began to whimper, lying there between the others.

'Eddying, dizzying, closing round...'

She disengaged herself and took his hand and drew him with her to a distant corner, stooping and fumbling through the darkness. For an instant she stood above him, her body a deeper blur, then knelt at his side, preparing to lie on the coat and jacket he spread out for her. She unbuckled her belt and slid the blanket pin out of her kilt. Now she drew it over them both. She searched for his hand again and carried it down to her thighs. 'Yes,' she murmured.

Her breath, like his, was heavy with the sweet rotting tang of beer. He made no move to kiss her lips, nor she his. After a moment he reached up and fumbled at her blouse, seeking her breast. Gently she thrust his fingers away, 'No,' she said. 'Not there. I'm ticklish there,' and drew his hand back to her thighs.

'O, now you're teasing me,' she said, breathing the words in his ear. 'You're teasing me.' He felt her fingers tugging at his belt.

He awoke in her arms to grey daylight and church bells ringing. She had straightened her clothes and his. She sat up now at his side, and dragged a comb through her hair. 'Sunday,' she said. 'And you'll be off to church, I shouldn't wonder, to confess your sins.'

Sins? He'd learned her body's mysteries with his fingertips, last night — a night ago already — in the gentle darkness. And nothing more. Nothing more. They hadn't... How could there be sin in that? Simply to touch? His mother's voice in his head countered his question, 'Do you need to ask?' But he was not listening, would not listen again.

He sat up, aware of grit and splintering floorboards, and looked around. George and Ernie were gone, and he heard their voices outside, below the wall.

Ellen Green stood up, straddling over him. She had found her knickers and put them on. He gazed up at her body, seeing her for the first time. She grinned and reached a hand down to him.

'Come on, lazybones,' she said. 'Upsadaisy. You haven't got time to lie back and admire the view. I must be off home. If I'm not indoors before dad starts shouting for his breakfast, he'll give me such a leathering.'

As they reached the edge of the village, Ellen stopped and turned to kiss him briefly on the lips. 'You'll be starving, I shouldn't wonder,' she said. 'If you can hold out till then, slip round to the garden door round about half-past ten if you like. I could make a couple of egg and bacon sandwiches. Her ladyship won't know the difference — we've got a party of twenty-nine arriving at teatime.'

He watched the swing of her legs and her plaid kilt as she climbed over the stile and walked away diagonally across the meadow.

She. Ellen Green.

Him.

Her body in the darkness.

And now it was Sunday morning.

Ahead of him, George and Ernie watched Ellen pass out of sight and stopped for him to catch them up.

The bells were brawling in the church-tower across the meadow. In the clear daylight, the fume of last night's beer ached in his head.

The smell of her on his fingers.

*

When she'd unpacked his case and put the dirty clothes aside to wash, his mother followed him about the house, trying to catch his eye.

'You're *different*,' she said. 'Something's happened to you. You're not the same person. What's been going on?'

'Nothing,' he said. 'Nothing at all.'

'Phhh! *I* know. I can read you like a book. *Something's* happened. You might as well admit it.'

'I *told* you. Nothing. Nothing. Nothing.'

'So *you* say. If *your* father—'

'If my father *what?*'

'Hmph.'

And it had *been* nothing.

Certainly nothing to do with his mother or his father. An adventure of a night, with no sequel and no consequences. And that was that. During his second week at Pargetting, Ellen had grinned at him when they encountered one another in the kitchen but said nothing. If George and Ernie had had thoughts of discussing the exploit, they sensed his attitude, and held their tongues.

Remorse? Guilt? No. Not at all. A dark shamefulness that his mother was hinting at but didn't have evidence enough to convict him of? We have erred and strayed from Thy ways like lost sheep? No.

That's the way she *would* think; she'd like him to feel guilty. But he didn't. Whatever he chose to feel was nobody's business but his own.

Acts. Afterthoughts. Whatever you did you *did*, you had chosen to do it, you couldn't shrug it off later. Not onto alcohol, not onto some abstract notion of temptation. Why should you, anyway?

What was it that he'd told Dusty? How could you know where the limits were until you had contemplated them from the far side? A Wildean witticism, said for the sake of effect: but there was a germ of truth in it. Take nothing on trust. It was part of the process of learning. Thomas, Doubting or not, was still a Saint.

It was time his mother untied *her* end of the apron-strings, and let him go.

And yes, of course he felt guilty. His face was hot with blushing, as he scrambled among the roots of the forest beeches with Pat, when they'd escaped from the house together. But only because it so obviously upset his mother to sense that he was withdrawing from her. That at Pargetting he had already withdrawn a little. O, one day there'd have to be such a showdown.

But not now. Not about *this*.

Sex. Male and female, reaching out to touch. *Ellen*. And him.

The remembrance of the events of that night thinned away as he tried to recall them, dissolving into an effervescence.

What had it had to do with love or falling in love? With those romantical fantasies of cyclamen-framed, flower-scented kisses, making innocent havoc in his heart? Nothing. *'Je fais souvent ce rêve étrange et pénétrant/D'une femme inconnue, et que j'aime, et qui m'aime…'* that was Verlaine's familiar dream of a not-impossible She. 'And I taste on your lips the taste of red roses and wasps.' All that lingered, unaffected. As it would, for years yet.

Back from his walk with Pat, he got out his bike and free-wheeled down to the Library in the Village, to ask for *Ulysses*.

'We don't keep that kind of book on the open shelves, and I certainly don't have a copy in this library,' said the Librarian. 'How old are you? I see… O, very well. I suppose I shall have to put in a request for an inter-library loan.'

*

Walter Mason left Monkswood school in the same term as his pupil Robert, having been appointed to a post in the north of England as an Inspector of Schools. Robert biked to Thornbrake Way to thank him and say farewell. Books that Walter gave him then still stand on the shelves at the far side of the room: *Tu viens en France, Les plus belles pages de Paul Verlaine, Le Géranium ovipare. Les Indiscretions de l'écriture*, inscribed on the flyleaf, 'Walter Mason, bought with holiday money, 1929', the year of his pupil's birth.

In October he went back to Monkswood School for Speech Day, sitting with his mother and father in the hall, collecting his prize, and staring up at the high oak panelling. There, close to David Verity's, his name gleamed in gold leaf. His mother patted his knee and, at his other side, his father nudged him from time to time, brimming with pride.

At last the music and the orations were at an end, and Dusty Rhodes presented his annual report. He wished the late fifth year and Upper Sixth godspeed, and turned his thoughts to Walter Mason.

'It is difficult for me', said the Headmaster, 'to do justice to his professional skill, loyalty, conscientiousness and devotion to his pupils without seeming immoderate in my terms.'

Robert's father nudged him again, and whispered: 'You should remember that.'

*

A hand stretched out and cupped his testicles.

'Cough.'

He cleared his throat.

'*Cough, lad, COUGH!* That's a bit more like it. Turn around. Bend over.'

Blunt fingers were prising his buttocks apart.

'Sit on the chair there. Cross your legs.'

A rubber mallet rapping under his kneecap, his shin jerking upward.

'Cross 'em the other way.'

Tap, again. Again jerk. Now the pointed end of the mallet-handle was scraping along his footsole.

'That's my Babinski reflex you're testing, isn't it, sir?'

'You a medical student? No? Word of advice. Keep your chit-chat to yourself. I've finished with you, now. Move along, don't keep my colleague waiting.'

In a drill-hall in a North London street with twenty other naked men, he was padding across the lino from one doctor to the next. Three doctors in all, each with his own batch of questions. Through an open kitchen door they could see an orderly, boiling batches of urine in a test-tube, looking for the scarlet telltale of diabetes.

One of the potential recruits hadn't been able to produce a specimen of urine on demand. He'd been sent to the café across the street, told to drink two or three cups of tea. He wasn't back yet.

'D'you have a family doctor? What's his name?'

' *Her* name, actually.'

A sharp stare. 'All right then, laddie, *hers*. Can you remember *her* address? I see. All right. Mouth open wide.'

A metal tongue-depressor, rattling against his teeth. Antiseptic tingling in his throat.

'Aaaah. Well, *SAY* it. Aaaah.'

'Aaaah.'

The tongue-depressor clanking back into the beaker.

'You dirty little bastard!'

From the haemorrhoids-and-reflex doctor's station there came a shout, and a crashing slap. Druce, R. turned round to look. A naked eighteen-year-old stood rubbing his left buttock. A scarlet handprint was blossoming across the pimply whiteness, like a photographic image in a dish of developer.

Wait a second. *Left?* Then that doctor must be left-handed. Which hand did he use to grab my—? Yes. That's right. The left.

He felt the cold end of a stethoscope on his chest.

'Deep breaths, now. Wake up, laddie, pay attention.'

'What was that all about?' he asked the victim of the doctor's rage, when they had both completed the circuit of tests and been sent to sit in the waiting-room.

'I couldn't help it, could I?' He spoke in an aggrieved whine. 'Wasn't *my* fault. He shouldn't have grabbed my arse. Made me blow off. I tried to hold it in.'

More naked examinees trooped in to wait.

"Ammer toes,' one lanky lad was wailing to anyone who would listen. "E said I got bleedin' 'ammer toes... Only fing I ever really wanted all me life was to join the Guards. "You can't get inta the Guards wiv 'ammer toes, my man." Thass wot that ol' fucker tol' me.'

The anuretic returned from the café. He still couldn't manage.

One of the doctors thrust his head around the door.

'Ah yes, you. Have you had a piddle, yet? What? Now listen to me, lad. Get over to the kitchen there and drink a pint of cold water. My colleagues and I are going to take a twenty-minute tea-break. When I come back I want to find your water in that flask, and that's an order. Right, then.'

He slammed the door.

Five minutes later the sufferer was back again.

'Any luck?'

'Naar... It's because I'm nervous, see? I can't ever go if people make me nervous.'

Druce, R. looked along the row of faces.

'Well?' he said. 'What about a whip-round?'

One by one, they padded out to the lavatory, and added their teaspoonful or two. The mixture, carried off to the orderly in the kitchen, passed the test.

'Blimey, all that piss,' somebody said, when they had been dismissed, and stood about in the street outside.

'Teamwork,' said Druce, R. 'That's what it takes. That's what the future of Britain is all about.'

'Here, you could have shown up with anything, mate. You could have come up with all the diseases under the sun.'

'Yeah, he could have fooled the doctors and dodged the call-up, the lucky sod.'

Three weeks later Mr Druce brought the OHMS letter up to his son's attic room at High Cedars.

'*You are required to report to… Failure to comply…* There was no doubt what that entailed: police at your door, Absent Without Leave, hounded as a deserter before you even started… *Britannia Barracks, Bury St Edmunds… Rail warrant enclosed… I am your humble and obedient servant,* printed scrawled signature, *Minister of War.*'

Well, there it was. Ask for the Navy, you get the Army.

Your humble and obedient servant giving you orders: fail at your peril. You couldn't overlook the paradox. Humble servant, my foot. It would be a wheeze to write and tell him so.

Didn't PC Druce have a colleague years back who signed every declaration to the Inspector of Taxes, 'You are, Sirs, My Humble Servants—'?

'Now you *must* practise getting up early,' his father said. 'It's imperative. It's going to hit you like a ton of bricks if you don't.'

*

On the November day that Princess Elizabeth married Prince Philip in Westminster Abbey, he took Pat for a last walk beside the river. Scrambling through lank grass, down to where Bren and he had waded through thigh-high water nine months before. Poking about under hedges. Pulling out a note-book and scribbling down notes. Wanting to keep on record what he saw.

Jungle-swamp by the bridge. Fronds of rusted iron. Coils of wire. Odd-shaped cans, square, pyramidal. Quaint lettering half-rusted away. Dregs of water in them, or oil, or half-filled with congealed stuff. Higginson's Patent Petrifying Liquid. Painters' Knotting. Wood sogged & unvarnished, lying in pools of orange water. Blue medicine bottles with peeling unreadable labels & retching smells. Meat-paste jars. A basin crazed with a trellis pattern etched in blue, & where it's lain in the water, orange-red. Five-pounder hunks of flint. Broken light-sockets. Caved-in radio sets with torn fabric & peeling plywood fretwork, like a badly shuffled pack of cards. Chunks of concrete. Car mudguards. Bike-frames. Wheels & torn strips of inner tubing, sprawling under mud & silt. Fragments of machinery, cogs rusted together indissolubly, beyond the reach of paraffin & burning newspaper. Among it all, clumps of rotting stems & leaves that still bear traces of marigold flowers & mombretia. A legless chair, forlorn but the right way up, facing me across a shallow sea of slime. Who last sat on that? Clanking drums & churns from a dairy, powdery galvanised iron. Long, black, elegant-shouldered wine bottles. A Welsh hymn-book — how did that get there? & a mystery novel from a sixpenny library. It must be odd for an author to come across his book in a place like this. Like being in hell, or having someone walk over his grave. Turn over the matted pages, look for a chance significance... None. & all around elder shrubs cluster their tom-cat-smelling leaves & untrustworthy stems, & wild roses offer shrivelled, blackening fistfuls of scarlet beads. Skeleton leaves half-submerged in festooning grass; tug them free & they're like the winter shapes of trees against this rim of sky & sunlight dipping in over hedges & under willows. One fine day the sun'll finger the water & ripen mosquito larvae & make showers of midges dance. I climb out with my pockets jingling with little bits of brass prised out of bakelite sockets. Volts & amps went zinging through them once, they're crusted now with dried slime. But it'll come alive to stink again when I rinse it off under the kitchen tap.

His and Bren's last summer's wasteland: '... fragments I have shored against my ruins...'

A ceremony of naming.

23

HER PRIVATES WE

Friday, December 6th, 1947.
Britannia Barracks, Bury St Edmunds.
The barrack-square was sugared with half an inch of snow. He was marching with the rest of his platoon, his fingers sticking to a brass rifle-butt, a khaki beret draped across his forehead and over his right ear like a monstrous cow-pat.

And now the draw-strings of his army-issue underpants were coming untied. He felt them slither down until they hung like an empty shopping-bag across the crotch of his trousers.

You! That man there!

Me? O23, Private Druce, R.

Time you woke your bloody ideas up, soldier.

*

By New Year's Eve, he'd witnessed dawns enough to satisfy him for a while.

Jo'burg platoon. Which was to say, Johannesburg. The Boer-War battle which men of the Suffolk Regiment — whose troops, half a century on, were training them — had fought and won.

Twenty men, quick-marching through icy darkness in step and three abreast, from the barrack hut to the cookhouse, with golden sparks spurting from the steel studs in their boots. Then, bellies filled, hastening back in twos and threes through the red twilight of winter dawns.

Back to all the bullshit to be got through before the bugle for Company Orders began their working day. Blankets to be folded, kit laid out on beds and aligned with a length of string that two men held taut from one end of the hut to the other. Windows polished with wadded newspaper. Lino swept free of ash and cigarette butts, and buffed to a shine. Stoves burnt red with overnight rust now gleaming with a coat of blacklead. Coal in the buckets whitewashed; and the buckets, their galvanized surface long worn away, freshly scoured and glittering like silver. But if they got all that and a hundred other details right, Jo'burg would end the course with a 48-hour pass, while all their rivals would be left to moan about a pathetic 36.

Before the echoes of reveille had died away, Corporal Haskard, who dossed in his own walled-off room at one end of the hut, was striding about haranguing them. At night, stripped to a vest and braces, he stood and watched them, grinding out his dog-ends on the floor. His talk was a stream of obscenity, as they hunched on their beds and rubbed their badges and buckles with Brasso and smeared spittle and polish in circles on their boots. Haskard, mindful of his rank, had sewn Corporal's stripes on his short-sleeved vest.

In a nest of cotton-wool in his room Haskard kept a pair of boots brought to a glassy shine with a coat of clear nail-varnish, strictly forbidden. Five minutes of marching through snow would have stripped their surface down to the leather, but these were for display only. 'That's the way I want to see *your* fuckers look this time next fucking week,' he said, producing them from time to time by way of encouragement. His own 48-hour pass depended on theirs.

On his third night in the Army, 023 Druce counted thirty-five variants on 'fuck' in an anecdote of Corporal Haskard's and ventured to tell him the total, as a point of mild interest. 'Right! You're on a fucking charge,' replied Corporal Haskard. But he couldn't make up his mind under what sub-heading of Conduct to the Prejudice of Good Order and Military Discipline 023 Druce's remark had fallen, and nothing came of it. 'You just fucking watch your fucking tongue, that man,' he said.

Amid the drizzle of obscenity, Haskard spangled his Suffolk speech with fragments meant to remind you, and himself, of service he had seen under alien suns. In Urdu he asked you what o'clock it was: '*Kai budgie?*' and yelled '*jildi*' to get his recruits moving faster. He demanded a sight of anything in Arabic with '*shoofti*'; if he liked what he saw he said '*quaiss ke-ter*'. Anything '*buckshee*' was going free, unwanted by its owner; although the owner might not be aware of the fact. Every woman, loose or not —

apart from his own mother — was a *bint* to Haskard. Beds, Urdu again, were *charpoys*: 'Now then, Jo'burg: stand by your charpoys! Move it! *Jildi, jildi, JILDI!*'

Jo'burg.

Twenty men, drilling by numbers, covering off and marching in step. Five stable-lads from Newmarket, foul-mouthed and bitter with rivalry; a scatter of lads from Suffolk, Hertfordshire, and Essex who had never met before; a midlander; three Jews from the Whitechapel rag-trade.

It didn't pay to be Jewish: the Suffolks were recently returned from Palestine, where they been sniped at by Israeli freedom-fighters. 'Yids,' snarled Corporal Haskard from time to time. 'Lazy as fuck. If we don't get that forty-eight, we'll fucking well know who's to blame, won't we, lads? Hoi! You there, Goldberg! *Jildi, jildi!*'

*

CCFZ 273/3, LW 810459 D: Druce could effortlessly recall his Identity Number; his National Health number, when he was allotted one; his passport, and bank account numbers. But in December 1947 his Army number was jammed somewhere in the cogs of his brain.

It wasn't that he hadn't wanted to join the forces: he'd applied for early call-up, foregoing the deferment that it was his right to claim with a scholarship and university entrance. After the vaccine fever it seemed sensible to concentrate on getting fit. Just one pound lighter, and he would have been drafted to a physical development centre; so one of the doctors at his medical had told him, sliding weights along the bar to balance it.

21064023. He had inked his number inside his beret. The 21-million-64-thousand-and-23rd soldier of the King? Surely, even with the Somme and the Dardanelles and Gallipoli, it couldn't have reached that total over the centuries, could it?

'Name and last three!' That's how a soldier had to identify himself. Surname, and the last three digits of your Army number. *Druce 023*. That he *could* remember. But whenever he was asked for his number in full, he had to take the khaki cowpat off his head and look inside.

It was all part of the process of cutting you down to size. Of making your compliance with an order unthinking, immediate and automatic. *Yours not to reason why.* But, Corporal — 'Shut it, sunshine! You're here to do as I *say*, not do as I do.'

So every morning they whitewashed the coal, and polished the brass light-switch to jewel-like refulgence. For a radius of three or four inches around the switch, the wall was caked with a slime of ancient verdigris. But that wasn't the point. 'Swank': that was the point. That every scrap of brass should gleam, that was the point.

The lace-holes of army boots were eyeletted with black-lacquered brass. So you pulled out the laces and scraped off the lacquer. And when you'd smelted Kiwi or Cherry-Blossom into the leather with the not-quite red-hot handle of a spoon and built up a coat of polish with a spit-lubricated rag, you shone the eyelets with Brasso, and threaded the laces back again. And then you polished your boot-soles and scoured any hint of rust away from the studs and the heel- and toe-irons with a scrap of emery-cloth.

Swank paid off.

Daily Part I Orders detailed men from each platoon to parade for guard duty. The smartest man — the 'stick' man — was rewarded by being excused, while his platoon gathered points towards the coveted 48-hour pass. So every potential stick man was a group creation: an assemblage of the best-looking boots that could be found to fit his feet, the shiniest cap-badge, smartest belt, most glitteringly pulled-through rifle. If he wasn't much cop at pressing his uniform, someone did it for him. With minutes to go before guard parade, his mates fussed over him like dressers around a mannequin. Then they carried him, unbending for fear of scuffing his blanco or filming his boots with dust, to the edge of the barrack-square, and lowered him to the asphalt as gingerly as though he were a painted icing-sugar groom on top of a wedding cake.

There were town-bred lads among the conscripts for whom guard-duty at night was two hours of terror of the dark in a Suffolk field where every rustle of grass or creak of branches in the wind was a menace, where the cry of owls, or the bark of a dog-fox and the scream of a vixen set their nerves alight.

But how you squared up to the bullshit and the discipline, to the force and the illogic — 'You're a dozy, idle nignog: what *are* you?' — to *forza e frode,* was up to you. You had three choices: fight, submit, or take flight.

023 Druce chose to submit — in public at least: your thoughts were your own.

He discovered a fierce and undreamed-of joy in the tasks of Psyche and Sisyphus: in spit-and-polish, in the gleam of brass, in the earthy clunch-pit smell of wet blanco, and the tang of cordite smoke. There were things to be learnt about yourself in foot-drill on the barrack-square, in your running stumble along the length of a tree-trunk above water, in the kick of a rifle against your shoulder, in shaving before dawn-light in icy water, stripped to the waist.

Life might have been a whole lot worse. We were peacetime soldiers, never hearing — as the Suffolk NCOs unwearyingly reminded us — a single shot fired in anger. We were jammy fuckers: we'd struck it lucky. We dwelt in the middle of Fortune's favours. Faith, her privates we!

Provided that a man embraced his fate, and made the best of it. *O, the easy way ain't easy; and the hard way's fuckin' hard.* Day in day out, they heard that warning in the parrot gabble of every NCO who had been given recruits to train.

Private Haslet of Jo'burg platoon did it the hard way, trying to fight the system. Half-way through basic training, Haslet's brasses were still tarnished, those parts unseen in daylight green with verdigris. His boots were a disgrace. His uniform was smeared with blanco, and spotted with grease where he'd spilt his food. For days at a time he got away with not washing below his neck or above his wrists. At night, hunched by the fire, he stank.

'Right, you filthy man, you are going to be scrubbed,' said Cpl Haskard, detailing half a dozen men to manhandle Haslet to the ablutions.

He was stripped and flung into a shower-cubicle along with his kit, even his greatcoat: everything, barring his rifle and barrack-box. Haskard threw him a brand-new scrubbing-brush straight from the Quartermaster's stores. When he'd washed and scrubbed it all with yellow soap, 'Right then, Haslet: throw your kit out here,' said Cpl Haskard. 'You two men — Druce, Brown — strip off and get in there with him and scrub the dirty fucker white.' But that was a pleasantry; for by then the worst of the dirt had been rinsed off Haslet. It was enough to make a distant pass or two with the scrubbing brush. Haskard flung Haslet a towel. Then, clad in dripping underpants and boots, he was marched at the double to the blanco-drying room, to drape his kit over the hot-pipes.

At the close of the six-week course, Haslet was confined to Jo'burg hut, while the rest of the intake marched in the passing-out parade. He was almost the last figure that Druce and Robin Brown and Danny Wheeler glimpsed, as they clambered with their kitbags and rifles into the truck that was taking them to the railway-station. That night Haslet would sleep in Jo'burg hut with Corporal Haskard for company, and next day he'd start again, back at square one among a new intake of rookies.

So much for fight, and trying to buck the system.

There was always flight, a third choice. There was an easy way to that, too; and a hard way.

Desertion was the hard way; chancing your arm and going AWOL — Absent Without Leave. It wasn't easy. When 023 Druce joined the Orderly Room at a camp on a Dorset hillside in August 1948, he arrived in time to take the place of Lance-Cpl Ray Doggett, who, two days before, had failed to return from weekend leave. Refused the 48-hour pass he felt entitled to, Doggett had gone AWOL in a fit of pique.

From time to time policemen, Civil and Military, made irregular descents on Doggett's Suffolk home but failed to ensnare him. More than a year after his disappearance, his old mate in the Orderly Room at last got news of Ray. After three days without food, he and a fellow-stowaway had given themselves up on the high seas to the crew of a German freighter bound for Dublin. Doggett had been court-martialled for desertion, and sentenced to complete his outstanding thirteen months of service, after eight weeks in the glasshouse.

So much for doing a runner the hard way.

In the October intake in 1947, there had been a recruit who fled from Britannia Barracks by a quicker route. Found hanged in his braces late at night in a lavatory cubicle, he was cut down alive and sent to hospital in Colchester. Three days later, so the story ran, he broke into a poison cupboard and completed his escape.

*

Christmas leave found Private Druce crunching up Fairmead Drive towards High Cedars, eyeing the lead flashing around the window sills of the Edwardian houses. There wasn't a scrap of lead in sight for miles around Britannia barracks. Barring church roofs, that is, and there were post-war gangs of professional thieves stripping them and flogging the rolls of lead to scrap-merchants.

Army recruits had a more personal and insistent need for lead. Flattened into strips half an inch wide and tightly rolled at close intervals around a loop of string like beads on a necklace, it made you a gaiter-weight. You needed two necklaces, one for each leg, to weigh down the slack that remained when you'd strapped the last inch of trouser-leg under your gaiter. They would put you on a charge if they caught you using gaiter-weights, and all the regulars in the Suffolks used them.

Without weights, the thick serge of each trouser-leg rumpled like a concertina: 'You are a sack of shit tied up in the middle; what *are* you?' yelled every NCO at the sight. *You and Odo of Cluny*, thought 023 Druce, remembering that medieval cleric's vision of womankind, while dutifully shouting, 'I am a sack of shit tied up in the middle, Sar'nt!'

But *with* gaiter-weights, the trouser-crease, such as it was, hung taut. More swank. Before his Christmas leave was over, Pte Druce had a set of gaiter-weights, and the roof of High Cedars was fractionally lighter.

Getting a lasting crease into the serge was another headache. But smearing a bar of yellow soap along the inside of the crease seemed to help it stick.

'Well, you amaze me,' said his father, eyeing him up and down in the kitchen at High Cedars. 'I thought the army was going to have its work cut out to make a man of you. Turn round. Let's have a look at you. Anyone would think you'd grown a couple of inches taller.'

But Mrs Druce looked at her son's cropped hair and reddened hands and sighed. 'Are you getting enough proper sleep?' she said. 'Are they feeding you properly? I want the truth.'

'Yes,' he said; 'yes, of course.'

'Dorothy, don't mollycoddle the boy,' his father said. 'That's been half his trouble all along.'

He didn't tell her about his third or fourth day in khaki, when he'd fallen into a daydream in the cookhouse. He had taken his turn at the counter, pint mug hooked over his right thumb, pudding-plate in his right hand, with the meat-plate held at arm's length in his left. He passed along, watching and not seeing, as helpings of stewed beef, potatoes, cabbage, gravy were flumped down onto the plate, and followed by a slab of suet pudding and a cupful of custard. He only woke up as the cookhouse orderly at the end of the counter poured a pint of tea over the lot. 'Wake up, Dolly Daydream,' said the grinning Corporal who had watched his progress. 'Now tip that lot in the bin, and get to the back of the queue if you want any dinner today.'

But his father enjoyed the tale. And it was the nearest he could get to sharing it with his Irish granny, long dead, who'd grown up in India in the cantonments and two of whose sons had been Warrant Officers in the Guards. She'd have relished it.

*

When you moved directly from school into the Army, basic training was no hardship, and the loss of freedom easy enough to knuckle under to. And they kept you on the move: there was little occasion to be bored. That would come later, as you lit a ciggy and dealt another round of cards and, staring out across the months ahead, groaned your life away: *O, roll on death! — demob's too slow.*

Army life was tougher for those who'd been at work since they'd reached fifteen. With the fragmented periods of a school-day long behind them, they hated the loss of freedom. They resented the break in their lives, too: until national service was behind you, few employers were likely to offer you anything more than a dead-end job. What wages you might have been accustomed to were scarcely matched by four shillings a day (five, when you'd weathered the first six months). Four shillings or five, the figure was notional. What with stoppages for clothing and the never-explained deductions for 'barrack damages', you were lucky if the Company Commander handed you as much as twenty-five or thirty shillings on Friday pay parade.

Each intake was confined to barracks for their first fortnight, until they'd learnt to look a bit like soldiers. Tom Wallis from Birmingham, whose bed was alongside Druce's, read his girl-friend's letters over and over and sighed his evenings and weekends away, pining for his motorbike: 'At this maoment, Oi should have bin beltin' me Matchliss reound the bypass, wiv Doreen snooggled oop be'oind me. Aw, fookin' roll on!'

In those six scurrying weeks there were moments when they all gazed across at the unregulated lives beyond the perimeter wire, and tingled with a sudden envy of the old man walking his dog, the housewives pausing to chat. They were a hundred yards or so and, for a moment, light-years distant from the reality beyond the wire, contemplating lives and landscapes never so alluring as when you were forbidden to stroll away and into them. Then 023 Druce would remember Rupert Brooke's 'meads towards Haslingfield and Coton/Where das *Betreten*'s not verboten' — meads where 023 Druce had romped as a child not thirty miles distant from this Suffolk field.

Shades of the prison-house hovered for a moment, and were swept away. 'Wake up, soldier!'

Twenty-year-old Second-Lieutenant Whoever-he-Was was slapping his thigh with his swagger-stick, and rocking on the balls of his feet. 'Get down behind the Bren, that man! Carry on, Cpl. Haskard.'

023 Druce hugged the butt into his shoulder and pressed the trigger and, 'Gun's firing all right… gun's firing all right… gun's firing all right — Gun stops!' yelled Haskard.

'Mag off, mag on, cock the gun, carry on firing,' you shouted back; wrenching an empty magazine off, clouting the catch with the heel of your hand, slamming an empty magazine on, and cocking, and squeezing the idle trigger. Idle; because all this was imaginary stuff, 'going through the motions'. They wouldn't be *firing* the thing for a fortnight yet. But lying there, just going through the motions, you could safely draw a bead on the white of Haskard's eye in your own mind's eye.

You learned about yourself and, side-spying other members of the platoon as you all crawled through mud-filled trenches and threaded lengths of telegraph pole through motor-tyres and stabbed your bayonet into straw-filled sacks — 'Scream, lad! Scream as you charge; terrify the enemy!' — you learned things about *them*.

Things sometimes surprising. How ex-schoolboys like Brown and Druce and Glover, weedy of stature beside the lads who had laboured on building-sites and farms, could outshine them in the gym. How, in the showers or before a medical inspection, while others blushed and looked away and cupped their hands to hide their genitals, the same three were at ease with nakedness. How, faced with an injection needle, it was the toughest of the tough guys whose eyes rolled up as they fell in a faint.

And you made friends. Robin Brown, yes, of course. He and Druce had gone to nearby schools, and had a range of acquaintances in common. But there were others whose warmth of friendship, and yours for them, was not to be predicted. Like Tom Wallis.

Tom was a Birmingham motor-mechanic and the gaiter-weights he brought back from Christmas leave he'd made by threading handfuls of steel nuts onto his loops of string. He was obsessed by motor-bikes and plans for his future: his own garage, and a suburban house and Doreen and three teenage kids.

And Lou Goldberg, who worked a steam trouser-press in Stepney. Lou approached Druce one evening, perching on the bed beside him, stretching out his hands towards the stove. 'Could you do me a favour, Perfesser?' he murmured. 'I just got a letter from mum, could you help read it to me?' Druce went with Lou to the Quiet Room, and wrote an answer at his dictation. 'Coming to the Sally Ann?' he said, as Lou licked the stamp. But Lou excused himself:'Nah, if you don't mind. There's things I got to do back in the hut.' An hour later Druce came in from gulping down tea and fruit-cake in the Salvation Army canteen, to find his uniform pressed and his brasses glittering, and Lou, with a smile on his lips, glancing towards him from time to time out of the corner of his eye.

And Danny Wheeler. They'd eyed each other for more than a week before offering one another cigarettes. Danny, half-Irish, a barrow-boy and cheapjack, sharp as a tack, sold shellfish from a horse and cart in Woolwich. It was Danny who taught him to pitch his voice at its loudest, to relax his throat and let his belly-muscles do the work. It came in handy later, calling school assemblies to attention.

It was Danny who carried him off to a New Year's Eve dance in the final hours of 1947. That morning Bob had been called off muster-parade to have a pre-molar drilled.

'*Novocaine?* You expect me to give you an *anaesthetic?* You can't stand a bit of pain? Forget it, soldier boy, you're in the Army now.'

When the army dentist had got the tooth looking like an upturned table, or Battersea power station with its chimney at each corner, he had given up trying to save it, and pincered it out in fragments. Then in the afternoon Jo'burg platoon had been given their booster injections, and by five o'clock everyone's left arm was throbbing.

'This calls fer a bit of initiative, squire,' said Danny, massaging his ache. '*Nil illegitimis carborundum*, eh? Know what that means, don't ya? Never let the bastards grind ya down.'

So they pushed a couple of girls around the floor of the Corn Exchange later that evening and, defying the need to be back in barracks before 23.59 hours, stayed on and held hands with them for 'Old Lang Syne'. Then Danny said it wouldn't be the act of a gennelman, would it? not to escort the girls, who were sisters, home. 'I mean, we're already AWOL. So in fer a penny, in fer a pound: might as well get hung fer a sheep as fer a lamb. What d'ya reckon, Bob?'

Miles they trudged along country lanes, and kissed the girls goodnight outside a pair of cottages. Then, guided by a far glow of light above the railway sidings, they found their way to the edge of town and the back of the camp where Danny had heard there was a way in through the barbed wire. It was past two o'clock before they slid under their blankets.

Jo'burg platoon was detailed for a five-mile route march the following day. They were half-way round the course when Danny, marching at Perfesser Druce's side, gave him a swift jab with his elbow: 'Should old acquaintance be forgot?' he intoned through clenched teeth. He had recognized the cottages where they had snatched a kiss a bare eight hours earlier. 'Whoever that is who's singing, jack it in,' Cpl. Haskard shouted.

The night before they climbed aboard the train to Liverpool Street, posted to different army corps and never to meet again, Danny and he cocked their last snook at authority. They went to a fish-and-chip shop in the town. They tucked their rolled-up berets under their epaulettes (a chargeable offence), and unbuttoned their tunics (a chargeable offence), and sauntered down a lamplit street, eating their fish and chips out of a newspaper (a chargeable offence). As they turned a corner a Military Policeman hailed them from the far pavement. 'Get over 'ere, you two! You're on a charge. Yes, you with the grin on 'is face: woss ya name n' last three?' But he had a prisoner with him under arrest, and could not, under regulations, leave him. 'Tell 'im bollocks!' called the prisoner.

'Bollocks,' said Danny.

'Don't worry, sunshine,' said the MP, 'I'd recognize you two bastards anywhere. Improperly dressed. Conduct to the Prejudice of Good Order and Military Discipline. Disobeying a Superior Officer. I'll fuckin' sniff you out.'

'Is that right?' said Danny. 'You'll have to be quick, then. Tomorrow morning we'll be sixty miles away in opposite directions. So, bollocks! Put *that* on yer needles and knit it.'

*

February, 1948. Aldershot. Marlborough Lines.

At Ash Vale station, his own mob of half-trained recruits had scrambled themselves and their kitbags and rifles onto a couple of three-tonners and jounced through line after line of nineteenth-century barrack blocks. The disciplined trunks of the trees along the streets were ringed like football shirts with bands of whitewash.

'What a pleasing prospect,' said Private Glover.

'And only man is vile,' said Private Druce.

They'd travelled down from Bury St. Edmunds together, glad to find themselves on the same draft.

Nick Glover lived just outside Cambridge. He'd been awarded a University Scholarship on the strength of his French and Spanish and, like 023 Druce, had chosen to get his military service over and done with first. At Bury St Edmunds they had been in different platoons, but two days after the aptitude tests, had met in the psychiatrist's office at Britannia Barracks. The psychiatrist, who wore a major's uniform, had called them into his office, smiling and shaking their hands. He proposed that they should sign on for three years and apply for a commission. When they declined, he flew into a rage.

'Your sort are no bloody good to the Army, and you're no bloody good to yourselves,' he told them. 'Stand to attention! You're too bloody cocky to make decent NCOs, and you're too bloody idle to sign on for a commission. Now get out of my office! About turn and quick march.'

After the aptitude test, Nick had put down his name for the Education Corps, the Intelligence Corps, and the Signals. Druce had chosen the Education Corps, in which John Robbins seemed to be having a cushy time; the Service Corps, where they'd teach you to drive everything from a motorbike to a heavy lorry; and, failing that, the REME, where he could at least learn about engines. It was the mad psychiatrist's revenge, perhaps, to post them both to the Royal Army Pay Corps Training Centre.

'The *what?*' said Robert Druce Senior, when he heard. 'The *Pay Corps?* Well, I never expected them to put you in the Brigade of Guards. But the *RAPC!* Rob All Poor Comrades, eh? God help the Army, if they put *you* in charge of money, that's all I have to say. You can't add up for toffee-nuts, you.'

Nick was quicker at arithmetic, but he and Druce made a pastime of asking naive questions during the six-week course of daily lectures. A five-week course in 023 Druce's case, who snatched the first chance of escape.

A week before the end of the course, a chit came round from the Orderly Room asking for someone who could type.

'I can type,' said Druce, standing up to attention.

Well, fair play. He'd had two lessons at the Youth Centre in Joslin Road. How to clean the machine, and change the ribbon, and set the margins. How the keyboard was laid out, and what happened when you pressed the shift key.

Nothing venture, nothing win.

After watching as he hunted all over the keyboard for each letter, the Orderly Room Sergeant came and stood over him. 'Well, well,' he said; 'So you're a typist, are you?'

But he took pity on Druce's crestfallen face.

'All right, all right. I s'pose we shall have to be grateful for small mercies. You can move your kit across to HQ company lines this afternoon, but you'll have to doss down with the general duties lot for a day or two. I'm Sar'nt Day to you. Understood? And in the absence of senior officers or NCOs, my name's Cliff. And you are *who*, exactly? Bob? Right then, Bob, cop hold: these are your shoulder-flashes.'

He produced two strips of crimson felt sewn to loops of elastic. Blushing with relief and pleasure, Bob unbuttoned his epaulettes, and slid his crimson HQ-company flashes into place. When the bugle blew, he tipped his typewriter up onto its back, and went to move his kit.

There was nobody about, and only half a dozen beds in his new barrack-room. He found a bed that seemed to be unclaimed, piled his mattress and blankets on it and stretched out and lit a Woodbine. In a while he'd fetch his kitbag and his rifle, and ask Nick Glover to give him a hand to shift his barrack-box. He'd miss Nick.

But that was that. He was in HQ Company now. Taken on strength. For the next few weeks, Cliff Day had explained, he'd be learning the ins and outs of a new system of documentation, to be ready for the first intake of new 'National Service' recruits. The Pay Corps Training Centre was moving to Wiltshire. While everybody else stayed on in Aldershot to strike camp he, along with Cliff and a handful of other Orderly Room and HQ staff, would find themselves in Devizes a month in advance.

For 023 Druce there'd be no more lectures on pay and family allowances and elementary accounting. No more rifle drill either, racing up and down the square at a hundred and twenty strides to the minute, the light-infantry pace that was a burden after the heavy-infantry march of the Suffolks. No second farcical passing-out parade. No evenings of unrelenting bullshit getting ready for it.

And, anyhow, hadn't he stood already on his own saluting-base, and taken the salute from a gaggle of top Army brass headed by the Secretary for War himself?

On the morning of the Minister's visit to Marlborough Lines a week or so earlier, all recruits been ordered to remain in their quarters, not so much as daring to show themselves at the windows, while their instructors paraded on the square. It was freezing cold in the barrack room, and the coal-buckets were empty.

'Well, I'm going to chance my arm, seeing that no one else will,' said Private Druce, and armed himself with the coal-shovel and a bucket. He could easily abstract a few lumps at the unattended coal-yard and be back again within minutes.

He sidled round the corner of a barrack-block, and froze.

Yards away, Emmanuel Shinwell, Labour-party veteran and now since 1947 Secretary for War, was striding towards him, flanked on either side by scarlet-tabbed Staff-Colonels. Or were they Brigadier-Generals? Something of the sort. Behind them trailed a wake of senior officers.

Druce crashed to attention, clanged his shovel into the bucket in his left hand and, desperately gazing straight ahead, threw up his right in a rigid salute. As they drew level, the Minister's immediate escort coldly stared at him and saluted, while Manny Shinwell nodded and waved his hand. Rank by rank, the remaining officers drew near, looked to their right, scowled, saluted, and went on their way. When they had all passed out of sight, Druce scampered out of the danger-zone with his shovel and empty bucket. Nothing ever came of the incident.

Now, at some time after midnight on his first day on the strength of HQ Company, he woke to the sound of men guffawing. His unknown room-mates were back.

'Wot 'appened *then*, eh?' someone was saying.

'Wot 'appened then? Wot d'yer fink? I stabbed 'er wiv me mutton dagger, thass wot.'

As the conversation rambled on, there were variations on the phallic metaphor: 'beef bayonet', 'pork sword'. Words, words for his word-hoard. He fell asleep giggling, and trying to think up phrases of his own.

Veal cutlass? Venison sabre? Ham stiletto?

*

At Aldershot there was no respite from Good Order and Military Discipline, in or out of barracks. If your boots slithered under you on a pavement rutted with ice, there was an even chance that a Military Policeman would jack-in-the-box out of a doorway to charge you under Section 44 of the Army Act with Conduct to the Prejudice Of. As the National Anthem cleared its throat with a drum-roll at the end of the last reel, cinema projectionists in Aldershot slammed the house-lights up. Military Policemen stood there in ambush, spaced out along the aisles. Woe betide a soldier caught unbuttoned or cuddling his girl at that moment, not standing to attention and gazing to his front. When you were so obviously a serviceman, civilian clothes were no safeguard from interrogation.

But for the advance party at the new Pay Corps Centre, for four exhilarating weeks, life in Wiltshire was a doddle. Nothing to do but organize the Orderly Room, while squads of general-duties wallahs loafed around slapping paint on appropriate surfaces, and three or four cooks showed off what they could do when they put their minds to it.

A straggling three-mile march from the back of the camp, by field-paths across billows of downland, lay a village pub. It was lit by oil-lamps and the flare of firelight, and a ten-penny pint of the landlord's rough cider would rattle your skull and unhook your tongue. Half a pint more, and your eyeballs slewed in their sockets as you held up the glass and peered through a cloud of motes and flecks and couldn't tell whether they were in your eyes or the smoky air or the scrumpy. A fourth half-pint and you were drunk and barely capable. The faces of the locals leaned and leered in the doorway as they saw you off on the three-mile stagger back to camp by starlight.

In the town itself, a mile and a half to the south-west, there were more prostitutes in the pubs and on the pavements than there had been in Aldershot itself.

'Aha! Oho! The meaner beauties of the night,' said Cliff Day, never at a loss for a quotation, as the Orderly Room staff sat over pints of scrumpy in the *Pelican*. 'A Sergeant in the Wilts was telling me they come down from London at week-ends for a change of air.'

'There was an old man of Devizes, who was had up before the Assizes,' said Private Druce. 'And that is the sum total of my knowledge about this town.'

Outside in the cold air once again, he felt the cider at its old game of twisting his tongue.

'Who's that over there with a statue and a fountain all to himself?' asked Cliff, as they reeled out of the *Pelican* and set off across the market square on the mile-and-a-half trudge back to camp.

'Southern something,' somebody read, holding a lighted match close to the stone plinth. 'Yeah, and then Ex Ex Ex One One One it says here.'

Bob wandered on to a nearby monument. He flicked his lighter, and found the name of Henry, Viscount Sidmouth, who had presented the town with a market cross. Suddenly there came to his memory the lines from Shelley's *Mask of Anarchy* that he had copied down from E.C. Greenleigh's blackboard. He struck a pose on the steps of Sidmouth's market cross, and declaimed them:

Clothed with the Bible, as with light,
And the shadows of the night,
Like Sidmouth, next, Hypocrisy
On a crocodile rode by...

But nobody was listening.

24

OFFICERS' CLERK

Once the main party had arrived from Aldershot and settled in, the halcyon days were at an end. Birdsong and the twitter of hedge sparrows was replaced by bawled commands and the crunch of boots. Lorries decanted the first intake of National Servicemen. They were documented, and kitted out. Drill Sergeants infested the place again, with their glittering boots and brasses and every raised stitch of their chevrons highlighted with white ink. Guards were mounted, and stick-men carried like precious parcels onto the square.

By a quarter to seven each weekday morning, the hot water was running icy from the taps before the first week was out. When the main boiler failed completely, the Orderly Room staff scurried back from breakfast and tried to lather their shaving-soap in lukewarm tea. Soon the familiar smells were clinging about the cookhouse, and the drains stank. At least, the CO assumed that the drains were responsible for the pervasive stench. In a mounting passion twice he had the sewers flushed before he learned that the smell came from rotting flax in the flax-dams across the hill.

Once the day-long flurry of documentation of each new intake had been completed, life in the Orderly Room ground on in its old way. Part One Orders expanded from a few typed lines into Gestetnered sheets three pages long, and Private Druce spent every weekday morning with his left eye shut against the smoke from the Woodbine in his mouth, while he squinted with his right eye at the keys of his typewriter. From minute to minute he stopped to curse and dabble magenta-pink correcting-fluid over another mis-type on his stencil.

Towards eleven o'clock, Captain Cletterton, the Adjutant, began to prowl in and out of the Orderly Room, waiting to sign the stencils before they were run off. 'Come along, come along, come along! Jump to it, laddie!'

he barked, pacing the floor with a mug of hot Bovril in his hand. When too dense a shower of magenta assaulted his eye, he ripped the stencil in two and demanded that it be retyped.

In the evening once or twice a week, a Reginald Cletterton transmogrified, pink-faced and hail-fellow-well-met, drifted across to the Orderly Room sleeping quarters in sports jacket and flannels, and sat around handing out fags. From time to time, in gigglesome mood, he sought to enlist the Orderly Room rank-and-file into teams to debag one another.

The Training Centre was the staging-post for officers going overseas or coming home, and a full Corporal, a lance-jack and two privates were occupied in running the officers' section. The moment Reggie's signature was safely scratched on Private Druce's stencils, he joined the other three at their table, as they invoked the mysteries of FORIN leave and BISKIT leave, collated additional information, copied it onto file-cards, and passed it round the table. Each one of them filed different details on his cards, and the day was spent in passing requests for information to the others, or in complying with their requests. One man could have run the section single-handed — filling out travel-warrants, ration-cards, and all — if every detail had been entered once only, on a master-card.

Druce spent an hour or so designing one, but Cliff was not amused.

'Forget it, mate,' he said. 'Work *your* system, and three of us are going to be shunted out into the cold. The way things are we've all got a cushy little number. Comprenez? Yours not to reason why.'

Which is how office-empires are built.

So Druce consoled himself by exploring the personal files which Captain Cletterton ought to have kept under lock and key, and the warning comments clipped to their covers by the Major at the transit office. 'Watch your step with this one!', 'A pissy but well-meaning bugger', 'Better give this silly sod what he wants'.

*

Halfway through that first intake, the NCOs and other ranks were ordered to the garrison cinema in mid-afternoon. They found themselves watching *Pickup Girl*, a black-and-white movie about syphilis: a spiritual prophylactic made for the United States army. Opening with a jazz soundtrack and dough-boys hitting the town on furlough, it ended in a deluge of Gothic images. Stained spirochaetae under the microscope; a middle-aged man walking down a street, his spine corroded by *tabes dorsalis*, stamping his feet as if he meant to burst through the paving-stones; close-ups of rotting eyelids and nostrils; babbling quarterwits in the terminal stages of general paralysis of the insane. Unbidden, 023 Druce's memory retrieved across a decade the fairground hues of Dr Foote's *Plain Home Talk*, and fleshed out the black and white.

'Ee, well, it's nowt to do wi' me,' said Private Accrington, the latest recruit to the Orderly Room staff, as together they strolled back to their quarters. 'A've never bin wi' a woman. Don't want to, neether.' Accrington, whose chin was innocent of a beard, looked about fourteen years old.

'Let the galled jade wince,' Druce mused aloud, unthinkingly. 'Our withers are unwrung.'

'Yeh what?' said Accrington.

At the end of that week somebody screwed a sign to the wall of a hut a few yards inside the Main Gate. 'E.T. ROOM'. Investigating, Private Druce came upon a wash-basin and an electric geyser, printed step-by-step instructions, a collection of packets on a shelf, and a locked ballot-box.

E.T. *Early Treatment*. What to do after sexual intercourse.

Scrawl your name and last three on the form supplied in the packet, and drop it into the ballot-box. Anoint your mutton dagger inside and out with ointment from the tube, wrap it in the square of Japanese tissue-paper, and secure it with the rubber band for a minimum of four hours.

Now you were safe: if not from infection, at least from being charged with unlawful self-wounding. Now, if you *did* catch a dose, they'd unlock the box, check that your name was in there, and you'd be in the clear.

Militarily, if not medically, speaking.

Three weeks later, Druce was sent for by the Adjutant. Reggie Cletterton hummed and hawed, pacing back and forth across his office.

'Sit down. Er, now, see here,' he said. 'This is not easy for me…'

Druce had to keep twisting his head to look at him.

'I didn't believe it, when it was brought to my notice. Thought you were a decent lad. From a good home. Listen, how old are you? Eighteen? Is that all?'

Reggie clicked his tongue several times.

'So, I made it my business to see for myself. I've been coming down here early every morning for the past week.' He nodded towards the window. 'I've been watching you.'

The door of the ET room was visible a dozen yards away.

'Every single morning for five days on end, I've seen you visit that room...'

Private Druce said nothing.

'Look, lad, your morals are your own. I don't *have* to take an interest in how you spend your time. But what would your parents say if they knew you were leading this kind of life? Eh? Think of that. You don't answer... And you can damn well wipe that smile off your face! Stand to attention!'

Reggie was getting the rats again.

Then Private Druce explained that the electric geyser — not sex — was the reason for his daily visit to the ET room. He'd kept the knowledge to himself, otherwise there'd have been a queue every morning, jostling for the sink. For the best part of a month now he'd been the only private soldier in the Orderly Room shaving in hot water.

*

In his way, Private Accrington was a model of foresight to them all, as they lounged on their beds and sighed their lives away, and wondered how much longer they could put up with Accrington.

Each evening, weekdays and weekends alike, Accrington hastened back from the cookhouse, sat on his bed, unlaced his boots and delved into his barrack-box. Still in khaki, he wriggled his feet into dancing pumps, donned an opera hat and white gloves, produced a walking cane and strolled out, closing the door behind him. Seconds later, the door was thrown back on its hinges and Accrington struck a pose in the doorway: 'Ter DUM!' It was the opening bar of the *Mephisto Waltz*.

Still humming between clenched teeth — 'Ter-Dum, Ter-Dum, Ter-DUM' — Accrington patrolled the room, clouting his cane against convenient surfaces: cupboards, walls, bed-legs, the stove. He was demonstrating that the cane was as solid as it looked. 'Ter-Dum, Ter-Dum, Ter-DAH'.

He stopped and held the cane aloft between gloved fingers, and with a flick of his wrist it resolved itself into two fluttering silk handkerchiefs.

He bowed into the silence, acknowledging the applause he heard inside his skull.

'Ladies and Gentlemen, you are most kind. I thank you...'. He delivered his patter in a nasal imitation of Oxford English. 'And now — 'Ter-Dum, Ter-Dum, Ter-DUM,' — he swept off his top hat, balanced it on the nearest bed and, in a flutter of silk, dropped into it the hollow knob and coiled steel spring that had been his cane — 'Ter-Dum' — and now he was drawing off his kid gloves — 'Ter-Dum, Ter-DAH' — and the gloves joined the litter in his hat.

'And now, Ladies and Gents, *by way of a change*' — the phrase set the barrack room's teeth on edge — 'I should like to entertain you with—'

He paused dramatically and, out of thin air, produced a fan of playing-cards.

'—the Cards!'

One by one, he began to flick them into his hat.

And so on through his fifteen-minute routine, as he strolled among the beds, and tried to catch the eyes of his fellow-clerks: 'Now, I know this gent here will be willing to assist me. Kindly pick a card, Sir. Any card at all — '

(Sod off!)

'Would you care to write down an item on this note-pad, Sir? Madam? Any item at all. Just write down its name.'

(Shut it, Accrington!)

'Nothing embarrassing, Madam. Ooh, I know all about you young ladies out on a spree. I'm easily embarrassed—'

(Accrington, I'm bloody warning you.)

'No, don't show me what you've written!

(Oi, Accrington! I dunno how to spell it. How d'you spell 'bollocks', Accrington?)

Impervious, his face set in a winning smile, Accrington carried on to the end, bowed right and left and swept out, swinging the door shut behind him. A minute later, with his cane resurrected and re-assembled, and his cards back in their packs, he flung the door back on its hinges.

'Ter DUM!'

Three, sometimes four times each evening, he went through his routine: Mephisto Waltz, cane, handkerchiefs, gloves, cards, the never-varying patter.

'Ah *moost* practise,' he shouted above the groans and catcalls.

'Do it under your bloody breath, then.'

'Ee, don't be daft,' he'd answer, 'It's not the same at all. Ah've got to practise for my professional career.'

'One of these days, mate,' somebody said one night, 'when you say *By way of a change*, just once too often, just one more bloody time, we'll blanco you all over.'

One Monday when Druce and Garrett arrived back from weekend leave, there were whisperings and meaning looks in the Orderly Room.

'Accrington. Tell you in the NAAFI,' somebody said.

At NAAFI-break the story came out. On Saturday night those three or four of his comrades who had not gone home on a weekend pass had fallen upon Accrington. Accrington, wrestled onto a bed and stripped naked, had sported an erection. So when they'd blancoed the rest of him with Khaki Green No. 3, they anointed his penis with black Cherry Blossom boot-polish, and his balls with oxblood purple. Tears streaking his cheeks, Accrington had fled to the shower block with his soap and towel, a naked green man.

'He can't take a joke, see, that's his trouble,' somebody told Druce, earnestly. 'It was just a laugh. Didn't mean him to take it serious. We was all pissed on scrumpy, anyway.'

No need for Druce, or Garrett, to feel involved. But he couldn't shake off the knowledge that, had he been present he, too, would not have failed to jeer at Accrington.

That same evening, Ter-dum, Ter-dum, Ter-DUM, Accrington, his face red with defiance, flung open the barrack-room door once more, 'Ter-DUM!' Thereafter, they let him get on with his practice for a career in civvy-street; they even stretched out a hand for his proffered playing-card and memorized it when he asked them to.

A week or so later, and with Accrington's single-mindedness as an example, Druce arrived back in camp from a weekend at High Cedars with a stack of books in his case. He lined them up on the shelf above his bed-head. More than six months had passed since he had opened a single page.

*

Piddlehinton, when he arrived on posting in late August, seemed almost as idyllic as, at the outset, Devizes had been. A thousand men and some fifty members of the Woman's Royal Army Corps were housed in wooden huts on a rain- and gale-swept Dorset hillside. They spent their days calculating the pay and family allowances of the entire Royal Army Service Corps at home and overseas, and the Army Catering Corps.

Druce took over the work of the Orderly Room Officer's Section from Ray Doggett, Absent Without Leave. At the adjoining table sat Don Francis, from Beckenham. He was as loquacious as Druce, and they struck up a friendship. Don slept in the next bed in the barrack hut.

Every weekday morning, back from the cookhouse, Don sat hunched on his bed, and waited for the bugle to announce the start of work for the day. When he heard it, 'Right, then,' he said. 'Always shit in the firm's time. Make that your golden rule.' And he set off for the latrines, grinning. Night after night, as the Last Post echoed across Piddlehinton camp, Don began the ritual of anointing his hair with gel and combing it into waves.

'No, well, listen, you never know, I might meet a good-looking bint in my dreams. I wouldn't want to look scruffy, would I?' he invariably announced, when anyone caught his eye.

By day, Don was responsible for the 'Statistics' section. It was his job to compile the Daily State — a listing of all personnel on regimental strength that day. Continuously falsified by a backlog of earlier errors, it could never be more than approximate. Don kept the truth to himself, and lost no sleep about it. On the 20th of each month, whatever the day of the week, it fell to Private Druce to compile a shorter, but infinitely more detailed list of commissioned officers, with copies to HQ, the War Office and Southern Command. He and Don quickly shared the secrets of how they kept their files and where the suppressed errors lay. They told no-one else. Soon they were taking care to apply for leave at different times, so that each could keep the other's section ticking over without fear of outsiders muscling in and learning too much.

Together they typed the stencils of Part I Orders every day and checked them, reciting abbreviated gibberish aloud at breakneck speed: 'fol pers sos this bn wef 28 8 49...', or 'Pte Mackay 798, chdgd sect 40 AA cond prej good ord n mil disc n tht he, at 33rd Bn RAPC Pid Cmp Dorch Dors, 28 8 49, did say to Stf-sgt Davies, "I'm not going to do it," or w.t.t.e.'

Which was to say, 'the following personnel have been struck off strength of this Battalion with effect from 28th August'; and that, yet again, Private

Mackay had been charged at Piddlehinton Camp under Section 40 of the Army Act with Conduct to the Prejudice of Good Order and Military Discipline, for refusing to carry out an order.

What Mackay normally told Staff-Sergeant Davies or anyone else, was 'Aw, yu kin fook off, jock!' The words uttered by a defaulter were set out on the CO's charge sheet. But in the high-minded context of Part I Orders, 'I'm not going to do it, or words to that effect' sufficed.

Mackay, a diminutive Glaswegian tearaway, kept Druce and Francis busy all summer with his appearances on charge-sheets and Part I Orders. He was doing everything in his power to be discharged, as of no use to the Army. One morning, informed by the CO that he was a useless character, Mackay retorted, 'Och awa! Ye're a wee waster yersel.' It seemed to do the trick at last.

'Rennie,' said the Colonel to his personal clerk, when the Regimental Sergeant Major, hoarse with fury, had double-marched Mackay out onto the verandah, 'Rennie, I have just spoken to the bravest man in the British Army. Telling his Commanding Officer to his face that he's a waster! Give him his discharge? I'd give him the bloody VC if it lay in my power.'

Dorchester, Thomas Hardy's Casterbridge, was six miles distant from Piddlehinton camp, along a road that wound its way up and down between hedgerows heavy with honeysuckle. Across the meadows near the town there was a sluice-gate and a weir where he and Don Francis and the others swam and dived and sprawled in the grass to dry off. A mile and a half away from the camp gate in the opposite direction, between White Lackington and Piddletrenthide, lay the nearest pub. There, once or twice a week along with the rest of the Orderly Room crew, he sank a pint of scrumpy laced with rum, and at midweek bought a two-ounce packet of Black Beauty shag and mixed his hoarded dog-ends into it. By Thursday, the Orderly Room air was rank with the stench of their roll-ups until pay parade brought a reprieve and fresh supplies of Player's Navy Cut, and Senior Service.

Discipline was minimal. When Private Druce first arrived and the five-tonner from the Training Centre had drawn up outside the Guard Room, Druce and his travelling companions had been inspected by the CO. The Colonel was wearing for the occasion a striped pyjama-top, khaki trousers and carpet slippers. From Friday midday to Monday morning almost everyone, regulars and national servicemen alike, wore civilian clothes.

Even in uniform, most people wore civvy shoes, except on the rare parades. Their webbing equipment gathered dust in their kitbags. Their rifles were all stacked in the armoury.

Before Lights Out, and during much of the day for Druce — who had soon arranged a barricade of metal cabinets around his one-man Officers' Section — there was leisure to read. On the shelf above his bed, Marie de France, Villon, Verlaine, Ronsard, Henri Bosco, Alphonse Daudet came to join the bright tangerine-spined novels and stories of Chesterton, Wells, Maugham, Sherwood Anderson and A.E. Coppard. Alongside them were ranked Quiller-Couch on *The Art of Reading* and *The Art of Writing*; the plays of Shaw and Wilde; Pelicans clad in the cobalt blue of science; and, in unaggressive grey, John Hersey's *Hiroshima*.

Romantical — all but the grey, and blue-clad volumes — they were an escape-route during the ten-and-a-half months of the Russian blockade of Berlin and the Allied air-lift, and the threat of a perhaps nuclear war that, since the beginning of July, had been suddenly renewed. They were a counterpoise to the sight of the dismantled Orderly-Room 'RELEASE SECTION' sign now gathering a film of dust on top of a cupboard. To the postponement for an unknown period of everyone's return to civilian life, regardless of his demob-group number.

One day they led him to the brink of trouble.

A civilian visitor, returning from the CO's office to his car, found the scatter of books he had left on the back seat gone, presumably stolen. The CO detailed the Orderly Sergeant and his crew to search the barrack huts. In the middle of the afternoon, a Corporal and escort marched into the Orderly Room.

'Got somebody here of the name of Druce?' said the Corporal. 'Right. Cap and belt on, you, and get fell in.' The Corporal led the way to the Orderly Room barrack hut, while the escort marched hard on Druce's heels, to cut off any attempt at escape.

'Stand by your bed, Private,' said the Corporal, once they were inside the hut. And as Druce started to speak, 'Shut it! You'll find out soon enough.'

Shadows passed the window, and the Orderly Sergeant escorted the owner of the missing books through the doorway. 'We've caught him, Sah,' he said. 'Just look at that little lot, Sah. Books!' And he pointed to the shelf above Druce's bed.

The owner of the missing books was red-faced and profuse in his apologies.

But not the Orderly Sergeant. 'I've got my beady little eye on you, soldier,' he said, as a parting shot.

*

He could reach Aldershot from High Cedars in three hours, but being stationed at Bury St Edmunds and later on at Devizes had meant lengthened journeys to and from home on steam trains. At Liverpool Street and at Paddington, there were fights for seats every Sunday night. More often than not Druce had settled for standing or lying in the corridor, cursed and trodden on by those who wanted to get past him to empty their bladders.

Half-awake and shivering, a dozen comrades-in-arms would find themselves staggering along a railway platform God knows where in the small hours. Then stretching out on the floor of a waiting-room, where the air was sour with tobacco smoke, and a row of paraffin signal-lamps stood winking and stinking in a corner. There — *Aw, roll on death: demob's too slow* — they waited for rosy-fingered dawn and the branch-line milk-train that would give them just time enough to scramble back to camp for muster-parade.

Never mind, Saturday night in his own bed under the skylight at High Cedars was worth any amount of travelling, sleeplessness and grime. And now, at Piddlehinton Camp, with a regular Friday-night coach that ferried thirty-two bodies from the Main gate to the Waterloo Road and back again late on Sunday night he became even more of a weekday soldier. As 1948 drew to a close, his mother was anxious for him to come as often he could. She was becoming more and more concerned about his father's state of mind.

Within a month of moving from High Cedars into a brand-new council house at Honey Hill in the Village, at a time when there should have been a lightening of his thoughts, Robert Kitchener Druce had begun to sink into a deep depression.

Home on a week's leave in late autumn, his son walked through the door to hear that his father was in a hospital ward at St Katharine's. Once Superintendent of Saint Katharine's Casual Wing, now he lay staring upward, his eyes from time to time brimming with tears, speaking in a whisper, possessed by shame.

'Get me out away from here. I'm *known* here.'

Private Druce was granted a moment's interview with the doctor in charge of his father's case.

'I'm afraid he'll do something stupid. Try to kill himself, even.'

'You are a trained psychiatrist, I assume,' answered the houseman.

'I know my father,' he said. 'And from now on I hold you responsible. I've told you what I think.'

'I see.' The man was not as crass as his first remark had made him appear. 'Very well. I'll get the psychiatrist to take a look at him tomorrow.'

Tomorrow proved to be too late. That evening Mrs Druce and her son arrived at St Katharine's to learn that soon after they had left the previous day, her husband had gone to the washroom and hacked his throat across with a razor-blade. A nurse had found him in time, and he had been transferred to a psychiatric ward in a hospital fourteen miles away.

The ward-sister rang through on Mrs Druce's behalf. Her husband had already started a course of electro-convulsive therapy. At that moment he'd been back from the treatment room for half an hour, and was still asleep. They'd be able to visit him in the morning.

The ward-sister put her arm round Mrs Druce for a moment, and poured them both a cup of tea.

'Sisters of Mercy, they call themselves,' his father greeted them when they saw him next, his cheeks unshaved and ashen. He jerked his head towards a coiffed and habited figure who was leaning over a nearby bed. 'Mercy? They don't know the meaning of the word.'

As the few days of Druce's leave, and the subsequent weeks and months passed, his father's personality continued to appear unrecognizable and alien. Back at Honey Hill, one moment he was shifty-eyed, seeming to rack his memory for words. Minutes later, he would erupt into a crazy euphoria. But at least his suicidal frame of mind, and the conviction that he was suffering from the cancer that had killed his mother, seemed to have been burnt out of his skull by the electric shocks.

As she coaxed her husband out of doors to help her plant out a new garden, his wife was a lot happier. In Piddlehinton Camp, his son could relax again, laughing at the antics of Don Francis, and reading until Lights Out, he began to be quit of the images that had sprung up between his eyes and the printed words.

*

In the new year, two Warrant Officers in B Company were arrested, and Piddlehinton Camp changed overnight. The pair had invented wives and dependants for long-serving unmarried soldiers in the RASC and ACC. They had forged appropriate Family Allowance books, and for months had been cashing them at a dozen London Post Offices at weekends. Now they sat in adjacent cells in the Guard Room, awaiting court-martial. Keeping them company nearby was the Staff-Sergeant who had gone AWOL with the Sergeants' Mess fund, and sundry less picaresque offenders.

Overnight the place became more disciplined than Aldershot. Six Military Policemen were taken on the strength of HQ company, and half a dozen infantrymen joined them as Camp Police. Suddenly, unwonted quantities of Brasso and Duraglit and paper-wrapped blocks of Khaki Green No. 3 were changing hands across the NAAFI counter, and people rummaged through their kitbags for gaiter-weights. Civilian clothes were forbidden except for soldiers on weekend passes. There was a outbreak of drill-parades, and the Fire Picket was put on permanent alert.

One morning, Don Francis strolled around Druce's Officer-Section barricade, and lit a cigarette.

'There's a couple of dustbins on fire round at the back. Can't you smell burning?' he said.

They both went out and clapped the lids back on the dustbins. Seconds later, the fire picket arrived along with Major Lomax, the CO's second-in-command.

'Who the hell put the fires out?' screamed the 2 i/c.

'We did,' said Lance-Corporal Francis.

'We put the lids back on the dustbins,' said Private Druce.

'They're not dustbins, you stupid, idle man.' The 2 i/c was in a towering rage. 'They are burning huts! Use your imagination. This is a serious exercise. Light the bloody things again, Picket Commander, and extinguish them in the proper manner.'

*

As long as the court-martial lasted, 33rd Battalion RAPC was infested with staff officers. They put up at the King's Arms in Dorchester and motored to Piddlehinton every day. You had to be ready to fling up a salute at any moment.

At the end of it all, the prisoners were sentenced to be discharged with ignominy, and to two years in a civil prison. The cells in the Guard Room slowly emptied, back went the rifles into the armoury, and along the cool sequestered valley of the river Piddle life resumed the noiseless tenor of its way.

Don Francis, who had been called up a month before Druce, was released in mid-September. They parted promising to keep in touch and look each other up from time to time.

Don paid a visit to the Orderly Room after hours to leave a parting gift for the slimy sycophant of a newly-promoted lance-corporal who couldn't wait to take over his section. While Private Druce kept watch, Don pulled out all eight drawers of his filing cabinet, and shuffled handful after handful of the cards among themselves and from tray to tray. Accrington could not have done it with greater panache. In the chaos which ensued, it was touch and go that L/Cpl Francis would be recalled to duty, and his release leave cancelled.

With Don no longer around, Druce's final month at Piddlehinton was a bore. It was common practice among national servicemen for them to construct an elaborate Advent-style calendar for their desks or the shelf above their beds, with a count-down number changing day by day during their last weeks of service. Archer, the Quartermaster-Sergeant, forbade any such insubordinate display on 023 Druce's part. He failed to observe that the number chalked in a six-inch circle under the 'Officers Section' sign was counting down from each day to the next.

It was the rule that men who served in Southern Command were discharged on the last day of the fortnight allotted to their group. Druce applied to sit a civil service exam which ensured his leaving on the first day of the fortnight. That morning the duty bugler, bribed with a packet of fags, blew reveille inside a barrack-room full of slumbering Orderly Room clerks. The effect was gratifying. Minutes later 023 Druce collected his kipper —

the time-honoured early breakfast for men on release — and hung it up by the eye-hole on a hat peg in the canteen — the time-honoured way of dealing with it.

Then he tipped his kit out onto the floor of the QM Stores, and clambered into the driver's cab of a truck. As the RASC driver let in the clutch, Druce lit a Wills' Whiff cheroot for both of them. He'd bought a packet for the occasion and, a man of leisure once again, savoured them along with the glee of travelling alone and unregimented on the train from Dorchester to Waterloo and down again to Aldershot for the last time. There was a parade-ground adjacent to the release centre. Two rookies were running around its perimeter at the double, with their rifles held above their heads. For a moment he loitered to watch and give them a sympathetic wave.

Then, a soldier no more, he hastened back across London to the Village, and All Saints, and Joslin Road Youth Centre, and John Robbins, and Bren Slaney. And his own bedroom in the Druces' new home in Honey Hill.

25

DOING THE SPITS

On early shift in the tuberculosis ward at St Katharine's Hospital in December 1949, Druce the orderly was clattering around in the sluice by ten past eight. He wore a surgeon's smock that fastened with tapes at the back, and over that a rubber apron. He was rubber-booted and rubber-gloved, and the side-pieces of his spectacles were trapped under the strings of a sterile mask. There was a tuft of cotton-wool squeezed out in Lysol in the corner of his mask. He was doing the spits.

By half-past eight, he would have finished scalding the urine-bottles and shining the bedpans. After that he'd get on with boiling up the urine of the five or six patients who were diabetic as well as tubercular, while he watched for the tell-tale scarlet stain of sugar.

But that all had to wait until the spits had been collected up, examined, and cast into the flames.

The 'spits' were cardboard sputum cups, folded to fit into metal holders. One stood within arm's reach on every patient's bedside locker. Replacement cups were brought round first thing, when the overnight spits were labelled and taken to the sluice. There Sister Hanson or a staff nurse peered down into them one by one, stirring the sputum around with a glass rod and writing comments in a register. It was left to the male orderly to stack the spits together on a thick layer of newspapers, douse them with sawdust, fold the whole thing up into a parcel, and carry it eighty yards to the boiler-house.

The stokers would be on the lookout for him. The instant his shadow fell through the open archway, they clanged the door of a furnace open, cranked the damper as wide as it would go, and retreated to either side, turning their heads away, terrified of contagion. He swung back his arms and pitched the parcel of spit and bacilli as far as he could into the roar of flame.

Instantly the stokers latched the furnace-door shut, and waited for him to leave before they drew breath again. They wanted him in and out fast. They had no time for chit-chat. He was Mister Death.

One morning Druce's ramshackle parcel buckled in his grasp and spilled sawdust onto the boiler-house floor.

'Get out, fuck off, we don't *want* you in here!' the stokers shouted as he stood hesitating. He left them dragging rakefuls of bright cinders back and forth across the concrete, cauterising it.

Back in the sluice, as soon as he had clanged the sterilised bedpans onto the shelves and blasted the urine bottles with a jet of scalding water, he would set about the diabetes tests. He added a dose of Fehling's solution to the morning piss in the row of boiling-tubes and lit the bunsen burner.

Then he set the window ajar, pulled his mask down around his neck, and took a quick drag on a cigarette. He left the hot tap running into the sink, and breathed his smoke out of the window along with a cloud of steam. Sister Hanson, the Terror of the TB Ward, was usually on the prowl at this time of day. Although she chain-smoked in the fastness of her office, Sister Hanson played hell if she caught anyone else sneaking a quick lungful on duty.

She often loitered in the lane behind the row of open chalets, at a vantage point two yards away from the window of the sluice, spying. She was at it one morning, with her back to the open window, peering intently at something. Druce, craning his neck at the window, tried to see what she was gazing at, and took his attention off the tube that he was holding in the gas flame.

Never allow liquid to boil at the bottom of a test-tube, or a gush of steam will gob the contents out: Fitz Fitzroy had drilled that into them in the chemistry lab at Monkswood. And now, unwatched, the flame played on the danger spot, the liquid gave a sudden cough and a steaming scarlet stain splashed across the back of Sister Hanson's veil. Intent as a tomcat on a heedless robin, she failed to notice.

Sister Hanson never encouraged idle chitchat, and although the nurses and patients wondered about the stain among themselves, nobody mentioned it to her. She carried it around the wards, blood-red, all through the shift: a virulent symbol, so it seemed to him whose inattention had flung it there, of the phthisis that had robbed the world of Keats, and Kafka, and Chopin and the Brontës.

Given commonsense precautions, he did not fear infection for himself. To be employed on the TB Ward was conditional upon your having antibodies in your blood. Of having — like most of the British population in the days before immunisation by BCG — got over a mild and probably undiagnosed attack. When he applied for the job in late November, he'd been given a Mantoux test and x-ray. Both announced his recovery from a very recent infection.

It wasn't difficult to look back to the earlier months of that year, recall the days he had spent in a military hospital, and put two and two together.

*

Private Hanwell was the Orderly Room orderly at Piddlehinton Camp. He burned the waste-paper all the year round, and in winter carried coal for the Orderly Room stove and shovelled up the cinders. He was Lord of the Gestetner duplicator, forbad anyone else to approach it and, late each afternoon, minutely cleaned away the day's impacted ink and fluff from it as tenderly as a lover. As soon as he had tucked the machine away under its canvas cover, Hanwell fetched a broom and swept the floor clean of ash and cigarette-butts, coughing, and spitting into the dust. Clearly, it was Hanwell who, in the barrack-room fug in the early months of 1949, had carried the contagion among his comrades. With hindsight, Druce could now recognise Hanwell's daylong dry cough and his nightly habit of spitting towards the open fire-door of the stove.

Druce and Trent and Francis all caught summer colds and sprouted boils on their buttocks. When they turned up on sick parade the MO's first question was a seemingly offhand: 'Any coughs or colds lately?' After which he packed them off one by one for an x-ray.

In the event, Druce 023's suspected boil proved to be a deep-seated abscess which would need to be lanced under a general anaesthetic. So off he jounced in the back of a jeep, each pothole in the road a microcosmic agony, to Tidworth and the military hospital.

Up and about again at Tidworth, he wore 'hospital blues' for a week: his own khaki battledress blouse along with the blue trousers, white shirt and red tie of the wounded. When he walked out in blues, interestingly pale, no doubt, and limping slightly, the world was welcoming. Elderly ladies, hard-faced in the looks they cast at the soldiery, now gazed at him with tenderness. Working-men grinned and called him 'chum'. When anyone got too close to asking how and where he had been wounded, 023 Druce shrugged the question away with a sad smile.

During his ten days at Tidworth there was a shortage of RAMC personnel and he was detailed to act as a hospital orderly. He snatched the chance to read his own medical report. The infection had cleared, though there was a telltale mottling on one lung. He was desperately grateful for his reprieve from a disease the name of which his mother mouthed in a whisper. Lending a hand on the wards became a way of giving thanks, as he recorded temperatures and pulses, changed dressings, fetched and carried for the bedridden. It pleased him to discover that, coping with excrement and pus, he wasn't squeamish, didn't feel his gorge rise. But it was impossible not to shudder in sympathy with the pain he couldn't avoid inflicting.

Jim, the recruit in the next bed, had been shot during an exercise. It is a military crime to point a fire-arm at anyone in jest, however convinced you may be that it is not loaded. A smart-arse in Jim's platoon, now in the cells and awaiting court-martial, had done just that, shoving his rifle against the cheek of Jim's backside and pulling the trigger.

Both men were lucky that they had only been firing blanks that day. Even so, the explosion drove wadding, cordite smoke and shreds of Jim's clothing all the way to the bone. The narrow puncture-wound suppurated. Twice it had to be cleaned out under general anaesthetic. Night and morning for a week, it was Druce who changed the dressings on Jim's hairy behind.

The only practicable way to remove the soiled dressing was to rip the sticking-plaster away — a merciful cruelty — in a single jerk. Night and morning, Jim's howl, and the tears that started from his eyes, were matched by the sympathetic shudder that raced through his tormentor's own flesh. After a week of it, Druce wasn't sorry to wish Jim all the best, and get back to the Orderly Room at Piddlehinton Camp, with an air-cushion on his own chair.

*

He was demobbed in late November. That meant waiting another eleven months to enter university, and he needed money. He decided to look for an office-job in London.

In 1949 the labour market still had not settled down after absorbing a flood of ex-servicemen. Times were austere. Petrol, soap, sweets and clothes were still rationed. So were many basic items of food. For would-be clerical staff it was an employer's market, and employers recruited their staff through agencies which required the applicant to sign away in advance a fee of ten per cent of what he or she would earn in the coming year.

More than a month's salary. Sight unseen. Before they dispatched you, cap in hand, to a potential employer. The instant an employer took you on, bang! the agency's bill fell due.

He wandered into an agency in Chancery Lane and filled up a stencilled form. Morridges were looking for an accounts clerk, wages £5 per week, the manager told him, and passed him an address on a slip of paper.

He found the head office of Morridge and Sons of Suffolk, Fruit and Vegetable Canners, at the top of a flight of stairs in Old Compton Street, Soho. The company secretary stepped out of an inner office and ran a languid eye over him.

'You can start when?'

'Why not today? Now?'

'I see. I'll take you through to Mister White, then. Our Chief Clerk. Leave you in his capable hands.'

The main office — a cramped Dickensian counting-house — was a long room at the back of the building, illuminated by a single window that opened onto a narrow light-well. At noon on that sunny November day, all the lamp-bulbs were lit. Four girls sat at a table typing invoices on festoons of paper. Seven men, all roughly his own age, sat elbow to elbow, facing one another across another table.

'That's your place there, Mister Bruce,' said Mr White, peering at the form which his latest underling had filled in at the agency.

'Druce.'

'What?'

'My name is Druce. Not Bruce. *Druce*. With a D.'

Mr White glanced at the form, and sniffed.

He looked about thirty. Thin-faced and pasty-looking, with a moth-eaten gingery moustache. There were lines seamed from his nostrils to the corners of his mouth, and his fingernails were bitten to the quick. Not much of an advert for Morridge's fruit and veg, thought Robert Druce.

'Well, as I say, that's your place there.'

The three others at his side of the table hudged up.

'You can start by totting the points up on this batch of invoices,' said Mr White. 'Canned vegetables and fruit. You understand about rationing points, do you? Here's a list of how many points *per* size of can *per* contents, how many cans *per* size of can *per* case. Go through the invoices, tot up the points, write down the totals on this list. Not too difficult for you, is it? You *have* got a School Sisstificate, have you? I don't see any mention of it on your application form here.'

Mr White, not used to being corrected, was bent on a little victimisation, it seemed.

'O, yes.'

Mr White wasn't satisfied.

'You don't seem very sure to me.'

'I have exemption from Inter-B.A. in point of fact.'

'No School Sisstificate, then,' said Mr White.

'School Certificate. Matric. Higher School Certificate, and exemption from the Inter-BA—'

'Well, *I'm* not satisfied,' said Mr White. 'Tomorrow I want to see written evidence that you've passed your School Sisstificate.' He stalked out of the room in triumph.

'That Mister White!' said one of the girl typists, unscrewing the cap of a bottle of nail varnish. 'Here, tell us your name, love, and I'll paint it on your coffee mug. So it don't get mixed up. Now Kenny's gone, this'll be *yours*.'

From time to time during the next three hours, Mr White prowled around the table and leaned across him to peer at his columns of figures, and sniff. At a little before five o'clock, there was a tap on Druce's shoulder.

He looked up at the pasty face of his overlord.

'*Now*, then,' said Mr White. 'I don't know if the agency informed you of *all* the details. Office hours in this establishment are eight a.m. till five p.m. Monday till Friday. Eight a.m. till one p.m. Saturdays. That's clear, is it? *However*, pro tem, during the week, office personnel are required to put in half an hour of voluntary overtime; that is, i.e., we go on till half-past five.'

'Ah. No. The agency didn't mention overtime.'

'It is, as I say, pro tem *and* voluntary. Your wages, as you *will* be aware no doubt, are five pounds sterling per week, less deductions. *However*, the additional hours will be taken into account if there should be an Exmass bonus. Are you with me? *However—*'

Mr White sleeked a hand over his head.

'*However,* being as this is your first day, I will not require you to do overtime—'

'That's very kind of—'

'*However,* in return, I expect you to take the post round to the G.P.O. before you catch your chube. All right? And I expect to see you here tomorrow mornin' by eight a.m. at the very latest. Preffably earlier. I got no time for slackers.'

Druce was half-way down the staircase with his stack of postal packets, when Mr White pushed open the swing-door at the top.

'Ah, and Mister Bruce, you won't forget, will you, to bring along your School Sisstificate tomorrow mornin'?'

The Post Office, when he found it, was streets away. At a ten to six, Morridges' latest employee was still standing in line at the counter.

The following morning, he waited until ten-fifteen before telephoning Morridge and Sons, to tell them that he'd decided, now that he had given the work a trial, *not* to accept the position.

Mr White was scandalized.

'Now jest you get it into your head, Mister Bruce, that *I* am the one what puts the persons under *me* on probation, not vicy-versy! I shall report this matter to the company secretary forthwith. *And* to the agency. O, it'll be interestin' to hear what *they* 'ave to say, won't it? O yers, I fought there was somefink fishy about you, I did—'

Mister Bruce gently hung up the receiver while Mr White was still spluttering.

And you can put that where you put your Exmass bonus.

He found more pennies and dialled the number in St Katharine's advertisement. They asked him to come for a Mantoux test and x-ray that same afternoon.

*

When the employment agency's invoice arrived, he returned it with a brief note of explanation. He ignored a second letter. At the end of a fortnight, a third letter came by registered post.

During his lunch-break at St Katharine's, he dialled the agency's number.

'So you're this Druce person, are you?' said the voice at the other end of the line, 'Yes, I've been wondering when I was going hear a squeak from you. I have your file on the table right in front of me, as it happens. Now then. Three times have I written to you, while all I have received from your end is an impudent note.'

'Well — '

'Your behaviour has been beyond belief, d'you realise that? I may say I was treated to a lengthy telephone call from Morridge and Sons. From a Mr White. He was thoroughly dissatisfied. How dare you simply walk out of the place? Well?'

Dissatisfied? Mr White? He was probably thrilled right down to his moth-eaten moustache. What a story to run to teacher with, all his suspicions proved!

'Yes, and I may say I'm now looking at the answer you had the bloody effrontery to write after receiving my invoice: you have changed your mind, you don't want the position after all. What the hell is that supposed to mean?'

'It means that I'm no longer seeking an office job. I have a scholarship to university.'

Well, the man's entitled to an explanation, I suppose. And there's no need to tell him that I had the scholarship all along.

'Oh, yes? I wonder if that's true. Well, that's your affair. But it's *my* business that you are in debt to this agency to the tune of twenty-six pounds. For which I require payment forthwith. In full.'

'Twenty-six pounds.'

'Twenty-six pounds. By Friday next, at the latest.'

Greed. Greed. He would have sent the agency a day's pay without demur to cover the minuscule amount of trouble they had taken. But ten percent of a hypothetical year's salary?

'I was never employed by Morridges,' he said. 'The position in no way matched the description you gave me of it. I received no pay, and no insurance contributions were paid on my behalf. Therefore the hour or two I spent there, and standing in line at the Post Office after hours, you may take as a free gift. From me to Morridges' Fruit and Veg. I was not paid, and therefore not *employed*. Do you see?'

'How dare you take this tone with me, you—' The man was enraged.

'Unless you hand over twenty-six pounds by the end of the week, I'll take you for every penny you've got. You've got no leg to stand on in a court of law.'

It was time to call the man's bluff with a counterbluff: truthful, if equivocal.

'I think you'll discover that the law says otherwise. What subject, may I ask, do you imagine I shall be reading at University?' *Let him think that out.* 'But keep your hair on. You shall have your ten per cent of my first year's salary. Which, since I was never employed, is nil. I'll write you a cheque for that amount, shall I?'

There was a hiss of indrawn breath and a moment's silence at the other end of the line.

'All right. Now, listen, you. I've had my last dealings with you. Your type are not worth bothering with. And I never want to see your bloody face in this office again.'

The telephone in Chancery Lane went down with a crash.

*

And the typists, and the seven clerks around the table in Old Compton Street: had any of them walked into the same trap? Were they still contributing their pounds of flesh to an agency? And the tens of thousands of city office-workers, strap-hanging through the morning and evening rush-hours: how many of *them* had been pushed into working 'voluntary' overtime? Half an hour a day, when you added it up, was three full weeks of work without pay in a year. Would a notional Christmas bonus match *that*?

As he stepped onto the train that took him to early shift at St Katharine's, and settled into a seat, he watched the office workers on the opposite platform scrambling into their city-bound carriages.

His own twenty-five-minute journey carried him into the countryside; *they* travelled into the daily grime of London. *He* wore what he liked: a tweed jacket, old flannels, a sweater. *Their* positions depended on their keeping up appearances, on wearing a suit and putting on a clean blouse or shirt and collar each morning. They gulped down cheap food in their lunch-break, and travelled for an hour or more night and morning in sardine-packed trains. He pitied them and found himself raging on their behalf.

Even on behalf of a petty jack-in-office like Morridges' Mr White: with the ineffectual moustache that attempted to assert his masculine authority, and the gnawed fingernails that betrayed his lack of it. Assiduous boss's man that Mr White was, who could tell what private insecurity — what family distress, perhaps? — lay behind his toadying to his employers?

*

The Tuberculosis Ward at St Katharine's, in the winter of 1949 and the following spring, was a place of other purposes, of long-term nursing and brisk compassion. Above all, at that point in the twentieth century, it was a place of growing hope.

Not for all. During his brief time there, there was a man among them whose sheets were soaked with his nightly sweats and whose eyes glittered in his skull, for whom there could be no hope. He had TB-peritonitis. He was a 'sick man': hospital jargon for the dying.

'Give me a hand to change the sick man,' Sister Hanson told Druce at mid-morning the day after Boxing Day. So he squeezed out a second tuft of cotton-wool in Lysol and tucked it into the corner of his mask, and went to help her. He slid the sweat-dank bed-sheet, hand's-breadth by hand's-breadth across the rubber under-sheet, while she unfolded clean linen into its place. Mr Manning's flesh was bruised with bedsores like patches of rot in a windfall apple. He whimpered as they rolled him sideways to ease the soiled sheets from under him.

At last the misery was over and Sister Hanson bustled away.

'Here, take a look at my locker before you go,' Mr Manning told him. 'See that new razor? My Christmas present from my little boy, that is. He saved up his pennies. I'd think he was trying to be funny, if he was any older. But I s'pose he doesn't realise I'll never shave myself again.'

The sick man's eyes brimmed with tears.

But for the fifty or more other patients, streptomycin injections and sodium aminosalicylate were bringing a cure within reach. At times Druce exulted in that dawn of hope to be alive, to be close at hand to an evolving miracle. Isoniazid, the third ingredient in the magic cocktail, was not yet in use — not at St Katharine's, at any rate. But soon, when it was, tuberculosis wards and hospitals all over the country would close their doors, and be fumigated and put to another use. Twenty years later, he visited a sick friend in St Katharine's, and found the TB wards transformed into a maternity block.

In the winter of 1949 for the nursing staff, who couldn't snuggle under piled-up blankets with a hotwater bottle, the TB block was a chilly place of open windows and airy wards. All day long the inter-connecting curve of chalets stood open to the sky, unless there was driving rain or snow. Giving a bed-bath demanded sleight-of-hand skill, as you laid bare an inch or two of a patient's flesh, swabbed it, scrubbed it dry with a towel, and covered it again in the space of seconds.

Every few hours there were rubber hotwater bottles to refill from the perpetually steaming kettles. They had to be filled with a funnel and Sister Hanson slammed in and out to ensure that her rules were followed to the letter. The bottle was to be emptied, plugged with a funnel and laid flat on the table, then slowly raised by the business end as the boiling water plumped it out, and lowered again until all the air had escaped. Finally the stopper was screwed in; firmly, mind! and with care to see that it wasn't cross-threaded. *That* way the boiling water couldn't belch out and scald you. Sister Hanson went through the rigmarole four or five times a day.

Between times you spun hot water around a metal bedpan to take the chill off it, carried it to the patient in a folded cloth and helped him onto it. More often than not, you had to prop him up there, wobbling from buttock to buttock. Manoeuvring Daddy Bass's wasted thighs on and off the bedpan was a twice-daily trial of force of character and bodily strength for Druce the orderly.

Daniel Bass was a huge raw-boned ruin of a man. He was eighty-four years old, a former farm-labourer. His day was ruled by the rituals that he enforced on everyone around him. He refused to put his false teeth in until his cup and plates had been positioned, just so, on his bed-tray, and a heap of salt poured out. 'On me alminack! Salt! On me alminack! Goo on, boy,' he snarled when Druce first carried him his dinner.

'He wants you to get his book off of his locker, and pour out his salt on it,' said the patient in the next bed.

Old Moore's Almanack. A stained copy lay on Mr Bass's bedside locker.

'You want me to pour it out on *this?*'

'Yis, yis. Goo *on!* On me alminack!'

Between mouthfuls, Daddy Bass sprinkled huge pinches of salt over whatever was on his plate. When he'd finished, he sucked his false teeth clean, and stood them on his locker.

He had been allotted a stone hotwater-bottle ever since his beaky toenails had burst the second rubber bottle in the space of a week. Positioning it at the foot of his bed was precision work. He'd wait until you were half-way to the door before raising his voice.

'Come back 'ere, that in't no good! Can't get no warmth out of the bloody thing. Me toes are freezin' fit to drop orf.'

So you opened the bedclothes at the foot of the bed and tried again.

'Get back 'ere, you! Thass worse! Here, tryin' to scald my bloody feet now, thass what *he's* after.'

At visiting time most evenings, Daddy Bass's sixty-four-year-old son hobbled down the ward to sit by his father's bed. He cringed and ducked his head while the old man shouted at him.

Robert Druce age 18

26

WAKEFIELD-AINSWORTH LIMITED

At Joslin Road Youth Centre one evening in early April, Don Brown said, 'Here, Bob. If you're free this weekend, what about going down to Pargetting? I had some fun there a couple of years back. We could be there by bike in two or three hours, eh?'

They went that Sunday, pedalling mile after mile through Essex lanes. It was a landscape that would imprint itself on his brain in the months to come, as he gasped up hills and flew swerving down under overhanging trees in sun and rain and starlight.

Pargetting Vicarage was empty of guests that weekend, but Mrs Somerville was there, sorting through papers in her sitting-room. She welcomed them at the door and invited them to stay to tea.

At tea-time Nadia, the black-haired, blue-eyed, elder daughter of Leo Brant, came over from Malmesey Green. She was fifteen years old to Robert's twenty. The sun danced in the sky, and all his worlds imploded.

While Ron and Mrs Somerville chatted and washed up the tea-things, he loitered with Nadia in the garden. They paced the gravel paths side by side, drifting in a maze of talk for almost an hour — although it seemed as evanescent as a fistful of seconds and as long as a lifetime when again and again he recalled it later. Then Ron came out and wheeled his bike to the gate and rang his bell and called, 'If we're going to get back home before dark…'

Robert swallowed and took a deep breath and said, 'Will you write to me?' And, 'Yes,' she answered. 'I'd like to. Yes.'

Before long they were exchanging weekly letters. Fat packets of ten sheets of paper at a time crammed front and back with her driving, left-handed calligraphy, or his loops that convoluted across the paper like bunches of squashed wire. He carried her most recent letter around with him, reading and re-reading it and elaborating answers in his head until the next arrived, and it was time to add the present text to the gathering pile in a drawer.

By the end of May he'd biked three times to Leo Brant's music school at Malmesey Green for the sake of an hour or two in Nadia's company.

But, working at St Katharine's, he could not make plans for more than a day or two ahead, because Sister Hanson always waited till the last moment to inform you when your next free day would be. In early June he left his job at St Katharine's, and started to work from eight to five as a site-and wages-clerk for the firm that was extending the gasworks at Woodlands Green. There at least he could be sure of having every Saturday afternoon and Sunday off.

*

The office of The Wakefield-Ainsworth Coal and Coking Oven and Retort Construction Company Limited was a one-roomed wooden hut. It smelt of shag-tobacco smoke, wet duffel-coats, sweat, tar from the cresol tank, and bad-egg sulphur fumes from the pile of spent oxide dumped a few yards from the window. Gas wheezed and bubbled in the radiator pipes, and a gritty dust drifted down over the litter of invoices and report-sheets.

As site-clerk, it was his job to write letters. To make up the time-sheets and wage-packets. To check truck-loads of steel and pipework and firebrick against the invoices as they were shunted into the gasworks siding. To parcel up samples of cement and send them away for testing. To calculate the building work completed week by week, and report it to head office. Everything in longhand, white-knuckled, scoring the letters deep enough to carry through five carbon copies.

'A typewriter, son? Where have you been living — Buckingham Palace?'

When Mr Holden, the site-manager, put his name to a wage-sheet or a letter, he used to brush the grit away, and lick the paper, and sign the wet patch with a stump of indelible pencil.

'Useful they are, indelible pencils,' Sid, the steel-erector foreman, told the new clerk one afternoon. 'Once you wet 'em, they stain the paper, see. So's they can't be rubbed out. Indelible...

'Listen, whenever I'm away on a contract, staying in digs for a month or two, my old woman signs 'er name with a dry indelible pencil across the flap after she's stuck down her letter every week. It's got to be dry, see? Then it don't look no different from blacklead.'

'What's the point of that?'

'Use your loaf, son. It goes purple if it gets wetted, dunnit? So if yer landlady's the sort of old cow who steams open people's letters, you can tell what she's been up to from the purple stain, see?'

'But surely they wouldn't—'

'Where was you *born*, son? Always at it, they are, landladies. Specially once you've 'ad their drawers down a time or two…

'I remember this landlady in Preston. I 'ad 'em alternate, 'er *and* 'er daughter. Course, I 'ad to keep it from the one what I was gettin' up to with the other, see? and vicy-versy…'

Whenever the talk was about sex, Sid would push out the tip of his tongue in a wet pink blob, and waggle it from side to side. He was a bow-legged, leathery midget of a man, an 'iron-fighter', getting on for sixty, and proud of his head for heights. His party trick was to shuffle out in space to the centre of a horizontal girder. He paused to check that people were watching. Then he rolled and licked and lit a cigarette.

Back again in the office, ostensibly to consult the plans, it was never long before Sid was journeying among his endless sexual reminiscences. The same was true of the other foremen and deputy foremen who crowded into the office three times a day, to roll up their fags and swallow a pint of tea. Only Jack Holden, fearful of undermining his authority as site manager by permitting too much familiarity, and Tom McCabe, a church-going Ulsterman, both decent men, ever told anyone to give the subject a rest.

Bob swallowed his tea, keeping his own counsel, while his thoughts went boomeranging back to Nadia. None of this talk had anything to do with her or the love that flooded through his flesh at the thought of her.

*

Work as a site-clerk was a daily challenge, a juggling with fact and fiction, complex enough to be pleasurable.

Week by week he reported on the progress of the contract: so many cubic yards excavated, so many cubic yards of concrete poured. So many tons of material unloaded, and checked against the time-sheets and the waybills. So many girders, so much chequer-plate and pipework bolted into place. So many yards of flettons or firebrick laid. And regardless of the thickness of any brickwork, everything had to be calculated in terms of 'superficial' yards of a notional wall nine inches thick.

These were supposed realities.

So, and in fact, were the times of a man's clocking on and off, and the rates of pay, different in every detail from union to union: steel erectors, pipe-setters, carpenters, brickies, day-labourers, and — cocks of the walk — retort-setters. So, too, were all the extra pennies or twopences an hour. 'Dirt-money'. 'Height-money'. 'Heat-money' for those who laboured close to a working furnace. 'Silica-money' for those who handled silica firebricks. All of that, along with tax-deductions, had to be balanced page by page on the wage-sheets, and translated into the bank-notes and the scatter of coins that Jack Holden handed out on Friday afternoons in the wage-packets.

Each packet was patterned with punched holes. That was so that a man could check what he was getting before he tore open the flap. The flap was fastened down with rubber-glue, so that no one could abstract a note or two and claim that a mistake had been made. Mr Holden explained it all on Bob's first day.

On Saturday morning, the weekly report had to be posted off to head office, along with an outline plan on which the week's construction work was coloured red, and the cumulated work of previous weeks in blue. Both had to dovetail with the time- and wage-sheets and the schedule of target costs. At this point reality faded into guesswork. And the pious hope that head office wouldn't spot the discrepancies.

The fly in the ointment was that no site-clerk had been taken on during the first three months of the job, while Jack Holden had struggled on as best as he could. It was his first time in charge of a contract: his reward for years as a skilled retort-setter, and he'd made a pig's breakfast of the paper-work. By June, he'd written off hundreds of man-hours to 'excavation' and 'unloading', far more than the target costs allowed. A quarter of the foundations still remained to be dug, and truckloads of bricks and metalwork were still arriving every week. On the other hand, a quarter of the building work completed had never been declared.

So Wakefield-Ainsworth's new site-clerk made trial runs backwards and forwards from the target costs and juggled them until they might seem plausible enough to match the hard facts of time- and wage-sheets and the brickwork and steel that was there for everyone to see. Each week he edged Jack Holden's signed report closer to reality, but for months it was a travesty of the truth. Later that year, when he read Orwell's *Nineteen Eighty-Four* for the first time, Winston Smith's task of adjusting forecasts to fit the facts was all too familiar.

So, given his parents' unashamed scrutiny of whatever he did, were the activities of the Thought Police, and their unending surveillance.

Or so it seemed.

*

At eight-thirty one Saturday morning in early August, the gasworks manager pushed open the site-hut door. 'Just had a queer sort of phone-call from your boss,' he said. 'Mr Holden. Asking was the chimney still up. What was *that* supposed to mean? Any idea?'

'Yes.'

'He said to let you know he won't be coming in for a couple of days. He's not feeling too well.'

But it was a month before Jack was back, and between whiles Wakefield-Ainsworth's area manager dropped in from time to time to sign the letters and keep an eye on the work on site.

'All your fault, that was. D'you realise that?' said Jack Holden as he hung his hat on the peg on a Monday morning in September. 'Yes, it's you I've got to thank for that little packet. You blowing a kiss to the chimney that Friday. Remember that, do you?'

O, yes. He remembered that Friday. Sid and his iron-fighters had been getting ready to erect a twin to the gasworks chimney. Before that could be done, an additional concrete foundation would have to be poured, and the existing chimney-stack had been undercut and propped in readiness. It was sixty feet high, steel-clad with a firebrick lining. It was hot and still in use, and now a fraction of its weight hung over the excavation. Propping it was a risky business, and the danger period wouldn't be past until Tuesday or Wednesday the following week. And if the wind should get up overnight…

Bob sat opposite Jack on the Central Line train that Friday evening. As it drew out of Woodlands Green station and clattered across the points by the gasworks sidings, Jack turned in his seat to peer across at the retort house, and the looming chimney-stack.

'Well, goodbye chimney,' Bob said, and blew it a kiss. 'Let's hope you're still there in the morning.'

The remark played on Jack Holden's nerves. He had nearly got out at Stratford, he told Bob later, to catch a tube back to Woodlands Green, futile as that gesture would have been. That night, suddenly waking out of sleep to his accountability as site-manager, Jack had lain and listened to the blood pounding in his head. For the rest of the night, he tossed and turned in panic as the chimney toppled in his nightmares.

Mrs Holden called the doctor at first light. He took her husband's blood-pressure, gave him a sedative, and told him to stay in bed, if he didn't want a heart attack.

*

Bob was appalled by Jack's tale. Not just by the effect of his frivolous remark, but also by the enormity of responsibility which rested on a site-manager's shoulders. Even on so minor a contract as that at Woodlands Green. Any hankering he might have had for a career with The Wakefield-Ainsworth Coal and Coking Oven and Retort Construction Company Limited evaporated there and then.

Not that he'd ever considered it seriously. But for a month or so he'd been poring over the blueprints and technical manuals locked away in the site-hut safe. He read idly at first, but soon with a growing interest in the mysteries of coal carbonisation and its chemistry. While Jack Holden was away with his heart trouble, Mr Dobell, the area-manager, stood Bob half a pint of bitter one Friday lunchtime before they collected the wages from the bank, and offered him promotion to another contract once the work at Woodlands Green was wound up. The pay, with a tax-free lodging allowance on top, was alluring. The three years he faced of living on a grant while he read for a degree in French would not entitle him to a third of that amount.

'And consider the opportunities for travel,' said Mr Dobell, the tempter. 'Not just in the UK. Overseas. There's a contract in Brazil that's still got three years to run. A couple more in the Far East. You could be there...

'Look, I've kept my eye on you here, running the office. That's the way the firm takes on its permanent staff: you hire a brickie, say, on a day-wage. Then after a bit you realise that you've got a first-class craftsman on your hands. So you put his name forward. The firm takes him on and trains him up as a retort-setter. A skilled man's pay, and a job for life. The chance of coming off the tools in the fullness of time and managing a contract of his own. Like Jack Holden.

'When this contract's wound up, you come to me at Chelmsford, and I'll put you on the right track. You could qualify as A.M.I.Chem.E. — Associate Member of the Institute of Chemical Engineers — easy as kissing your hand, if you want my opinion. Go right to the top. Eh?'

'Well...'

'Think it over. No rush. Now, could you shift another half-pint?'

It was tempting.

Out from under his parents' gaze, cash in his pockets, the challenge of a bigger site. The flattering knowledge of a job offered out of the blue, to *him*. He watched images stream through his head all afternoon.

But all those pettifogging regulations a contract manager had to pick his way through: were they worth facing?

When lightning struck the naked girders the previous week, every main fuse in the gasworks blew: lights, elevators, control systems, everything. The works electrician replaced them. There followed an afternoon of telephone calls from infuriated union officials to the gasworks manager. Didn't he realise that his electrician had no business to touch the fuses? A senior man should have been called in from twenty miles away to restore the power. Union rules of procedure had been infringed.

The talk of disciplinary action rumbled on for days.

And the endless living out of a suitcase, rootless, no home of his own? A future of randy landladies, and letters signed 'Nadia' in indelible pencil across the flap? Days, weeks, months cut off from that kingdom that she was already fast becoming.

The flattering images streamed away into emptiness.

That night he went back to reading François Villon...

Hé! Dieu, se j'eusse estudié
Ou temps de ma jeunesse folle

Et à bonnes meurs dedié
J'eusse maison et couche molle…

'O God, if only I had studied in the days of my heedless youth, and lived a decent life. I'd have had a house and a soft bed…'

When Mr Dobell arrived the following week, he avoided his eye.

*

The seaside arcades of the 1930s had been lined with cast-iron Edwardian machines. What-the-Butler-Saw machines, that flipped through a pack of yellowing photo-cards as the viewer turned the handle and the butler's Lady stripped to her corsets and a bare bottom. Machines that invited you to emboss your name on a strip of aluminium. Try-your-strength machines, where the player squeezed a pair of brass hand-grips and matched the strength of his grasp against an electric current. Now, after almost a decade, the barbed-wire and the mines had at last been cleared away from the beaches. The arcades were open for business again, and the rows of machines had been refurbished and given a splash of paint.

When Robert dropped his penny into a try-your-strength machine, he felt nothing but a fine effervescence against his fingertips. He tightened his grip and the current intensified. The fizz became a shudder, and the shudder a convulsion of the muscles of his arm, as he tried to force the needle across the dial.

And now here he was sitting on a grassy bank alongside Nadia, gazing out across the shimmering estuary. It was a Sunday afternoon in mid-August.

Four times he counted up to ten, and swallowed hard, and panicked and started back at nought. 'Come on, Robert, be bloody, bold and resolute,' he told himself. At last he put his arm around her. His hand brushed across her dress and onto the bare flesh of her shoulder, warm in the sunshine. The instant his fingertips touched her skin, he felt that test-your-strength electric effervescence.

Nadia trembled under his touch, but did not draw away.

He caught his breath, and the blood began to pound in his head.

Her dark hair was brushing his cheek, and his fingers had not stopped tingling. The air seemed to curdle around them, thick with pollen and

323

sunshine. They both began to babble, both staring straight ahead across the dazzling water. Talking of God knows what, anything, nothing, that would break the weight of the silence.

In his throat and his numbed lips, words trapped themselves, as if he were drunk. Each time Nadia began to speak, her teeth were chattering.

Dans mon coeur fait outrage... Making havoc in his heart, and hers. *O, my America, my new-found land...*

When it was time for them to walk back to the village, she held his hand until they came in sight of house windows and prying eyes. Around them, the hedgerows were a bright haze of birdsong. The bell of Pargetting church ringing the hour was the chiming of the spheres as they slid in their crystal courses. He found himself treading as he sometimes trod in dreams, on a floor of bubbles.

They both stayed on to tea, at Mrs Somerville's invitation, and then to supper. After supper, they loitered inside the gate in the lengthening shadows.

'Well...', he said.

He took her in his arms and kissed her, and they trembled, clinging together.

Once clear of Pargetting village, he bicycled the homeward thirty miles and more, shouting songs into the gathering dark, saving his breath only when he had to stand up on the pedals to climb a hill. Oblivious to the racing landscape, he missed a turning and found himself lost in a tangle of lanes.

The twilight was fading. He couldn't read what it said on the signpost; and when he managed to spin the back-wheel dynamo he couldn't keep it going and shine the front lamp upwards at the same time. He shinned up the post and clung there, deciphering the cast-iron letters by feel. BILLERICAY. Brimming over with love and singing again, he found his way there helped by the sky-glow of the railway sidings.

On the outskirts of the town a policeman waved him down with a flashlamp.

'You didn't come through Crays Hill — did you, sir? — a while back?'

'Crays Hill? Yes. Probably.'

'Singing, were you?'

'I suppose so. Yes.'

'Ah. The village bobby there phoned through. Reporting it. A drunk on a bicycle, he said. Weaving all over the road. You *haven't* been drinking, have you, sir?' The policeman stepped closer, laying a hand on the handlebars, and sniffing in his direction.

'No. No.'

'More caterwauling-like than singing, that's what he said.'

'I was singing because I'm happy.' He could have embraced the entire world in his joy.

'Ah,' said the policeman. 'All right for some. Well, just cut it out when you get to a residential area, there's a good lad. There are people trying to get a night's sleep.'

Driven into the mazes of his own illogic by Nadia once, Robert, me, I, oppressed by the weight of scholars who haunted her father's house, made a bid to assert his own intellect. Nothing less than chapter and verse would do. 'Our sixth-form master was working for a PhD in Psychology. He tested our IQs. So I know what mine is.'

Why insist? She loved him, didn't she, lying in his arms?

But today, time swoops backwards two thirds of a lifetime, and launched on self-aggrandizement, he does not know how to stop.

Music wells out of the music-room windows in a flood of honey and mathematics and sunshine and lacy intricacies of fingering. He leans against the door to the walled garden, his hand on her arm, inhaling her breath, searching and failing to recall the score vouchsafed to him by the master whose favoured pupil he was. All he remembers is that 100 is an average, with a swooping curve falling away on either side.

He longs to make Nadia proud of him before her family, thirsting for her eyes' continuing caress.

So he conjures from out of the throbbing air a figure plausible and impressive.

It was not.

Even as he uttered it, he saw her face and knew that it was not. Dreading to betray himself in an overweening lie, he had plucked too low a score by far. He trembled, shame searing his flesh. When he checked with Walter Mason and learned the truth, the knowledge came too late. Uttering the lie had made it irrevocable.

Nadia's eyes gleamed. O, but she still loved him. There was no doubt of that, was there?

But now that pathetic and unnecessary lie divided them, delving the first spadeful out of the grave of their immature and over-ripe passion.

Nadia.

Nadia, dear heart, *how like you this?*

27

UNIVERSITY COLLEGE

It wasn't long before he was biking back and forth to Pargetting every other weekend. There was usually a chance of a bed at the Old Vicarage, where Major Somerville seemed to have taken a shine to him. Failing that he put up for the night at the Three Colts, or with a widow who did bed-and-breakfasts in the village. All the while and week after week, the letters that Nadia and he exchanged grew longer.

He went to London for an interview at University College, and was offered a place there for October. He began to carry French texts around with him in his pockets, reading them on the train and at idle moments in Wakefield-Ainsworth's site-office. In the moments that he was alone he sat writing letters to Nadia in his lunch-hour, quoting Ronsard and Verlaine alongside Eliot and John Donne.

'Cunt-struck. That's what you are,' said Sid the iron-fighter one afternoon, catching him unawares, not quick enough to smuggle his letter under a pile of invoices. 'I've seen it coming.'

Sid broke off to lick the cigarette he was making. He wetted the end, rolling it between his lips, and flicked his lighter.

'Just don't let yourself go like that bloody draughtsman at head office. So busy daydreaming, he makes a bollocks of the pipework drawings, and then buggers off on his honeymoon. Three days now I've been at it cutting and welding so the pipes won't foul the charging car. Cunt-struck. Daft as a brush. You'd better get on to Mr Dobell for another two six-foot runs of steam pipe.'

He couldn't wait for Sid to finish his roll-up and get out of the site-hut, so that he could go on with his letter to Nadia, and rinse his mind with poetry.

Sid hurried up to him at Saturday lunchtime, as Bob was wheeling his bike past the coke-tip. 'Here,' he said. 'Have this one on me.' He tucked what looked like a fat aspirin into Bob's top pocket.

'What?'

'Rendells,' said Sid, and waggled the pink blob of his tongue. 'Better than all your french letters, Rendells are. Just pop it inside, give it half a minute to foam, and Bob's your uncle. Safe as houses, that is, and no rubber to burst and let you down.'

'But it's not *like* that. We don't — ' He was appalled at the assault on his vision of Nadia. Filth, filth! He *loved* her.

Sid cackled in his face. 'Don't you? Well, it won't be long afore the pair of you *do*, if you ask me.' Sid waggled his tongue again. 'Judging by the way you've been mooning around. So save it up and use it when you *do*. And don't fergit to let me know how you get on.'

Sid turned on his heel, and went back towards the hut, still cackling.

Bob prised the contraceptive pill out of his top pocket. As he pedalled out of the main gate of the gasworks, he flicked it into the gutter.

*

The Woodlands Green contract was due for completion in December. Half way through September, Bob told Jack Holden that he'd be leaving at the end of the month. The University term began on October 3rd.

'Well, *I* don't know,' said Jack, turning to look him in the eye. 'You announce this right out of the blue. Listen, are you *sure* it's what you want to do with your life? There's a career for you with Wakefield-Ainsworth for the asking. And a damned good one, at that.'

It was hard to explain things. Hard to break away from Jack's fatherly concern. Hard to convince him that Bob's next three or four years would be an investment for the future.

But how was he going to manage for money? A *scholarship*? How much was *that* worth? Where would he live? At *home*? Good God, boy! Wasn't it time he broke free of his mother's apron-strings?

The site-manager watched him with narrowed eyes as he answered.

Then what about this girl of his, Nadia? He seemed to think of little else nowadays. Would *she* wait?

'She'll be taking her own entrance exams for University within a year or two,' he said. 'We couldn't even think about getting married for years yet.'

'I hope for *your* sake you know what you're doing,' said Jack. 'I must say I'd been counting on your help with all the paperwork, now the contract's winding up.' He sighed.

'I've still another fortnight yet. I'll do everything I can.'

'Humph… Well, come on then, lad! Buck your ideas up, I can't sit here gabbing with you all the day long. Get over to the gasworks office and see if they've got any news of the operator.'

*

The operator was the man who would set the seal on the contract. His skill alone would bring the six new retorts up to working heat from their present damp and untempered state. At first there'd be no more than a few handfuls of straw and a tiny bundle of kindling flickering alight in each firebrick kiln. Then more kindling, and more, and then a bare shovelful of coke. Day by day and night by night he would add to the flames and the surging heat.

He was condemned to live on the job, dossing down on a camp bed, checking the thermometers hour by hour, opening and closing dampers, ensuring that the jigsaw of brickwork expanded evenly and the layers of mortar — acid in some areas of the retort and alkaline elsewhere — slowly welded into the acid silica and neutral magnesite bricks that made up its lining. At the end of a week, the flues would be warm to the touch. Inch-thick softwood battens had been interposed between the old hot retorts and the new to cushion the expansion. By the end of a fortnight they would have been crushed into a charred line no thicker than a pencil lead.

It was an anxious time, the final test of months of intricate construction work. If all went well and nothing cracked, the extension would be officially handed over. The new retorts and producer-gas ovens would come on stream along with the second chimney. The operator and Jack Holden would be free to sleep soundly in their beds once more. But if anything went wrong, Wakefield-Ainsworth would be compelled to pay a heavy penalty in cash for every day the agreed completion date of the contract was overrun.

It seemed that it wasn't Bob's not being there to help with the paperwork

329

that Jack Holden resented and was hurt by, but the loss of his comradeship at the most trying time of all.

*

At the end of dinner-break the day before Bob was due to quit, a deputation tapped on the door of the site-hut. It was led by Jim Allen, a brickie whose name Jack Holden had forwarded to head office as a worthwhile recruit to the permanent staff, and Bill, foreman of the gang of labourers.

'What's this, then? Trouble?' said Mr Holden, slamming down his mug of tea.

'We had a whip-round,' said Jim, staring down at his feet and addressing himself to Bob. 'Just wanted you to know we appreciate what you did while you were here.' He held out a narrow parcel.

Bob unwrapped it. A fountain-pen.

'We heard you'll be doing a lot of writing now,' said Jim, his face crimson under Jack Holden's gaze.

'You can change it, if the nib ain't right,' said Bill, staring boldly around the hut. 'An' there was some money left over, after the pen. So we thought this might come in handy.'

A purse. Made of two leather trays, hinged and folding together.

'If you want to talk, do it outside,' said Mr Holden. 'I can't have the office cluttered up with people. And make it quick. The whistle will be going in a minute.'

Bob's heart was suddenly full. He gripped Jim's and Bill's hands in turn and led them outside, blurting his thanks. A cheer went up fifty yards away. The rest of the site-workers were grinning and waving.

*

'What's been going on?' said Mr Holden, when Bob stepped back inside the hut. 'That's the first time in all my experience I've ever known a site-clerk given a present. More likely to get sworn at, if he does his job the way it should be done. I want an explanation.'

'Bill and the concrete-breaker,' said Bob. 'That time he broke through into the foul main... He's mentioned that once or twice.'

330

The incident had occurred months earlier, soon after Bob arrived on the site. Bill had been drilling through concrete with a pneumatic concrete-breaker. The drill point broke through the cast-iron wall of a disused foul main, still half-full of gas-tar and dissolved ammonia, and the air-blast from the drill spurted the fluid up into Bill's face. Bob sent for a taxi, and spent the fifteen minutes before it arrived, mopping the caustic film from Bill's eyes with wadding soaked in Optrex, before dispatching Bill to St Katharine's casualty unit, eight miles away. Bill returned by bus, saying the swabbing with Optrex had saved his eyesight.

'All right,' said the site-manager. 'I grant you that. But it doesn't explain Jim Allen. What's *he* got to be beholden to you for?'

'Ah,' said Bob. 'That's a long story. It was while you were off sick. Jim's wife was expecting, remember? The day after the baby was born the doctors told Jim she'd been born without a lower bowel and there was nothing they could do. Jim's wife was mad with grief and Jim had to take time off just to sit with her.'

'And then there was the baby's funeral to pay for…'

'So I booked Jim down on the time-sheets for two full weeks. With overtime on top.'

'You *what*?' Jack stretched his eyes. 'And he grabbed the money, I suppose? Thought he'd got a windfall.'

'No. He brought his wage-packet back saying there had been some mistake. I told him no there hadn't, and sent him off again. Said I'd square it with you.'

'So you play ducks and drakes with the firm's money, and calmly expect me to back you up?' Jack Holden was enraged.

'I couldn't cut a man's wages at a time like that.'

'You falsified the time-sheets.'

'Wakefield-Ainsworth have got contracts all over the world. They make millions. They can spare a pound or two. Anyway, aren't they taking Jim on as a retort-setter? What do they want, a disaffected or a willing worker? Wakefield-Ainsworth won't lose by it. Sometimes a fair crack of the whip, and a fair share, ought to mean giving someone more than they're strictly entitled to, it seems to me.'

'Now, *you* listen to *me*. If he was in trouble, I'd have given him a sub on his next week's wages. I could even have found a bob or two out of the petty cash, if he'd come to me.'

'What's the difference? And you weren't *here* to come to…'

'But it wasn't your place…'

'No. But the way Jim works, Wakefield-Ainsworth will get their money back, won't they?'

'That's not the point. Maybe it's just as well you *are* getting out.'

By the time Bob came to leave on the Saturday, Jack was his old self again.

'Well, good luck, Bob. And look after yourself,' he said. 'You're a bit too fond of an arguing the toss, and you take too much on yourself at times, but I'll miss you. I can't persuade you to stay, I suppose? Well, if you ever come this way, drop by, eh?'

*

Seventeen women and five men met at University College London in October to register for first-year Honours French. Robert Druce and Frank O'Connor gravitated towards one another. At the end of the morning they lunched together on their own and went off to pay their respects to Jeremy Bentham, Founder of the College, encoffined in his glass-fronted cabinet. They spent the remainder of the afternoon in talk, cementing their alliance, and establishing an amicable rivalry, a jostling friendship, that would last throughout their time at UCL and for decades after. They were twenty-one. They both had their military service behind them. The women in their group were bright-eyed and friendly, but Robert was wrapped up in Nadia and Frank in his Audrey, and paid them little attention. The three remaining males, not yet nineteen, they both found naive, tiresome in their boyish eagerness.

There was more between Frank and him than their shared age. They were the only children of working-class parents, inflexible Tory-voters who aspired to a superior life for their children. Like Dorothy Druce, Mrs O'Connor eyed her son's every move, while assuming the role of a sweetly-yielding martyr. She too had married the son of an Irish Catholic mother. Like Robert Kitchener Druce, her husband was an authoritarian who ran into constant jarring conflict with the wife and son he loved too possessively for his own peace of mind.

'So this is what we slave our fingers to the bone for? So you can come back here and argue the toss? We deny ourselves, we skimp and scrape so that you can go to University. And what's our reward? You've grown too big for your bloody boots...

'Listen to me! He who pays the piper calls the tune: get that into your skull. If you're not happy with the home we provide, if your mother and me aren't good enough for you, you know what you can do. Quick as you like.'

They were both familiar with that litany.

While Robert tried to turn his father's rage aside, Frank met the conflict head-on. Still in his first year at UCL, he married and broke off all contact with his father.

Robert was sauntering down Gower Street deep in talk with Frank one afternoon when for a moment they came face to face with a middle-aged man. He glared at them, and pushed past. For a second, Frank stumbled in his speech and the air seemed to thicken and shudder. As they turned into Torrington Place Frank said, 'Did you see him? That was my old man.'

The ingrained attitudes of his family imprisoned Frank. Not only in ways he never thought to question but also, like Robert, in paradoxical acts of defiance. Yet, married man as he already was, Frank was fearful of looking even a male pharmacist in the eye, however fleetingly, and asked Robert to buy contraceptives for him.

Frank carried the war against his father's Tory principles into his student life, and joined the Labour Society, along with the Rugby Club, and the Bridge Club. He stood for office in the Students' Union, and was elected Secretary. Within a month he had organized a strike against the price of refectory meals, and forced the outside caterers to lower them. Political moves, every one of them, he explained, calculated to stand him in good stead in his future career.

Robert found the bickerings of students' union politics repellent, but joined Frank in his other ventures. In the Druce household, bridge was anathema, a first step towards damnation, like every other card-game outside Happy Families and Lexicon. But encouraged by Frank, he started to play.

He joined Frank on the rugby field, where he could sprint down the wing, and rejoice in the muddy violence that ten years earlier had appalled him on the soccer pitch. He had no idea of strategy other than to let his aggression rip. Invariably bruised and limping for the remainder of the week after every Wednesday match, he found the violence a release.

Within a fortnight, he had blown a quarter of his first year's grant on rugby kit, a college scarf, and a University blazer with a gold-wire badge encrusted on the breast pocket. Four years later he stopped draping royal purple and wedgewood blue around his throat, and gave his scarf to the cat as a lining for her basket. But, freshman as he at present was — and as much to justify his parent's pride as his own — he took the regalia seriously enough and, properly partisan, he curled his lip at the London School of Economics scarf that had been wound around John Robbins' neck for the previous twelve months.

'John Robbins came in like a lamb to the fold,
In his LSE colours, black purple and gold,'

he wrote to Nadia one evening after a visit from John.

*

Suddenly it was Saturday, the twenty-first of October. He was twenty-one years old.

And here was his mother opening the front door to sixteen-year-old Nadia, who'd been sixteen on 16th August. Sixteen on the sixteenth. Twenty-one on the twenty-first. The mere arithmetic of their birth-months seemed significant and auspicious.

And here was his father, obviously smitten, greeting black-haired and blue-eyed Nadia and ushering her in. *When you are twenty one and at university–and NOT before–we will be pleased to welcome the woman of your choice into this house...* His father was keeping his promise to the minute. Robert Kitchener Druce certainly looked pleased enough.

Before long Mrs Druce was sitting everyone down to tea. Her husband had already started teaching Nadia ju-jitsu throws in the front-room — *No, Dorothy, this is important, don't interrupt. A young woman needs to know how to defend herself nowadays... Come on then, go for my throat... Come ON, harder than that! You're supposed to be an attacker...*

That Saturday and Sunday whirled past in an undifferentiated blaze of joy. Robert's exultation even undercut for a while the sense of hollowness and loss that flooded through him when he'd kissed Nadia on the step of the Green Line coach, and waved her goodbye.

He walked back home to fondle once again the *Collected Poems* of Louis MacNeice that she had given him.

'With best wishes from Nadia, 21.10.50.' There it is, on a shelf at the far side of the room.

Today it seems a cool inscription, certainly less than an acknowledgment of love. But Nadia was careful with words, he told himself at the time, and perhaps she was guarding her thoughts from the eyes of any stranger who might take up the book.

*

He began to write for 'Pi', the University College newspaper, named after Dr Pye, a former Provost. He became its drama critic for a time, reporting on Dramsoc productions with what he calculated was a judicious mixture of praise and precept. For a couple of terms he was 'Jeremy' of 'Jeremy's Diary', a gossip-column named in honour of Bentham. It was the closest he approached to student politics. Frank O'Connor's barbed inside knowledge was a help.

Most important of all, it seemed to him, he joined the French Society. Before a year was out, he was gesticulating before imaginary footlights, rehearsing the part of Dr Knock in Jules Romains' *Le Docteur Knock; Ou, Le triomphe de la Médicine*. Meanwhile he hung on every word in seminars and lectures. He soaked himself in the medieval texts, and rejoiced in the casual and scholarly flamboyance of Leonard Tancock's mass lectures on eighteenth-century literature. Moonlighting in the English department for the subsidiary part of his degree, he ground away at Anglo-Saxon, picking out fresh treasures to share with Nadia. Week after week he tingled with excitement as Winifred Nowottny explored the poetry of John Donne, unravelling it layer by layer, as if it were a ball of wool or an onion…

> Twice or thrice I had lov'd thee
> Before I knew thy face or name;

335

So in a voice, so in a shapeless flame,
Angels affect us oft, and worshipp'd be…

With her text restored and somehow metamorphosed into a magical clockwork, she set its logics sliding on their interlocking courses, bright images all chiming together.

Grist, every moment and fragment of it. Grist for the letters to Nadia that he composed in his head minute by minute.

*

His first end-of-term vacation found him delivering Christmas mail around the village, earning a fortnight's pay to stretch his scholarship grant.

Blundering through evening or before-dawn dark with a cycle-lamp hooked onto his coat. Setting down his mail-bag to untie the next bundle of letters in the careful sequence. Snatching his fingers out of the jaws of letter-boxes or, among the forest-side cottages, thrusting an unlocked door or window open and tossing the letters into the room.

On parcel-delivering days he took turns with a pair of fellow students to swing on a rope at the tailboard of a truck, as it chuntered forward fifty yards at a time with a heap of packages and parcels sliding back and forth along the floor. When the truck halted he helped to rummage through them and carry them one by one through garden gates and up front paths, hoping that he wouldn't have to wait while an apprehensive householder rattled bolts and burglar chains or wandered off to hunt for spectacles. If you hadn't climbed back onto the truck in time, the driver pulled away and you'd have to sprint a hundred yards or more. As soon as the truck was empty, the driver drove to the nearest caff and they all sat warming their hands round mugs of coffee and egg-and-bacon sandwiches, and taking leisurely drags on their cigarettes. Then it was back to the GPO for another load.

John Robbins was at it too that Christmas, elsewhere in the village. Until a truck moved off as he was about to clamber on, and he pitched forward and broke his wrist.

The Post Office, Mister Drrr-yoose. Give them a lesson on the Post Office.
As he trudged home after a restaurant lunch on Christmas Day, the

memory of Mr Pritchard and his own shambles of a first lesson suddenly returned to him.

Five years wiser, with cold cheeks and a blue nose, he wondered whether he could hold Standard Four spellbound now.

28

NADIA

1951. A year of rejoicing.

On May 3 King George VI would stand on the steps of St Pauls, to declare the Festival of Britain open. On July 9 the State of War between Britain and Germany would officially come to an end.

Festival Year. Good times were just around the corner. With luck, a new era was about to dawn.

Dust was still blowing across city bomb-sites. Food was still rationed. British citizens were still required by law to carry an Identity Card, although few ever did. But at last it seemed as if an end to post-war austerity might be within sight.

In February at University College London, repairs to the wartime damage had been put in hand. Beyond the windows of the lecture-rooms, gangs of labourers were shovelling earth, slopping trenches full of concrete, and whistling at women students. You couldn't straighten up from tying your shoe-lace, so ran the nine-day's-myth, without finding that a breeze-block wall had mushroomed up between you and the person you had been chatting with a moment earlier.

A number of students had been enlisted to sort through the chaos left by the wartime bomb that had burst through the library dome. Within a week, Bjorg Janssen, who otherwise spent most of his days at the bridge-tables in the bar, was displaying to his male acquaintances the handful of rotogravured full-page nudes which he'd filched. He preferred to call it 'liberated', in the jargon of the day. He had pulled out a stained and shattered volume of *Femmes du monde* from the rubble, and pocketed the sections devoted to 'Women of Arabia', whose pubic and underarm hair spread across their limbs in monstrous birds' nests; and 'Mulatto women', page after page of whose almost hairless flesh gleamed like oiled silk.

Prostitutes patrolled the London pavements, but the same obscenity laws were still in force that in July 1929 had led to the seizure of thirteen paintings by D.H. Lawrence, and their imprisonment in the cellar of Marlborough Street police-court, under threat of burning. Representing pubic hair in a graphic image remained an infraction of the law. With only the clean-scraped nudity of *Health and Efficiency* — the vade-mecum of the adolescent male — to compete on the bookstalls, the *trouvailles* of Bjorg Janssen and the delicately obscene commentary which accompanied them, seemed to Robert and his fellow-males desperately exotic, desperately *French*.

*

Less than a mile away from UCL and Gower Street, a half-derelict site on the South Bank of the Thames had been cleared, and foundations excavated. Now the Festival pavilions were springing up that would exhibit British achievement once again to the world, in a centennial reenactment of the Great Exhibition, that smugly exultant brainchild of Prince Albert.

Frank O'Connor and Robert Druce cut the last class of a March afternoon to gaze down from Waterloo bridge at what was happening. This time it would not be an exhibition alone, a bombastic display potentially offensive to Britain's wartime allies. *Festivity* and *Festival* were to be the keynotes of the season.

Sweetness and light. 'Let the people sing together and watch the fireworks soaring in the sky and the little lamps twinkling among the trees...'

Not 'exhibition halls' but 'pavilions'. Pennons and ribbands and pageantry. Freedom. Rejoicing. A new harnessing of the British spirit. A splash of paint and a skylon tower of girders. Bauhaus Englished. Functionalism. Abstract sculpture. Utility. Social awareness. Open-plan model housing. Atomic-age materials.

Expanded polystyrene, waterproof laminboard, spun aluminium. Walls of poured concrete, left with the wire-brushed grain of wooden shuttering to encrust their surfaces; inner walls of red brick, unplastered, asserting their brutal truths. Lower-case sans-serif lettering, huge unseamed sheets of plasticized hardboard, panels of lacquered steel.

Acres of vinyl floor-tiles, thickets of tubular steel legs. With formica (*say, 'for MY kitchen...'*) tops that made them into tables; or washable foam-padded seats and backs that made them into chairs. Lampshades of wipable polythene parchment or woven vinyl ribbon. Coat-racks confected from a zigzag of chromium-plated rods and rainbows of wooden balls.

And alongside and counterpointing the functionalism, there was a mocking dismissal of fussiness and appliqued decoration for decoration's sake. It was an attitude which so easily backtracked into nostalgia and a self-subverting celebration of Victorianism and Victoriana.

Like Roland Emmett's pastiche of a Victorian railway in Battersea Park, where, soon after its opening, a woman passenger would be killed and thirteen others injured in a head-on crash on the single-track line between 'Oyster Creek' and 'Far Tottering'. Like the Lion and Unicorn Pavilion which proposed to represent the British Character and British Humour, and housed, among other things, a collation of dottiness and impracticality, presided over by a larger than life-sized model of Lewis Carroll's White Knight. With a machine for grinding smoke, Coarse, Medium or Fine; a tea-service fashioned out of haddocks' bones; and plans for a rubber bus, which would deflate itself while passing under low bridges.

Throughout Britain, town and borough and parish councils were busy endorsing and indulging the festival spirit. Stone facades gleamed white once more, scrubbed free of soot, and stucco surfaces were tarted up with paint. Everywhere enthusiastic amateurs were recruiting themselves into choirs and orchestras and drama-groups, and planning festival performances.

By mid-February Leo Brant was deep in rehearsals for an Easter performance of Bach's *St. John Passion* in the village church at Malmsey Green. In Pargetting, Mrs Somerville had already set about canvassing the village for players in the midsummer pageant she had been writing. Nadia was to play a part in both. Robert, it was agreed, would go down to Pargetting and stay for the weekend — this time with the Brants — and join the tiny choir that would sing the Bach chorales.

*

Early on Good Friday Nadia met him at Pargetting, and together they biked the three miles to Malmsey Green. From the Somerville's late-Victorian vicarage, where the one-time servants' quarters were divided by plasterboard into dormitories for the youth-club members who arrived there week by week to let off steam — to the elegance of Bennets, Leo and Mary Brant's rambling eighteenth-century house at Malmsey Green. From pinned-up notices, plastic tablecloths and fire-buckets at every turn of the stair, to Adam-green walls, framed engravings and polished mahogany.

The contrasts between those houses, as month by month he experienced them more closely — between a forward-looking brashness, an appeal to mass opinion, an assertion of democratic right: and nostalgia, a submission to tradition, a sense of cultural guardianship — seemed to encapsulate the conflicting, and in the long run irreconcilable, attitudes of Festival year.

Bennets lay alongside the village green, behind high, arrow-headed railings which miraculously had survived the wartime drives for scrap-iron. Through an archway at the side of the house lay a cobble-stoned courtyard and a stable block, now divided into cell-like rooms for the musicians who came to stay.

Nadia and Robert parked their bikes against the wall of the stable-block, and Nadia led him along a gravelled path to the back of the house, to bay-trees and a lawn, set out that day with hoops for croquet.

A face was pressed against a back window of Bennets, its nose and mouth flattened against the glass.

'Judith, my sister,' said Nadia. 'Excuse me.' She shook her fist at the face. Its eyes rolled up to show the whites and the flattened lips opened in a gap-toothed leer.

'Wait there,' said Nadia. She slammed into the house and there was a distant squeal. 'When she asks you to buy her an ice-cream,' said Nadia, returning, 'as she inevitably will, just don't.'

Then she led him through into the house to meet her parents.

*

Leo and Mary Brant were a striking couple. She was tall and pale and freckled, and theatrical in manner and appearance with her tawny hair and wide green eyes. She smiled and offered a limp hand, murmured something that he didn't catch, and excused herself to see to the other guests. Her husband was swarthy-skinned, with a shock of black hair and alert grey eyes that, as he gazed upon his daughter's boyfriend and crushed his hand in a friendly grip, for an instant narrowed. 'So this is your poet, eh, Nadia? Ha. Is he any good? Well, you can save telling me until later, when the rehearsal's over, and we all have time to think straight.'

Watching him that weekend, as he shamed and browbeat and flattered a tiny rabble of singers into the disciplined choir that would stand amid the white and gold of Easter Monday to sing Bach chorales in the parish church, Robert found himself confronted in Leo Brant by something close to his own bodily image in a darkened mirror, and heard in Leo Brant's bursts of passionate speech something of his own voice.

'We'll be seeing you again in Malmsey Green before many weeks are out, I imagine, if my daughter has her way,' he said, when it was time for Robert to leave.

'You'll be welcome, for Nadia's sake,' said Mrs Brant. 'And perhaps to a bed, if they haven't all been pre-empted for one of Leo's courses.'

He wheeled his bike to the archway.

'Are you going to buy me another ice-cream, next time you come?' said ten-year-old Judith Brant, materializing at his elbow. She clutched the handlebar and grinned up at him. 'Promise now, and I'll make myself scarce.'

Moments later, as he was embracing Nadia in the shadows, 'Ugh!' came the sound of Judith's voice. He glanced up to see her monkey-face peering round the corner of the arch.

'Kissing!' she said. 'Ugh! I find that quite *disgusting*.'

An instant later her face popped round the arch once again. 'I think you'd better make it a choc ice,' she said. 'Or, on consideration, two.'

*

Making ends meet on a grant, generous enough as it was, was not easy. By Easter at UCL, Frank O'Connor and he were making do with coffee and a bread roll and a wedge of camembert for their daily lunch. What they saved on food they spent on cigarettes that would turn the edge of their hunger. But French books, and above all medieval texts and texts in phonetic script, were not cheap.

Nor was his daily train fare to London, and the recurrent expense of bed and board at Pargetting. But, faced by his hovering presence, as the year passed through spring and summer the Brants would invite him to a meal and from time to time offered him a bed among the musicians.

There were limits to their welcome. 'Dad has taken to calling you Mr Ponds,' said Nadia one day. 'O, you know. Like the advert for Ponds' make-up. Spring, summer, autumn, winter, Ponds stays *on … and on … and on …*'

In the Easter vacation, with the balance in his bank account dwindling fast, he got himself taken on at Scott's nursery in the Village, where Bren Slaney and a group of his fellow-Catholics had been working, off and on, on Saturdays. It was unskilled work at half-a-crown an hour, the lowest agricultural wage. It amazed him that a farm labourer, even with free housing and cheap produce, could bring up a family on it. Yet somehow his mother's youngest brother was managing it.

Day after day, rain and shine, the rest of that vacation he spent skimming, quartering a tiny area of the nursery's acreage. 'Skimming' meant driving your spade horizontally, half-an-inch or so below the surface of the soil, and slicing off the layer of weeds. It was a futile, unending, stopgap task. As fast as you scalped them, the roots, still anchored in the clay, retorted with a fresh spurt of growth.

Before he went to bed each night, he dowsed the broken blisters on his palms with methylated spirits, his inward gasp of pain hissing between his teeth. But then, so what? Hadn't his mother blistered her hands as a child on rakes and hoes for no wages beyond food and handed-down clothing? Hadn't she dragged turnips out of the frozen furrows with chillblained fingers? And winced with pain, wrenching the handle of the turnip-slicer? Didn't she still come home from work with sticking-plaster on her fingers?

Sixteen years later he was in the room when Brian Patten, reading poems late into the night to a group of students, gazed down at his palms, scarred by a day's labour in a London park, and glimpsed there a fleeting kinship with the stigmata of Christ. As he glanced down at his own hands that night, his thoughts boomeranged back across the years to Scott's nursery, and to Nadia. And the aching scars on his hands that Festival Easter, when he clutched the handlebars and pedalled to Malmsey Green to join the choristers, as they gathered in the transept of the church to sing the *John Passion*.

Throughout his first summer term, he cut each Thursday's and Friday's scatter of classes, and spent those days at the nursery, working on through

Saturday when he wasn't meeting Nadia. Sweating and stripped to the waist, he laboured alongside Ted, the foreman, planting out runner beans, tomatoes and chrysanthemums. At the end of the summer, they harvested and sold them to the Village housewives. 'Runners', 'Toms' and 'Mums': Ted recorded the sales in a ledger, his tongue labouring between his lips. Later in the year, when they harvested gooseberries and blackcurrants, Ted added 'Gogs' and 'Blackies' to his lists.

Ted reminded him of old Daddy Bass at St. Katharine's, like Ted a huge-boned cadaver of a man whose body had fallen into ruin.

Daniel Bass was a true farm-worker, who had laboured in barns and fields all the working days of his life. A foreman Ted might be, but in agricultural matters he was a novice. Born in London's East End, Ted had been a regular soldier since his boyhood, a 'hard nut', a 'tearaway', as he described himself, more often in the glasshouse than out of it. When the Japanese overran Singapore, he and a mate had stolen a three-tonner, crashed it through the window of a downtown liquor store, and drunk themselves into a stupor. The Japs had stumbled over them hours later, still blind to the world.

They'd been transported to a prison camp in the jungle and put to work on the Burma railway. Ted rolled up a trouser leg. See those white puncture scars? That's where the Japs had held a bamboo stake behind his knees and forced him down on it so that the thorns were driven deep into his flesh. Punishment for being cheeky. Same on the inner side of his elbows, see?

There was a Major Churchill in the camp, Ted said. The guards took against him for having the same name as Winston. 'Used to ask him what he was called, and beat the shit out of him when he stood to attention and told 'em.'

'Getting a beating? Nah. That's nothing special,' Ted said. When one of the prisoners was accused of raping a village girl, the Japs handed him over to the women of the tribe. 'They cut off his cock and sewed it up in his mouth,' said Ted. 'Their idea of justice.'

'Here, watch this, then!' Ted said one afternoon, when the talk turned once more to life in enemy hands. He began to pluck thick tufts of hair from his legs, and giggled. 'Can't feel a thing. The nerves are all shot,' he said. 'Beri-beri.'

A year later he was dead. Thirty-three years old.

'I do not recognise this self,/At one with the machine…'

He made a poem in his head one evening, biking through the Essex lanes, standing on the pedals in a half-crouch to get on faster to Pargetting.

He was mesmerised by the lock of hair metronoming across his vision as the bike rocked from side to side. Fatigue sent endorphines racing through his bloodstream, drugging him into hallucination. He felt as if the bones of his arms and legs were changing their nature, merging into the steel of handlebars and cranks, and his muscles metamorphosing into electric and hydraulic rams.

He seemed to be gazing down upon a vision of himself, floating a man's height above the racing roadway and a foot or so above his own body, as he swerved at the road's turn under the trees and swept on through woodsmoke, past the gipsy encampment and over the rim of the world.

'O, your young man's a true Romantic,' said Mrs Somerville to Nadia, who'd gone over to Pargetting to wait for him. 'Love lends wings to his heels. Isn't that so, Signor Romeo?'

On his homeward journey that Sunday evening, there were wilder sensations to cope with. He arrived at the top of a rise, and was met by a headwind that forced him to a standstill and toppled him into the road. The thrust of wind was followed by a single crash of lightning, and he felt the hair rise on the back of his neck.

The sky changed colour. There was a sudden surge of rain, and another lightning crash. He threw his bike down into the roadside grass, and ran away from it to where the line of overhanging trees was broken by a stunted hawthorn hedge. There, with his trousers and socks and shoes already soaked, he squatted on the edge of a ditch, draped his raincape over his head and fumbled for his cigarettes.

Hopeless! They were sodden, falling apart in his fingers.

He pushed his head out again through the neck of the cape. In that instant the wind dropped as swiftly as it had struck, leaving the atmosphere alive with static. He stared ahead at a skyful of clouds that spilled sheet and forked lightning, while the leaves above him seemed to fizz with a faint blue aura.

Expecting to be struck at any instant, he talked to Nadia in his head. Twice an incandescent ball of lightning appeared to race across the surface of a nearby field, swerving away and back again at sudden tangents as though it were a live thing avoiding obstacles, and at last exploding in a flash that left him blinded, seeing only a mauve glare.

He stayed in the ditch for three quarters of an hour, until the storm had died away on the horizon. Then, plucking up courage, he thought of the miles still between him and the Village and went over to collect his bike, half-dreading a lethal shock from it.

A little later the headlights of a lorry flickered behind him and he got off and waved the lorry down.

'OK, mate, sling your bike up into the back,' said the driver. 'You'll have to ride up there along with it. With me and Bill in here, the cab's crowded enough as it is.'

They dropped him off on the outskirts of Brentwood, and he pedalled the rest of the way home. His mother came down when she heard his key in the door.

'What time d'you call this?' she said. 'It's just not good enough. I've been worried sick. D'you realise it's half-past four in the morning? What can Nadia be thinking of, I wonder, *encouraging* you? O, my God, what's that blood on you?'

He looked down at the dark stains on his trousers. Perched up in the lorry, clutching the tailboard with one hand and his bike with the other, he'd felt the wet mounds of vegetables shifting under him, on their way to Covent Garden market.

Beetroot. So that's what they'd been.

*

'Est-ce qu'on est maître de devenir ou de ne pas devenir amoureux? Et quand on l'est, est-on maître d'agir comme si on ne l'était pas?'

Diderot's restless, flashing, disruptive wit, when he encountered it in that year's readings, enchanted him: it seemed so often to chime with his own willed cast of thought.

As Diderot's Fatalist Jacques contrives to ask while knowing full well the answer: Take the question of falling or not falling in love. Is it a matter of choice, or out of your hands? And, once you're caught in the toils of love, will you still be master or mistress of your thoughts and deeds?

In any case what can you do, Robert asked himself, but accept with joy the fever in the blood, ride out the electric storm, fly with the ravishing whirlwind?

While rehearsals for the part of Doctor Knock in Jules Romains' play were giving him a sense of panache, sprezzatura, a confident stance which his newly sleek-styled hair and the pencil-thin moustache he grew for the role were intended to confirm, so his readings in the Metaphysical poets put flesh on his daydreams of Nadia. In Donne's 'Twice or thrice I had lov'd thee/Ere I knew thy name' and in Crashaw's celebration of a 'not impossible She', he rediscovered apparent truths which, looking back, he was convinced he too had shared. Throughout that spring and summer, he set out to make his days an open book to her, dedicated as he told himself, ad maiorem Nadiae gloriam: to the greater glory of Nadia. He wanted to hand his life and thoughts into her keeping, wanted to be possessed.

Unbrothered and unsistered, throughout childhood only ever having known surveillance as the manifestation of his parents' love, he knew no better, could not see the corollary, the fatal double-bind. As a result, he gladly sacrificed any other interest or occasion which might have intervened between Nadia and him. His feelings for her, as he envisioned them in a poem, were hourly 'tangling, like cinquefoil, a skein of possession/Over every moment and purpose' of his life.

It was an impossible burden to thrust on Nadia.

Or on anyone.

For a while Nadia joined him in the game, creating moves of her own, sharing her notion of 'boomerang thoughts'. Apart, and struck by any idea or feeling, each turned to a vision of the other to share it with, joy reaching out and boomeranging back to the other in a swoop of thought.

A conscious device at first, it became second nature to him, binding a spell upon him that would not lose its compulsion for many years to come. Invading his intellection, too, the instant he came across Lewis Carroll's game of 'Doublets'.

Problem: Change Oat to Rye (in as few moves as possible) by changing a single letter at a time. Solution: OAT—rat—rot—roe—RYE.

Or 'BRANT' into 'DRUCE'?

He lay awake and tried: BRANT—brunt—brune—bruce—DRUCE. No. Not good enough. 'Brune' was French, and 'Bruce' a proper noun.

Try it with 'SMITH': could that be done? He stared upwards into the darkness, trying to construct from both ends a chain of links that would meet at the middle and interlock. Then: SMITH-smite-spite-spice-slice-slick-click-crick-trick-truck-truce-DRUCE. Success! So he tried again with 'Jones'. JONES-cones-canes-cants… He fell asleep with the words parading through his skull, convinced he had worked the trick. But in the light of day, try to seize it as he might, the coalescence he had dreamed eluded him.

He made another attempt with 'Brant'.

Swift as thought there it was: BRANT—bract—brace—trace—truce—DRUCE. Done! With four sweet intervening moves. A growth, a binding, a following, a coming to terms.

Magic. And ineluctable. In his mind's eye he watched Nadia's driving, left-handed script setting down her altered name in a marriage register.

It was Nadia who coalesced their names into a single icon. One day they played the game of encoding the names of couples they were acquainted with. Topping and tailing them into a unit. So Ron and his girl-friend Molly became 'Rolly'. 'Or Mon?' — 'No, Rolly suits them better, don't you think?'

Bill and Phyllis were 'Bliss'. 'That matches their besotted look when you see them together,' he said. 'And us? Who are we?'

'Ra, of course.'

'Ra. A Sun God. I like that,' he said.

'Well, aren't we?' said Nadia.

29

RA

It was Saturday afternoon, and they still had half the weekend before them. They left their bikes leaning against a sunny wall and found a corner table in the teashop, and asked for lemonade. They held hands across the table while they waited, and eyed the customer sitting over by the window.

'The Duchess from *Alice in Wonderland*,' Robert whispered.

'And the moral of that is: O, 'tis love, 'tis love that makes the world go round!' said Nadia.

Elderly and many-chinned, the Duchess was gnawing a cream-slice, and frowning at the world from under the tapestry hat that was perched on her head like a hassock. Beneath the gate-legged table, her bulging toes turned inward together under her skirts.

'Her feet beneath her petticoat,/Like little mice stole in and out,' whispered Robert.

The woman was grist. Grist to their mill as would-be authors, like the whole blooming, buzzing confusion of the world itself.

'I recognize that: *blooming, buzzing confusion*. That's William James, talking about a baby's first impressions,' Nadia had said, when they talked about her ambition to become a professional writer of detective stories. Together and apart, they had soon begun to play a game of mapping the world, collecting characters as a cartoonist might collect thumb-nail sketches for future use.

Three cars drew up outside and the room filled up with the members of, it seemed, a church outing. The newcomers began to rearrange the furniture, four around a table for six and five at a table for three.

'Unmusical chairs,' whispered Nadia.

Their Duchess rapped a spoon against her cup, paid the waitress and left. Under their own corner table, Nadia trod on Robert's foot with her sandalled toes, and nudged her head at the nearest group. More grist.

A woman with hairy eyebrows and a face as yellow as the flesh of a turnip. Another with teeth that jutted from her smile-spread lips like the blade of a bulldozer. A little man in a clerical collar, with a beetle's face and thin pink lips. A woman with the face of a dairy-wench in a Rowlandson cartoon, and a rapid twitch in the muscle of her cheek. She had pale blue eyes. Too pale.

They all made a performance of settling down, occupying empty chairs with handbags and scarves. When the tea came, 'Who'll be mother?' the smiling woman smiled. 'Kitty?'

The dairy-wench twitched her jaw, and they gave her the tea-pot, and elaborate assistance — was she simple-minded or something? — humouring and mothering her at the same time, it seemed. There was a long pause in which each one's gaze floated around the room, seeming to see and not see it, avoiding one another's eyes.

'Which one's the murderer?' Nadia mouthed the question.

'Tell you later,' he silently replied.

At last, 'Well,' said the little beetle man, 'it looks as though the forecast on the wireless has indeed proved true...' There was a general murmur from around the table. 'Yes, oh yes, we've certainly been lucky, no rain, no, not a drop.'

Emboldened, the beetle said, 'I only speak for this area of course. I can't speak for elsewhere...' And again the general murmur, 'No, no, that's right, no,' while the Rowlandson wench went on rattling the teapot spout against the cups, splashing them full of tea.

And then Nadia had kicked off her sandal and was stroking his shin with her bare toes, and he gasped and was silenced.

'I'll plump for the vicar as the murderer,' said Nadia a little later, as they pushed their bikes along a woodland path in Indian file.

'If he *was* a vicar. Which I doubt. "Goodness me, the weather is most clement for late May, is it not?" His conversation was overdone, I thought.'

'Yes. Cliche upon cliche. "But let us not be precipitate. Ne'er cast a clout till May be out, as the weather-wise say." No, the dog-collar was a fake, and he's our murderer all right.'

'And the daft one is his victim.'

'Not just her. The man's a mass murderer,' said Nadia. 'They're *all* his victims.'

'He's after them for their money.'

'Their little bits of savings.'

'Welcoming the little fishes in with gently smiling jaws,' said Robert. 'Like Haigh. Polishing off the evidence in a bath of sulphuric.'

'Yes, but it didn't work out, did it? Haigh went to the gallows,' she said.

'And heard the stroke of eight, And not the stroke of nine.'

'Housman,' she said. 'Look! Primroses.'

They propped their bikes against a hawthorn bush and pushed deeper into the tiny clearing. He stripped off his jacket and spread it on the trunk of a fallen tree for them to sit on.

'Ne'er cast a clout,' said Nadia. 'It won't be June for another fortnight.'

'It's nothing to do with the months,' he said. 'May-*blossom*, that's what it means. When it comes into flower. Just look at that hawthorn.'

They sat in a tangle of green and white and gold, flower and leaf. An embroidery of Easter vestments.

'*Bel aubespin florissant,*
Verdissant
Le long de ce beau rivage,
Tu es vestu, jusqu'au bas,
Des long bras
D'une lambrunche sauvage.

'Pierre de Ronsard,' he said.

'What's *une lambrunche?*'

'A wild vine. Trailing across the flowering hawthorn, embracing it. Me. You.'

She snuggled her head against his shoulder.

A little later she shivered and said, 'No. Not there,' but did not resist his touch.

'No one,' he said, caressing her. 'Never before have I… No one.'

A lie.

Ellen Green. His drunken recollection of that night curdled into a nightmare and fled, whipped from his brain like a fading blasphemy.

'No one. Just you,' he said.

A gratuitous lie. But he so imperiously wanted it to be true.

When they pushed their way back through the greenwood to the road, his senses were tingling, shaking his blood, giddying him.

'It's like trying to walk on a carpet of bubbles,' he said, looking back into her eyes.

'Don't look back again until we're out of the wood,' she said. 'Orpheus, remember?'

Her voice was unsteady, as if she were fighting not to shiver again.

'I love you,' she said a moment later.

'And I have done one braver thing,' he told the trees at the edge of the wood, and the acres of green springing wheat beyond them; 'Than all the Worthies did./And yet a braver thence doth spring,/Which is, to keep that hid…

'Nadia — You: I.'

'Robert and Nadia. Ra. The Sun God. Us.'

'Our secret.'

When they came through an echo of distant music into the kitchen at Bennets, Nadia's mother eyed them narrowly.

*

'Cheap culture for the masses. That's the age we are living in,' Mrs Somerville was fond of remarking. 'The Century of the Too, Too, Common Man.' You could hear the capitals.

He arrived at the youth centre at Pargetting one Friday evening in early June, to find her still simmering from the shock of a day-long visit to a holiday camp a few miles along the coast. 'The Too, Too Common Man.' Her frequent phrase seemed to sum it all up for her; the chalets, the red-coats, the mass feeding, the tannoy announcements that fragmented and directed the holiday-camper's day.

'Damned efficient, though, mind you,' said Major Somerville. 'Given the fact that they don't have a guard-room to clap the defaulters in. Better organized from the top than many a battalion I've had the misfortune to serve in.'

But Mrs Somerville was affronted by regimented pleasure, mass-entertainment culture. Community singing. Bingo. The parade of bathing beauties all aspiring to be 'Miss Jaywick Sands'. Competitions for the knobbliest knees, the bonniest baby, the most glamorous grandmother. She was furious when a red-coat had approached her with an entry form for *that* contest.

The doorways to the holiday camp lavatories were labelled 'LADS' and 'LASSES'. For Mrs Somerville the last straw came when she misread 'LADS' as 'LADIES' and walked in upon a group of youths loitering by the wash-basins to comb their duck's-arse coiffures. They assailed her with ribald mockery and jostled her towards the door.

'Well, dammit, that's what they call them: duck's arses. Looks like a duck's arse, too.' Retailing the story, Major Somerville seemed to relish his wife's discomfiture. 'Mark you, if I'd had them under my command, they'd have been off to the regimental barber before their feet could touch the ground.'

Mrs Somerville shuddered, but at what aspect of the Major's military cast of mind it was hard to decide.

'Self-discipline, that's what this post-war generation lacks,' she insisted. 'Regiment people, make all their choices for them: and what do you get? Vulgarity. Licence. Teddy-bear clubs.'

She was getting into her stride. 'Those schoolgirls flaunting their lost virginity by wearing a tiny teddy-bear pinned to their lapels. You must have seen the story. It was splashed all over the tabloid papers. Teddy bears. What a pathetic symbol of childishness and irresponsibility! As though virginity was a burden, and losing it was something to be proud of.'

'Growing up straight from childhood into adultery,' ventured Robert, repeating something he had heard.

'Hah!' said the Major, grinning.

'Don't be ridiculous,' said his wife, rounding upon him. 'If those youngsters turn up here with their holiday-camp morals, trying to climb into each other's beds, you'll soon change your tune!'

'Ah, well, that's different,' said the Major. 'Can't tolerate indiscipline.'

'And I hope *you* two have got more sense,' said Mrs Somerville, turning her gaze upon Robert, and then on Nadia, who at that instant was walking in through the hall door. 'And now you can make yourself scarce, young man, while I take Nadia through her part in the pageant.'

He was glad to escape from under a threatened inquisition.

Leo Brant, taking him into his study for a word the following evening, was more blunt. 'Tell me this,' he said. 'Is my daughter still a virgin?' He cut across the confused horror of Robert's stumbling, red-faced, heart-pounding assertions, yes of course, yes, it wasn't like that, how could you think...'

'Then, I suggest we keep it that way, shall we?'

*

Summer. He assembled images in his head one afternoon, storing them to share with Nadia, as he rode on an ancient single-decker bus on his way to Pargetting.

Summer. A hollow husk of time, powdery dry, with a blue sharp-edged sky like cloisonné enamel, and dusty sunshine. Heraldic. Azure and or.

Underarm sweat and thin dragging clothes and dryness, shucked with soil and grasses, tractors and grasshoppers simmering in the distant hills and the roadside grass. Pools of water too far away for laziness. A dry poster with crusted paste flapping against a fence, with scarcely breeze enough to lift it away from the palings.

His feet were pressed against the silver bulge of the gearbox behind the driver's seat, urging the bus forward, willing it to sweep past the garrulous old granny who would have to be hoisted up the steps, with a hand under her behind. Only to clamber back down and hoist up another creaking basket to scrounch against people's knees as she lurched interminably past on her journey to her seat.

O, get on. Get on with it.

Slow drawn-out stops where one lane ended in another. And a slower start, with the engine throbbing through the gears under the soles of his shoes. Spires and rooftops. Swoops of countryside flattening out towards the estuary. The gipsy camp.

Another interminable halt beside the signboard of a pub, and passengers clambering up and down. Then the woods where Nadia and he had sat amid a white and gold tangle of blossom.

Then masts and a distant sparkle of water. The estuary. Pargetting.

And at last the stop where he climbed down into a parched and hissing silence with only the blur of a far-off engine and the barking of a dog in a council-house garden, battering about amongst the sweet peas and the phlox.

He half-walked half-ran to the Vicarage to leave his bag there, and then on to the meadow and Mrs Somerville's pageant, already long begun.

Fragments again. Cameos. Village schoolchildren circling a maypole. Morris dancers. Actors moving out across the grass. Much ado with smugglers and a seagoing scenario which at times owed no small debt to Crabbe. Seventeenth-century life, public and domestic. A servant girl scrubbing at a pewter candlestick to no avail.

'Oi can't git a shine on this'n, missus.'

'Do you spit on ut then, gel!'

'Spittin' in't no good. Oi sput, n' Oi sput, n' Oi sput, n' thet *'on't* come clean.'

And Judith Brant with her gap-toothed grin, rigged out as a disaffected turnspit.

Nadia in Elizabethan dress, a sixteen-year-old Juliet. Playing a Hippolyta twice her age in an inset slice of Shakespeare's *Dream*. Saying her lines in that clear, high voice.

He closed his eyes and his heart brimmed.

When the pageant was all over, they walked together in the twilight before supper and the country dancing which would follow. Nadia had read *Brave New World* the previous term, and recently he'd given her Huxley's *Chrome Yellow* and *Brief Candles*.

'What did you think of them?' he asked. 'A far cry from babies in bottles and Bokanovsky groups.'

She turned to him and clutched his arm.

'Remember *Brief Candles*? And "After the Fireworks"?' Her voice was shuddering, and she looked past him, over towards the estuary.

'I want to say to you what Pamela said to Miles Fanning in that story,' she said.

He did not dare to break the silence.

'Please. Perhaps not quite yet, darling,' she said. 'But soon.'

For a moment her eyes gazed into his. 'And now we must hurry back to supper like good children...'

Home again in Honey Hill that Sunday evening, he ran up to his room to find his copy of the book and check the words. Had he wrongly remembered the passage?

'Miles!' And sliding across the seat towards him, she threw her arms round his neck and kissed him. 'Take me, Miles,' she said, speaking in quick abrupt little spurts, as though she were forcing the words out with violence against a resistance… 'Take me. If you want me…'

*

But no. Not yet. Not yet.

'Soon', she had said. 'Soon.'

But not yet.

How exactly Huxley's words caught the sudden and relentless conflict of desire and dread: 'His body was uneasy with awakenings and supernatural dawn.'

There were other warnings in Huxley's tale. 'Stupid and mad,' his heroine said. As she pleaded to sleep with the man she was infatuated with. Begging him to lie with her.

He found the passage again and read it over and over again:

'Even if it is stupid and mad… And it isn't. I mean, love isn't stupid or mad. And even if it were, I don't care. Yes, I want to be stupid and mad. Even if it were to kill me. So take me…' She kissed him again. 'Take me.'

It was not measured thought. Was it truly what Nadia felt at heart? This sudden unthinking, crazy desire, unresisted, and irresistible? She was sixteen to his twenty-one. Could she be sure of what she herself wanted?

And if they did, and if it all turned sour, as Pamela and Fanning's love affair had gone sour in Huxley's novella? What then? She, Nadia, like Pamela determined to break away from her lover; he, Robert, snarled in a greed of possession. Such an outcome didn't bear thinking of. They loved each other too much.

No, not yet. If ever, in their present circumstances.

If at all.

And in any case, rehearsals for his own part in *Le Docteur Knock* were invading all his free time; he'd not see Nadia now for another month. Not until she came, at his parents' invitation, to watch him in the play.

Time enough then to talk again. He could put off any commitment until then.

He tried to force his attention onto his studies. But could not put off thought.

'Tis She, and here,
Lo! I unclothe and clear
My Wish's cloudy character…

But where's that wise man that would not be I,
If she should not deny?

Against all reason, Crashaw, Donne, the summer sun, the Sun God
Ra, French medieval verse, the exhilarating effrontery of *Dr Knock* in
rehearsal: 'To be healthy is a serious condition: it can lead only to disease!',
the wash of adrenalin through his own and Nadia's blood; the exploits of
the 'Teddy Bear Club' splashed across the headlines; 'After the Fireworks';
Nadia's 'I *meant* what I said,' since then twice repeated in her letters; the
unforgettable scent of her body: all fermenting in his brain, all conspiring.

Come, here are our hearts and hands against us.

Persuasive. Exhilarating.
Not yet.
But, yes. Yes.
Soon.

*

A few days before the performance, he called at the chemists in Tottenham
Court Road. On his own behalf, this time, not for Frank O'Connor. And
this time, ridiculously, he felt himself blushing to the roots of his hair
while he fumbled with his change and slid the packet away into an inner
pocket.

The following day, while his father was on duty and his mother out at
the shops, he opened the packet and tucked one of the three little envelopes
into his wallet. It ought to be safe enough there: as long as he took care
to keep his wallet on him at all times. He carried the remaining two little
envelopes into the bathroom and locked the door.

He thought of Lou Marsh, and the package of contraceptives Marsh had
been given by an American GI. At the back of the air-raid shelters in 1945,

Marsh had held a handful of members of 5A spellbound with the tale of how he'd secreted a french letter in his folded towel before running himself a bath.

Marsh lingered over every detail. Putting the bath-plug into the plug-hole. Turning on the taps. Stepping out of his pyjama trousers. Swirling the water to an even temperature with his hand, with the steam blurring his naked reflection in the bathroom mirror.

'Now, don't rush me,' said Marsh. 'All in good time.' He was a past master at making his hearers wait.

So they waited until at last they could watch him in their minds' eyes as he leaned out of the bath and reached for his towel, and carefully dried his hands. He fumbled the condom out of its little envelope.

He put it on, and gazed down at it.

It was greasy, and bright pink. Stretched over his tight-swelled knob, it gleamed in the steamy light, he told them, 'like pink bone-china'. Lou's audience grinned and shuffled, sharers in the vicarious charade.

'What did you do then, Lou?'

'Flushed it down the pan. Getting rid of the evidence… Hey, listen. Isn't that the bell?'

You could always rely on Marsh for that impeccable timing of an anti-climax.

In their grammar school days, coming across discarded contraceptives in the hedgerows close to the army camp, they often discussed the legend that the manufacturers were compelled by law to perforate one in every packet of three, before releasing them to the wholesalers.

Compelled by law? Whose law? The government's? The *Pope's?* Don't be stupid. How could *he* have any say in it? Well, I dunno. But that's what somebody was saying… Anyway, it's wartime, isn't it? They want to keep the birthrate up, I reckon, eh?

Now, ten years later, unwrapping two of those greasy inner envelopes behind the locked door of his parents' bathroom in Honey Hill, he prepared to test their contents to destruction. See how just how tough they were. You couldn't be too careful.

He unrolled one and blew it up like a balloon until, more than two feet long and stretched to a squeaking transparency, it burst. He unrolled the other and fumbled it over the mouth of a bath tap. It had become a mammoth rain-drop, holding what? — half a gallon? — when at last it gave up the ghost.

Like Lou Marsh before him, he flushed the evidence away. But now he knew. Nothing to be afraid of there. Unless there was a fatal pinprick in the third french letter in his wallet? No, that was a horror-tale for schoolboys.

As he unlocked the bathroom door, the realization flooded through his flesh in a surge of adrenalin. He'd made his choice. The die was cast. Nadia and he. For good or ill, the act lay between them. Then O…

Then O, then O, then O, my true love said,
'Til that time come again
She could not live a maid.

If, when he next saw next, she had not changed *her* mind.

30

NIGHTMARE

Le Docteur Knock; Ou, le Triomphe de la Médecine. High farce, gesticulation, *marivaudage*. Declamations, cajolery, asides across the footlights. The performance flooded past and through him in a high-octane blur.

At last, past midnight already, Nadia's footsteps echoed alongside his own as they walked from the Village station to Honey Hill and home. His father would be out all night on duty. At this late hour, his mother would have long been fast asleep.

They reviewed the plan yet again. Nadia would take a bath and go back to her room. Then, as Robert left his room to go to the bathroom, she would slip barefoot past him, and wait there for his return. If by chance his mother *was* awake and listening, she would not fathom their manoeuvre.

They stopped on the station path, and kissed.

'The gaslamps,' he said. 'Listen for a moment, when we reach the next… Irritably clicking prim deprecatory metallic tongues… Sorry about the tongue-twister. I used to imagine there was a little old lady sitting up there in every one of them. Clicking her tongue at me. Tt, tt, tt, tt…'

'They are clicking their tongues at *us* now,' she said. 'If they can see into our minds…'

Mrs Druce had left them a jug of milk, and sandwiches. She didn't come down. 'She's asleep,' he whispered.

The manoeuvre worked flawlessly. The running water didn't wake her. When he'd towelled himself dry, and brushed his teeth, and left the bathroom, he paused, quietly closing his bedroom door. His wallet lay on the bedside table. There was no sound from his parents' bedroom.

At first he could not see Nadia in the faint light of the street-lamp that filtered through the drawn curtains. Then found her, curled up on the rug by his bed, looking up at him, wide-eyed. They both shuddered, holding one another, then got into bed and pulled the coverlet over them.

'What needst thou have more covering than a man?' he whispered. 'Since our two loves be one, or, thou and I love so alike…'

'Yes,' she answered. 'Yes…' She kissed him. 'And stop wooing me by the book.'

*

Less than a minute later, they fell out of their dream of love to sounds stirring in his parents' bedroom. He heard his mother click on her light, and sigh. Nadia lay between him and the wall in the single bed, utterly still, holding her breath.

His door-handle turned and a wedge of light splashed across the floor. His mother was standing in the doorway.

'Are you awake?' she whispered. 'How did you get on? How did the play go?'

If only he had had the wit to yawn and murmur sleepily: 'O, fine, just fine, I'm dog-tired, I'll tell you in the morning…' But, panicking, he did not.

'I want to sleep,' he said. 'You woke me up. I don't feel very well.'

His mother, all solicitousness, crossed to his bedside. An instant later she retreated, and snapped the light on by the door.

'O, my God,' she cried.

She came back and stood looking down at them, her left hand clutching her dressing-gown, her right outflung towards the door.

'Go to your room! Go to your room!'

The spell shattered. Nadia and he, frantically groping with their toes for her pyjama trousers, failed to find them. Love was toppling over into nightmare, passion corroding into hysteria and low farce.

'Do as I say this instant!' His mother was stamping her foot.

'Mother, please,' he pleaded.

'I'll deal with *you* later,' she said. 'And as for what your father will have to say about this!'

Her search at last successful, Nadia leapt from his bed, her pyjama trousers clutched in her hand. She fled past his mother to her own bed, her bare bottom twinkling in the lamplight.

'Twinkling.'

He was torn between frustration, shame and rage. Between the lunatic asseverations of his role as Doctor Knock, and deference to his mother. Between a hysterical impulse to laugh, and a hysterical need to weep. The only escape route he could take lay in a detached nicety of words. *Twinkling*: that was it, exactly.

Unbidden, a cartoon — in *Punch?* In *Lilliput?* — flickered into his memory. A boy across his father's knee, being walloped. The father's electric razor lying on the floor nearby, and the family cat, shaved in stripes around its belly. 'Yes, I know, Dad. But in five year's time we're going to laugh at this,' the boy was saying…

But now was nightmare.

'That girl', Mrs Druce turned in the doorway of his bedroom, 'leaves this house as soon as she's had her breakfast. I shall be writing to her mother. And now you can get your clothes on and come downstairs. I want a talk with you. My God, you've got some explaining to do.'

*

His mother did not write to Nadia's parents. Nor, despite more than a fortnight of threatening to do so, did she mention the affair to her husband.

Perhaps it was because she dreaded the violence that his rage would lead to, fearing that it would shatter the family and her marriage with it. Perhaps she wanted to keep the threat of revelation hanging over her son, and was reluctant to cast away so powerful a weapon in her armoury of surveillance and possessive love. Perhaps she recognized that his love for Nadia might prove a force too powerful to wage war against; sensing that she herself might be the loser. Perhaps she felt that, after an act of such sinful intimacy, only eventual marriage could atone. Perhaps all of these things.

On a Friday afternoon in June, grim-faced, he set off once again for a weekend at Pargetting and Malmsey Green.

His mother stood over him as he threw things into a case. 'Just behave yourselves, the pair of you. That's all I ask,' she said, sighing. *Does she believe that we will?* he asked himself, kneeling on the case to snap the locks shut.

From his first words with Nadia when she came to meet him from the bus, he knew that they would not.

Broken in upon almost *in flagrante delicto*, — no, not in deliction but in delectation, they told one another, 'in flagrant *delight*', frustrated in their dream of sleeping and waking in one another's arms, of apostrophizing that busy old fool the Sun, peering in on them — they found another time and place. The following day and a mile or so from Malmsey Green, in the ruins of a medieval leper-house long crumbled back into the earth, they crept into a patch of ragwort overshadowed by elder-trees, and lay together, with only the midday sun as witness.

They were amazed by themselves, incapable almost of speech as afterwards they pushed their way, with blood on both of them, out through the blackthorn saplings and the tangling briars into open fields and the light glittering from the estuary.

Nadia and he, bright-eyed, her fingers interwoven with his.

There was so much, so much to say.

And love tying your tongue.

They lingered until dusk, delaying their re-entrance into the workaday world of Bennets and Malmsey Green, the world of parents and casual visitors, where they must be careful to be decorous in company. A world of thoughtful, prying eyes where too-elaborately-feigned indifference would betray them just as inexorably as their looks of longing.

As he climbed down from the bus in Billericay late that Sunday evening, and stood to wait for another, two men came to join him, in a miasma of alcohol. They eyed him, muttering together, while he sighed, *Heigh ho*, and lit a cigarette.

He clambered up to the top deck, and put his bag beside him on the front seat. The two men hustled onto the seat behind. After a moment, there was a tap on his shoulder and he turned round.

'Beg pardon fer askin', sor, but couldya see ya way to letttin' us have the price of a cup o' tay?' whined the taller of the two, between stained and broken teeth. 'Sure, 'n not a drop of tay has passed between me lips for a night and a day, sor.'

The smaller man ducked his head and snatched off his cap, as if he were in the presence of a superior. 'Ach, now listen to 'm, sor,' he said. 'That's God's truth. He wouldn't be tellin' ya a lie.'

'Tea? Perhaps not,' said Robert, through the fumes. 'But has nothing stronger passed your lips?'

'Gob, ye're an understandin' man, sor,' cried the little man, grinning and unabashed. 'Ye're a man o' the world, so y'are.'

He turned to his companion and smacked him over the head with his folded cap.

'N' didn't I *tellya* he was a man o' the world?'

With such fierce remembered joy still flooding through him, he was quite prepared to believe that he was. He fumbled in his pockets and presented the pair of drunks with half a crown.

'Ah, God bless ye, sor,' said the little man. 'May ye be the father of bishops!'

'Amen, Amen to that,' said the other. 'Ye wouldn't maybe let us have the loan of a coupla cigarettes, sor, wouldya?'

*

And did not fall away, bubble-hollow, a cardboard queen...

Fragments — phrases, images — sprawled through his brain in the succeeding weeks, assembling themselves into what he told himself were poems while, week by week as summer ran its course, Nadia and he snatched every occasion to be alone with one another, littering the landscape with our kisses, he said, stealing an image from MacNeice. Essex and Cambridgeshire; the Village, and the forest hollows by Maze Hill and Gregories and Long Ridings. Even the house in Honey Hill, where his mother's embargo suddenly ceased to run from one weekend to the next, and Nadia was made welcome.

In mid-July Mrs Brant exploded her bombshell.

She came into the kitchen at Bennets one Saturday morning, where Nadia and Robert were drinking coffee, and sat down.

'Ah, there you are, Nadia,' she said. 'It's hard to keep track of where you are nowadays. Now listen. In a week's time it will be August.'

With her Higher Certificate and university entrance looming ahead in less than a year, it was important that Nadia should visit Paris for a week or two, yes? Visit the obvious places, the Comédie Française, the Louvre, see the sights, get the feel of the place a little, hear the language all day. It was all grist to her mill. Very well, August wasn't the best of months to visit Paris, but it would have to serve, no?

Judith would go along too; she'd hate to be left kicking her heels in

Malmsey Green. Very well. Look, my dear child, it was no use arguing, Judith was included in the arrangement.

'Next point,' said Mrs Brant. 'You can't go on your own, the pair of you. You'll need a responsible adult with you. Someone with a good command of the language…'

Robert saw a vision of himself squiring Nadia and her sister around Paris. Judith would be a burden: how many ice-creams…? But Paris, with Nadia. Wet morning pavements. The Tuileries. The bouquinistes along the Seine. The theatre Olympia. Notre Dame, and a blaze of candles in a dark aisle. Saucers piling up on a sunlit café table. The sweet acridity of Gauloises Bleues, and a scribble of accordion music. Sous les toits de Paris.

Nadia's mother paused for a moment, eyeing him.

'So I've asked Lionel Voss if he'll escort you and Judith.'

'Lionel Voss?'

'Who else? Lionel is the best possible person. He knows Paris, he speaks French, he's adult, he's absolutely trustworthy.'

Voss. Robert was consumed by jealous fury. He'd met the man, talked to him. He was aged twenty-five, or so; a flautist, or oboist, or something; one of the musicians who frequented Bennets. Lionel Voss. Smooth-mannered. Ingratiating.

And Lionel Voss's eyes came to rest on Nadia a little too often for Robert's liking.

'Who else could there possibly be?' asked Nadia's mother, again. 'So this afternoon you and Judith can come into Colchester with me and have your passport photos taken. Just think, darling, a fortnight from now you'll be in Paris.'

Max, Leo Brant's corgi, scuttled across Mrs Brant's path as she walked towards the door. With careful calculation, she placed her instep under the dog's belly, and flung it out of her way.

'Get out from under my bloody feet,' she said.

'So much for me,' muttered Robert, as the door closed behind her.

He was dry-mouthed with rage and bitter jealousy.

'Paris!' said Nadia. 'Well!'

'With Lionel Voss.'

'And Judith. She'll be our greedy little chaperone. Don't look so miserable, darling. And I'll be writing to you, anyway, won't I?'

Mary Brant had not misjudged his reactions. He lay awake most of that night, lighting cigarette after cigarette, and staring up at the ceiling of his room at Mrs Lodge's bed-and-breakfast guesthouse in Pargetting village. When the dawn chorus had quietened down at last, he drifted into sleep, and fell into a dream of being trapped on a ice-wet rock-face, footholds crumbling under his boot-soles, his fingers slipping from holdfasts suddenly grown treacherous.

He was consumed by a rage of jealousy that clouded and soured the remaining hours of that weekend. When Nadia came home from her fortnight in Paris with all her excitements to report and share, she was affronted by his relentless and bitter cross-questioning. His work in French was no comfort. Manon Lescaut, as he read and re-read it at the time for a vacation essay, dripped its subtle vitriol into his self-inflicted wound.

They patched things together, loving one another too desperately to bear even a hint of parting. For the remainder of the summer they met and made love as often as they could. At his home and hers, in the rare absence of their parents. In the Forest thickets, and the woodlands near Pargetting and Malmesey Green, and among the grass-grown boulders of the clunch pit a swoop of hillside away from Rectory Farm. But now when they lay in one another's arms it was with a fierce passion close to tears, gentleness turned all to greed.

*

In September, a film crew turned up at Pargetting. Nadia and her sister Judith were full of the nine days' wonder, when they arrived together to meet him at the bus-stop late one Friday afternoon.

'There were great big arc-lights all along the river last night,' said Judith. 'You could practically see to read by them at Malmsey Green.'

'Look, I've no idea where you'll be able to stay this weekend,' said Nadia, 'All the pubs are full of actors and technicians...'

'Hard cheese, old boy, but this time your luck's out,' Major Somerville told him when he applied at the Old Vicarage. 'We're full up to the gills. Youth Club leaders on a weekend's training. Practically got people bedded down in the bath, what?'

Nowhere in Pargetting could he find a welcome. All the available accommodation in the village had been commandeered. 'You'll be lucky to find anywhere within a mile or more along the estuary,' they told him at the

Three Colts. 'Sorry, dear,' said Mrs Lodge. 'I would if I could, but both my rooms are taken.'

While Nadia and Judith hurried off back to Bennets for their tea, he trudged the length and breadth of the village in vain, before making a last appeal to Mrs Lodge. 'The thing is,' he said, 'if I'd come by bike, I could have turned round and gone home; but now there aren't any buses before the morning, and I'm stuck.'

Mrs Lodge hummed and hawed and at last agreed to make him up a camp-bed on her landing. 'Just for tonight, mind,' she said. 'Seeing it's you and I know you. But you'll have to leave as soon as you've had your breakfast. You can't stay on till Sunday.'

It was a poor start to his weekend with Nadia. He talked with her for a few bitter hours the following morning as they strolled through the crowd of village children who were watching the film-makers down by the estuary. He wanted to carry her away to walk alone with him through the yellowed and falling leaves up in the woods. But she was more than content to stand and watch the boatful of actors as again and again they rowed inshore and scrambled out onto the quay and then rowed away again for another take.

'Grist, darling, remember?' said Nadia. 'And I don't *want* to go for a walk. And certainly not with you in this mood, in any case.'

'This afternoon, then?'

'Not this afternoon, either. I'm sorry, I've got a date.'

'A *date*?'

'Well, I didn't know you were coming down this weekend, did I? You didn't say so in your letter, did you?'

'What sort of a date? Who with?'

'Does it matter? I'm going for a motorbike ride, if you *must* know. The film-company's clapper boy offered to take me to Jaywick and back on his pillion.'

'O, Christ,' he said. 'And you *agreed*?'

'I asked my mother,' she said. 'She doesn't mind. I don't see why *you* should.'

'If you can't see that…' he said.

'Look, I'll see you this evening,' she said, 'when I get back. If it'll make you any happier. You really are becoming quite impossible, you realise. We can't go on like this. I can hardly call my soul my own.'

*

'So, did he try to kiss you? Did you kiss him?' Filled with self-loathing, he heard himself whining through an endless litany, tearing down all that lay between Nadia and him, and incapable of stopping. Dusk was falling. The arc-lights were blazing once more along the estuary, and Nadia's clapper-boy was back at work.

Tears were running down Nadia's cheeks and his own as they paced the meadows beyond Pargetting church, and they both looked on the ruin he was making.

'I love you,' he said. 'I want to make you happy.' But, *C'est me vouler du bien d'une étrange manière*, he heard a woman's voice crying in his skull.

'O, give me a cigarette,' said Nadia suddenly.

She smoked it in the centre of her mouth, pouting it from pursed lips, talking past it, a glowing barrier, *noli me tangere*.

The field paths gave way to an alleyway and then to the village street. As they rounded a corner they passed a knot of young women outside the Three Colts. One of them turned to look in his direction, and he felt the blood draining from his face.

Ellen Green.

He had distantly heard — from George or Ernie, who had kept in touch with her for a while — that she had married her boy friend and moved away. Now here she was in Pargetting once again.

Ellen ducked her head, acknowledging Nadia, and then let her eyes trail slowly over Nadia's companion's face. She stared him hard in the eyes, frowning, for a long moment, then turned away, failing to remember, it seemed, who he was or might have been.

The blood lurched back and forth in his body, as he and Nadia moved on along the street, while a sudden insane notion took possession of his mind. Since Nadia failed to comprehend *his* jealousy, let her taste it for herself. *Then* perhaps she'd understand.

And if he only succeeded in pulling down the whole bloody box of tricks, what was there to lose? — it was already cracked and spoilt, its magics all turning sour.

'Ellen Green,' he said. 'Ellen Green.' *Tell the truth*, a paranoid voice prompted him, *and shame the devil*.

'And who am I to be blaming *you*?'

Her silence taunted him.

'I'm afraid I told a lie,' he said. 'I'm sorry. I told you a lie. You are the only woman I have ever loved. But you were not the first I ever touched.'

And he insisted on telling her, although she did not want to hear, about Ellen Green and the darkness of that August night in the empty boathouse down by the estuary where now the arc-lights were blazing into the sky.

He collected his case from Mrs Lodge's front hall, and together he and Nadia waited at the bus-stop. When the bus came, 'I'll see you next week… Yes? O, please, darling,' he said. They turned apart, not touching one another. Tears were streaming down her cheeks and his, as he hunched into a seat at the back of the bus, where he might go unnoticed.

*

When he got home from UCL on Wednesday evening, his mother handed him a parcel. 'It's postmarked Pargetting,' she said. 'Well, aren't you going to open it?'

He took it up to his room and locked the door.

Nadia had sent back his letters, shoving them into an empty Weetabix packet and fastening it with garden twine and brown paper. Underneath them at the bottom of the packet were trinkets he had given her: a paper-knife, and the two tiny cut-glass liqueur glasses he'd bought for her in an antique shop one afternoon in Colchester. He found Nadia's own letter sandwiched between two layers of the brown wrapping-paper.

She would keep Huxley's *Brief Candles* and *Chrome Yellow*, but she was returning everything else. 'I shan't bless you,' she wrote, 'for making me damaged goods. Nadia.'

*

For the remainder of that week he seemed to have fallen into a nightmare landscape of foul and feverish darknesses, haunted by succubi and their slobbered whisperings; a wasteland of pitfalls and thickets of hot shame, *antres périlleux, infectes*. He lay on his bed chain-smoking, his gorge rising at the mention of food. He composed bitter jeremiads to Nadia in his head, and

369

followed them with protestations of deathless passion. He had so desperately sought to wrap her round with affection, mistaking possessiveness for love, and now the trap had sprung upon its own maker, possessing him.

From time to time he heard his parents conversing in whispers, tiptoeing outside his bedroom door, listening. Only when he was sure that they had gone away, did he creep to the bathroom. He ran cold water over his wrists, staring back into the pits of his eyes reflected in the mirror.

By Saturday he had pulled himself together a little. He swallowed some breakfast, and went to walk with Pat for half the day among the forest trees, patrolling places haunted by Nadia's presence, littered with their kisses, trying to shake free of his longing for her and the guilt he felt towards her.

On Sunday he opened the drawer where he kept Nadia's letters. It was empty. So was the drawer into which he'd dropped the parcel she had made of his letters to her. He flung himself downstairs.

'Letters?' said his mother, tight-lipped and arms akimbo. 'I gave them to your father. He burnt them in the garden yesterday while you were out… Listen, it's for your own good. Brooding over them would only have upset you. And you needn't look at me like that. We're the best friends you've got, your father and me, if you only knew it.'

Back in his room, he discovered that Nadia's photograph had vanished from its frame on his desk. He searched his wallet. His snaps of Nadia were missing.

Everything. All of it. Burnt.

It was behaviour so breathtaking in its assumptions, such an insanity of possessive love flung back upon him, that he could not begin to find the words to tell his parents what he thought of it.

31

PROFESSOR KOCH'S TREE

'Druce. Right, that's DEE-ARE-YOU-SEE-EE then, is it? Not a name you stumble across every day of the week.'

Sergeant-Major Howell glanced up from the recruiting form.

'Ever have any relations in the Brigade of Guards, did you?'

'Ah,' said Private Druce 023 *redivivus*. 'You may be thinking of my uncle Leonard. He was a Warrant Officer — Class 1 or 2, don't ask me which — in the Welsh Guards. Or my uncle George, more likely? He was Regimental Sergeant-Major of the Irish Guards...'

'*That* bastard!'

Sergeant-Major Howell had slammed down his pen, and was glaring at the latest would-be recruit to the University Training Corps.

'A *bastard*, that man was. Worst-hated man in the Brigade of Guards... Well, I'm sorry to learn that he was a relative of yours.'

'He was my father's eldest brother. But they had no time for each another. I never even met him, to my knowledge,' said Druce. 'He may be dead, for all I know.'

'I'll knock you into the middle of next week,' said Sergeant-Major Howell in a sudden stiff-throated scream. 'I'll swing you round a threepeny bit, lad, before I've done with you...'

'What?'

But Sergeant-Major Howell was not to be halted.

'Duw, a spiteful tongue that man had. I'll *swing* you round a threepenny bit. That was his favourite saying. Sarcastic bastard... Trying to goad you, see? Never mind back-answering, just give him an old-fashioned look, and he'd have you on jankers for dumb insolence. RSM Druce, eh? So you're that man's nephew...'

Sergeant-Major Howell gave him a long look.

'Well, we'd better get the rest of this form filled up, and then I'll sign a chit for you to draw your kit from the stores.'

Sergeant-Major Howell laboured on for a moment.

'All right now, sign on the dotted line. October the fourth. Parade here every Thursday...

'Well, then, just so long as you don't take after your uncle, isn't it?'

His second year at UCL was two days old.

*

Joining the Territorial Army and parading at South Kensington every Thursday evening was a distraction, an desperate act of defiance which he tried to interpose between himself and the misery that gnawed at him. He joined the bridge-players most days at lunchtime nowadays, and took up rugger again with the new season, stringing along with Frank Connor on Saturday as well as Wednesday afternoons, trying to take to heart Frank's homilies on tactics. He knew that he was a hopeless player, a make-weight, but the rough-and-tumble gave him a chance to void some part of the rage that alternated with his despair.

Nadia possessed him. Waking, he could not shake her remembered voice or her image out of his head. He tortured himself with senseless hope, knowing that it was senseless:

Now at the last gasp of Love's latest breath...
Now if thou wouldst, when all have given him over,
From death to life, thou might him yet recover.

He could not shake off the habit so recently acquired, so deeply ingrained, of turning to her in his mind, *surprised by joy* — Wordsworth voiced so exactly the momentary surge of excitement and the ebb-tide of despair — seeking to make her a sharer still in what he saw and thought. With the passing weeks there was so much to share: Blake, Coleridge, and Keats in second-year English. Alfred de Musset, Théophile Gautier, Victor Hugo, Stendhal in the Honours course: for now Leonard Tancock's bi-weekly lectures were sparkling on through the early nineteenth century.

And away from the world of print and paper, people.

Stephen Spender at Engsoc, retailing anecdotes of Auden as an undergraduate; a frivolous and unsatisfying evening.

Bessie Braddock, Member of Parliament for Liverpool Exchange, addressing a meeting of Labsoc, making intellectual mincemeat of the Tory members of Consoc who had turned up to barrack her, thinking a Scowse housewife would be an easy target for their wit.

But Nadia was no longer there to share it all.

Nightly, she stalked through his dreams, shaking her head when he tried to explain, to ask for forgiveness, to make promises of a fresh start. Waking he was dumb, unable to write and tell her why he could not return her letters, incapable of blotting out the bitter final paragraphs he had written her, the memory of which made him hot with grief and shame.

*

He would be paid, of course, for the hours he paraded in South Kensington. After the summer camp in July, there'd be two weeks' full pay to collect, with a bounty of £48 on top of that.

But what had also lured him to join the University Training Corps, was the prospect of getting a licence to drive every sort of vehicle from a motor-cycle to a ten-ton truck. He'd been denied a posting to the RASC in 1948, but here was a chance to make up for it. The driving test at every level was a formality, so the stories went. Just chauffeur the Adjutant round to the nearest pub, stand him a drink, answer a couple of questions, and that was that. The day he signed on with Sergeant-Major Howell, he made certain his name went down on the driving-instruction list.

Two weeks later a War Office Order was posted on the board: 'Conservation of Vehicles: No driving instruction will be given until further notice. This order to take effect forthwith.'

He was bitterly disappointed, but that was that. Nothing to be done. And look on the bright side, there was still the weapon-training and he had always enjoyed that. The pay would help to eke out his scholarship grant. But above all, the comforting thing about the UTC, as opposed to serving as a conscript, was the escape clause. Any cadet could quit at moment's notice, 'under pressure of examinations'.

*

As far as a motorbike licence was concerned, he had a second chance. His father had bought a Cyclemaster Winged Wheel. A heavy pushbike with pedals and a chain, the centre of its rear-wheel housed a tiny two-stroke engine. You needed a licence to ride it.

In 1951 a motor-bike was a motor-bike and, as far as a licence was concerned, engine-size counted for nothing. Pass the test on a Cyclemaster's ink-bottle-sized engine and you acquired the right to throw your L-plates into the dustbin, and take a 1,000-cc Vincent Black Shadow for a burn-up along the by-pass. Three Easters later he would pass the test on his father's Cyclemaster and the following morning ride to Suffolk on a 500-cc BSA Shooting Star with Emily's arms around his waist.

You had to pedal the Winged Wheel to get the engine running, and to stop it stalling on a steep hill. On the flat it would bowl you along at an effortless twelve miles an hour, until the spark-plug sooted up. When that happened, the plug had to be jiggled out with a spanner, while you burnt your fingers and got yourself filthy scraping away the whisker of carbonized oil that was short-circuiting the electrodes.

He went to the Post Office for a Provisional Driving Licence. After a fortnight of pleading, and a homily from his father — *you've GOT a Provisional licence? And what made you assume that I'd give you permission? Taking a lot on yourself, aren't you, my son?* — he was allowed to take the Winged Wheel for a spin. With celluloid L-plates clattering from the handle-bars and the carrier, he set off after breakfast on a Sunday in late October. He turned at the top of Honey Hill, thumbed the throttle wide open and took the road toward Billericay.

He had been sailing along for half an hour or more when he woke up with a flutter of panic to the fact that he was heading like a homing-pigeon for Pargetting and Malmesey Green.

*

It was low tide, and the waters of the estuary glittered distantly beyond the mudflats.

Now at the last gasp of Love's latest breath…

Oh God, why be so idiotic? Can I never take no for an answer?

But since he'd come this far…

He throttled down and rode a little further, then stopped to light a cigarette.

Yes, there it was, just visible through the unleafing trees, the slated roof of Rigg's boat-shed.

'Come on, lazybones… You haven't got time to admire the view…' Ellen Green straddling, grinning down at him.

Go on, then. Twist the knife.

The Winged Wheel snarled into the Sunday-empty streets of Pargetting. At the left-hand fork, he took a deep breath and swung away towards Malmsey Green.

He stopped by the church, and kicked the bike up onto the stand.

A dog barked nearby. He turned and saw Max, Leo Brant's corgi, scampering across the green. Judith Brant was stalking through the grass no more than the length of a cricket pitch away. She froze for an instant when she saw him.

Then she yelled to the dog to follow her and took to her heels, scampering away towards Bennets, and vanishing under the arch.

Moments later Mary Brant came out through the archway and strode across the green towards him.

'Yes, you,' she said. 'I want a word with you…

'I don't know what game you think you're playing, but the sooner you make yourself scarce the better. Don't you think you owe that much to my daughter? Haven't you hurt her enough?

'The least that you can do for that child is to stay out of her sight.'

Mrs Brant's eyes were staring directly into his own.

O God, what agonies of inquisition had Nadia been subjected to?

*

But he was not free of her.

On the first day of term a new student had joined the French department. Now, as the days ran down towards the solstice, she loitered near him, seeming to seek out his company. Moira. She was half-Irish and, like Nadia, blue-eyed and black-haired.

Perhaps, he asked himself, perhaps she might break the stranglehold of Nadia on his mind.

Moira. Fleet of wit and sharp of tongue. She had been working in the Foreign Office, she told him one morning.

'Do? What did I do? I suppose you could say I was a diplomatic bag,' she said, printing wet circles on the table with her coffee cup.

'Listen, why not come over to Westbourne Grove for a meal or a drink tomorrow evening?' Moira said, as they met in the doorway after a Friday-morning seminar. 'We could go through this week's translation together.'

Glad of any opportunity to silence his grief, he went along to the flat she shared with another girl. After the meal Moira sat by his side, taking turns to ferret through the dictionary and argue over the phrases they unearthed.

At a quarter to midnight he said, 'I'd better catch my bus before the last one leaves.'

'It left twenty minutes ago,' said Moira. 'You'll have to stay the night. That's fine by me. You can sleep in my bed.'

She went away to clean her teeth and came back wearing a nightdress. She bent over and kissed him.

Her glasses chinked against his, and she took hers off.

Nadia.

Innocent of glasses, Moira's face was the face of Nadia.

Misery smashed into his stomach.

He slept in Moira's bed that night — *that* she insisted upon — while she spent the night on a camp-bed somewhere. In the morning he found her clattering cups in the kitchen and went across and kissed her. She wrenched away.

'No,' she said. 'Forget it. OK? In fact, I think you'd better blow. Now, if you don't mind.'

He caught an early bus to Paddington, dispirited and longing for Nadia. Comforting himself that he had not so casually betrayed his love for her. And angry for having failed Moira. For the remainder of their time at University College, Moira flinched away when he looked towards her.

Before long another recollected face twisted his senses. Late one evening he was facing Krishna, a new friend, across a table-tennis table when, without warning, he found himself swamped by a wave of murderous hatred that left him weak and trembling.

He was incapable of returning a service and when it was his turn to serve, again and again watched the ball clatter across the floor or into the net. He refused a third game, and abandoned the match to Krishna.

He was hunched on a bench by the wall, contemplating Krishna as he took on another challenger, when recognition hit him. Blanch Krishna's dark skin to white, and his were the loathsome features of Lionel Voss.

With understanding, his affection for Krishna flooded back. But he could not forget and was appalled by the intensity of that moment of insidious and sudden hatred.

*

As for Nadia, within a few years, with a degree behind her, she married a historian and bore him children. By that time John Robbins had taken to frequenting Pargetting, assuming intimacies with Nadia's family and friends. He carried back knife-twisting reports of Nadia from time to time, retailing them to Robert with an almost smirking satisfaction. It seemed to be his way of exacting punishment for a relationship which he had disapproved of from the outset.

Nadia, dear heart. For the next fifteen years or so of his life, prowling the music-haunted corridors of Bennets in his dreams, he would go on meeting her. Trying to explain, trying to negotiate a peace.

'I shan't bless you for making me damaged goods.'

Her words — or her mother's? — haunted him. Was that *all* she would remember? Nothing but *damage*?

Perhaps it was.

And what sorrow had it cost Nadia to write that?

Later she would make her name as a writer of detective-stories, winning awards. From time to time he would scan the bookshop shelves and buy her latest work. In one novel he thought he recognized himself, with subtle alterations here and there. The surrounding details of time and place were precise enough, and Nadia herself was recognizable in Sally, the narrator.

His own alter ego was Sally's lover, a thin-lipped would-be killer in a story of witchcraft, amnesia, and false identities. Accelerating away in panic from a botched attempt to murder her, he swerved and struck a wall head-on, spilling his brains through a shattered windscreen.

*

'What's the Time? Time We had the Liberals back!'

In March 1950, the Liberal Party slogan, and the image of Big Ben which accompanied it, had seemed trenchant enough. Across Britain, 479 Liberal candidates stood for election. Ted Willis, a fellow conscript from Robert's days at Piddlehinton Camp, was acting as the Liberal party agent in Horsham, and asked Robert down for the final week to help him canvass. Their candidate was Miss Marchant, the retired Headmistress of Horsham Girls' School. She stood, without the remotest hope of winning, against Earl Winterton, a former cabinet minister, now sixty-six years of age, and Father of the House.

Ted and his assistant bucketed around Sussex in the back of Miss Marchant's Morris Minor, trailing up and down garden paths and knocking on cottage doors.

'Lectrick?' said one old lady, opening to his knock.

'I'm sorry, I didn't quite catch…'

'I said *LECTRICK!*' shouted the old lady, clearly thinking him deaf or simple-minded. 'From the *Lectrick*, ain't ye? The meter's under the *stairs*. You'll want a *torch*.'

'No, madam. Not *Elec-TRIC… Elec-TION*,' he said, smirking at his own wit. 'Can I interest you in the Liberal party?'

'No,' she said. 'Ye *can't*. I votes *Conservative*. Allus 'ave, allus *will*. You can tell 'em *that*. If ye ain't come to read the meter, ye can bugger orf.' And she slammed the door.

Ted and he and Miss Marchant and the retired Geography teacher who was her friend all met the same blank refusal often enough. An old man in another cottage doorway had more to say.

'Look, sir,' he said, 'this is a tied cottage, d'ye see? I couldn't vote otherwise than the landlord, now could I?'

'Why ever not? It's a secret ballot. Nobody knows how you vote.'

'Oh ah, sir?'

The old man smiled pityingly at the fool on his doorstep.

The election results, which left the Labour government in power but without an overall majority, were a disaster for the Liberal party. Of their 479 candidates, seven were elected. Three hundred others lost their deposits, at a total cost of £45,000. And since so many Liberal candidates had insured themselves against not winning at least the necessary tenth of the poll, Lloyds was badly hit.

In Horsham the result was predictable: Marchant (Liberal) 5,539, Nicholls (Labour) 11,204, Winterton (Conservative) 21,627. But at least Miss Marchant had not lost her deposit.

Trailing around the countryside in her wake, he had learned a number of things about electoral law. As an official canvasser, you may *not* legally ask people how they intend to vote. But, subtle sophistry, it is not illegal to ask, 'May I know, Sir (or Madam), where your sympathies lie?' Convicted criminals serving their sentence, he learned, are disqualified from voting. So are Peers of the Realm. So is a lunatic — 'except he hath lucid moments'.

And, a practical point: blarney people into handing over a subscription, however minuscule, and you give them a stake in your organization. From that moment you can depend on their vote.

Thirty pieces of silver ought to be enough, he told himself.

*

Now again, in 1951, after nineteenth months of minority government, Clement Attlee had gone to the country once more. In a general election in the last week of October, Winston Churchill returned to power with a majority of 17. At last, Labour's ascendancy, won in the landslide victory of 1945 and fatally weakened in the March 1950 election, was at an end.

John Robbins and he sat up through the night in John's front room, just as they had in 1950, chain-smoking and gulping down coffee while they listened to the radio. As the results came in, they scribbled down the votes awarded to each candidate.

John, now in his second year at the LSE, was still a keen student of politics, but after his brief experience as a party sub-agent, Robert's interest had become perfunctory. As he had come to see it now, the whole affair was nothing but a slambang performance for the electorate, greedy and cynical, frothy with insincerity. 'Don't Knows' apart, opinions were rigidly entrenched. The majority of electors, it seemed, were driven by fear of the unknown, and a bitter hatred of what they did not understand.

If canvassing in Horsham hadn't demonstrated it already, student Union elections at University College in 1951 made the effects of prejudice clear enough.

'Root for William Plant!' 'Fish for Valerie Salmon!' The posters, each with its stark text and a simple image of fish or flower, stood out among the wordy screeds displayed by other candidates for Union office. William Plant and Valerie Salmon wasted no words. They offered nothing. No self-congratulating rehearsal of their own achievements. No claptrap about their political ambitions. Nothing to argue against or be offended by. Simply their names, take them or leave them.

Inevitably, it seemed with hindsight, Valerie Salmon and William Plant topped the poll.

At which point it was discovered that neither William nor Valerie existed.

The affair bore out W.C. Fields' maxim: It's not a question of who you vote *for* that counts; it's who you vote *against*.

'ONLY', ran the campaign leaflet of the Perpetual Democracy Party in a later election at UCL, 'AT THE MOMENT THAT PEOPLE CAST THEIR VOTES, can democracy be said to exist. As soon as the chosen candidates take office, the electorate loses its power. Therefore we, your Democratic candidates, pledge ourselves, if elected, TO RESIGN IMMEDIATELY, and thus ensure the continuance of democracy.'

And so they did, three or four times in succession, until the joke grew stale and someone with malice prepense left a ballot-box uncollected long after the stipulated time. The election was invalidated and another swiftly carried through without warning.

*

Through a fortnight of nights before Christmas Day that year, he worked in a gang of male students from UCL, shifting Christmas mail at Liverpool Street station.

Out on the floodlit platforms, cupping numb fingers round a cigarette and shivering in the frost, waiting for a train to draw alongside. Clambering in and out of mail vans and guards' vans, within minutes labouring in a muck sweat. Shouldering letter-bags and brick-hard sacks of packages and parcels, and hefting them onto barrows. Shivering again as the linked barrows trundled away to the Post Office's own underground railway, where another gang unloaded them into the chutes.

Deep under London the driverless strings of GPO trucks clanged through their own dwarfish tunnels night and day. Once or twice he blarneyed his way down to the narrow strip of platform to see for himself. A waterfall of packets and packages was streaming from the chutes. A gang of GPO workers trundled them to the string of trucks that would deliver them to the sorting office at Mount Pleasant, a mile and a half away. He went through to the switchroom to watch as a slowly turning shaft tripped the circuit breakers that slowed the locomotives to a stop or slammed them into action. Half-asleep and dreaming on his feet in the small hours of the night, it seemed as if he had dwindled down to matchbox size, and was trapped in the clockwork train-set he'd played with as a child.

Above on the wind-swept platforms, there were priorities of livestock and perishables to be adhered to. Wicker-baskets of racing-pigeons, off with the early-morning trains to be released at distant stations. Stacked gallon-cans of synthetic cream en route to bakers and confectioners. A dead weight of sausages in cardboard boxes that broke their backs if you picked them up by the middle and didn't get both arms under them. There were punnets of mushroom stalks to be made into soup in London restaurants. There were crates of ferrets for rural sportsmen on Boxing Day. He learned to pick up the ferrets with hands held flat against the wire-netting sides of the crate. But only after the first time, when his fingertip poked through the wire and he'd snatched it back bloody and bitten through almost to the bone.

At last — after the slog and the camaraderie and the yawning, reeling journey home to bed on Christmas morning; after waking to fetch his wallet and thumb through the money he'd earned — *double* time for night work and *treble* time for the after-midnight hours of Christmas Day; after shaving, and scrambling off to All Saints for midday communion and O Come All Ye Faithful; after dinner, and sausage-stuffed goose and whisky-flamed pudding and sherry trifle; after swapping presents, and kissing his mother, and sucking a cheroot alongside his father while his mother puffed a pink cigarette with a gilded tip — after all *that,* he was alone with himself again, and Nadia thrust herself back into his mind. And would not quit him.

'Don't sit there moping,' said his mother. 'Let me see a nice smile.'

*

On Boxing Day he sat down to draw a tree for Jacques, who was taking a course in psychology at the University of Brussels. *'Dessinez-moi un arbre.'* Jacques had written. 'Draw me a tree. Do it in ink. Don't give more than four minutes to it; time yourself.' It was a new sort of personality test, Jacques wrote, and he was gathering samples from his friends.

He fetched ink and paper and, recalling a hawthorn across the meadows, he drew it as well as he could. Leafless and autumnal, as he had last seen it, with a few scattered fistfuls of berries. It had been undermined over the years by floods, and its roots clawed the earth like finger-bones. He had always found it beautiful.

He knew its botanical name, *Crataegus monogyna,* and wondered whether to label his sketch. When it was finished, he picked it up from time to time to admire it, and he took it with him to John's, where Mrs Robbins had invited him to tea.

'Why don't *you* draw a tree for Jacques?' he told John. 'I can send it along with mine. Four minutes. I'll time you.'

John laboured for barely ninety seconds and was done. His tree looked like a shaving-brush, appliqued with fruit the size of medicine balls. What on earth were *they* supposed to be?

'Apples,' said John indignantly. 'You said an apple tree.'

'Not at all,' he said. 'I never said apple. Just "a tree". I've drawn Jacques a thorn-tree myself. An real one, down by the river. See? It's really a portrait, in fact. What do you think of it?'

Jacques' tone, when he next wrote, was strange. His letter was a tissue of unfocussed advice and thoughts about the meaning of life. Not a word about his, or John's, tree. Although prompted in subsequent letters, Jacques never remembered to report what his tutor had said about the drawings.

Not until three years later when he came over from Brussels, did Jacques speak about the test: *l'arbre de Koch*. It was a measure of personality, devised by Koch in 1949. Artistic skill was irrelevant. Brushing aesthetics aside, what Jacques' psychology tutor was interested in was the image of selfhood offered by each drawing. *That* was the point of the test. Koch's tree was *you*. In drawing a tree you drew yourself. John, laden with fruit — at the end of the academic year he would get a first in Geography — was someone well contented with himself. As for Robert's tree, 'That one is tormented,' said Jacques' tutor. 'Do not be surprised if he takes his own life.'

Which explained the tone of Jacques' letters at that earlier time.

Tormented? Yes, but the roots of his riverside thorn still clung to the racing earth, and had not been wrenched away. Even in the tree's name, the hindsight of later years would tell him, he had flung down a clue, all unaware. An insidious play on words. *Crataegus monogyna.*

Monogyna. Single. Female.

One woman.

Nadia.

32

SALISBURY PLAIN

He was sailing down Southampton Row on the back of a brewer's lorry, surrounded by a surging mob of duffel-coated men and blanket-draped and broomstick-waving women. As the lorry stopped and started they lurched into one another, chanting snatches of *Beowulf*. Their helmets were colanders tied under their chins with string. Painted banners — OUR BAWDS ARE WATERTIGHT — fluttered along each side of the lorry, port and starboard, *bækbord* and *stéorbord*. A snarling cardboard dragon's-head jolted from side to side above the cab. They were Viking warriors.

In 1951 he had kept clear of the goings-on in Rag Week. But in 1952, grateful for every distraction, he stayed around and gave the Rag Week harangues a hearing. The student-members of the French department, few in number, could not afford to hire a lorry for the parade. So he had joined the members of the English department on their Viking float. Throughout the voyage to Waterloo, a drunken stowaway in a hooded duffel-coat leaned out over the stern of the lorry shrieking, 'Come! Come! Wives and Virgins, Old Women and Maidens, come! Confess your Sins to the Venereal Bead.'

As the procession swung left into Aldwych, the chant of the Vikings switched to '*All* King's students *are* illegitimate, Buggering about in the Strand', bawled to the tune of *Here we Sit Like Birds in the Wilderness*. The berserker Viking maidens lobbed festoons of lavatory-paper into an enemy crowd that seethed along the pavements all the way to Waterloo Bridge. They walloped the knuckles of would-be boarders with their broomsticks and helped to fling their owners back into the road. In the Strand an attacker clung one-handed to the lorry's gunwale, and clouted Robert's jaw. Robert Hammerfist thumped him back and he fell away into the sea of faces.

At Waterloo, on the concrete wasteland alongside the Thames where the pavilions had stood in Festival year, they stripped the floats of their trappings. They heaped up all the debris in a pile and set it alight as darkness fell. Members of Queen Mary College, Kings and UCL jeered and struggled around the bonfire, leaping through the flames. Rival debagging-gangs marauded through the brawling crowds. Somebody was thrown into the Thames.

Grist, all of it.

But without Nadia to share the story, his presence there seemed futile. The Rag and all the effort it absorbed was childish and pointless. As pointless as the constant kidnapping and snatching back of Phineas, UCL's snuff-taking highlander mascot, and Reggie, Kings' tin-plate lion. As forced as the high-spirits which tradition enjoined them to lay down, like vintage wine, for future nostalgia: 'God, d'you remember the time we hammered Reggie flat? Hah! Have *your* lot forgotten how we sank Phineas in the Thames with a marker buoy? And sent him carriage forward to Inverness? And buried him on Hampstead Heath?'

Greying men and women giggling together.

In 1930 — newspaper clippings filed in Pi office told the story — the then comradely students of Kings' and UCL had battled with Imperial College, their common rival. A gang of them smashed down a hoarding in the Euston Road, stacked the planks around a lamp-post in Museum Street, and burned the Provost of King's College in effigy. When the cast-iron column cracked and gas began flaring at the main, the undergraduate mob attacked the fire-brigade and repelled the baton-charging police until reinforcements overwhelmed them.

With the Monkswood school election vivid in his mind, the escalation from farce into open riot and destruction was no surprise.

*

Julia, when he met her, did not exorcise the ghost of Nadia, although for a while he hoped she might. She was twenty years old, in her second-year of reading Law at UCL. Educated at a public-school, fluent in French, Julia was an disturbing mixture of self-possession and naivety, as at ease standing in for her mother at Masonic Ladies' Nights, as she was in disputing a point of law. She could be casually outspoken, surprising him one day by announcing out of the blue that she'd not begun to menstruate until she was eighteen. At other moments he found her ignorance difficult to believe. Confronted with the concept of 'unlawful carnal knowledge', she took out the pound note that marked the place in her textbook, read the phrase aloud, and asked him what it meant.

'Illegal sexual intercourse,' he said.

'But what *is* sexual intercourse? What goes on?' she said. 'What do people *do*? Please *tell* me.'

He could not believe that she was asking him a serious question. But she was.

It was her habit to leave banknotes in her books, to mark the place.

From her first term onward, Julia had been a dinghy captain in UCL's sailing-club at the Welsh Harp in Hendon, and now she taught him how to sail the club's twelve-foot Fireflies. He abandoned rugger, and after lunch on Wednesdays stood at her side in the courtyard, looking up at the revolving metal cowl on a high chimney. If it was spinning fast, there would be a good breeze at the Harp, so they took the tube to Neasden and tacked up and down, hooking their toes under the straps on the centreboard-case and arching the weight of their bodies back above the water, until night fell.

On windless Wednesday afternoons they sat in a cinema or, if the weather was warm and dry enough, they went to Hampstead Heath, and lay with their books amidst the gorse until it was too dark to read. From time to time they kissed, after that February day on the Heath when Julia gave him a sideways smile and said, 'You know, don't you, that there's a rule that you may only kiss when the gorse is in flower?'

He glanced around and detected a tiny blaze of yellow nearby. 'In which case—' he said. He brushed her cheek with his lips, still haunted by the memory of Nadia.

'Gorse blooms all the year round. Didn't you know that?' she said, kissing him on the mouth and seeking his tongue with hers. But that was the inviolable limit of their love-making.

They invariably wound up their Hampstead afternoons eating roes on toast in a cafe.

They wrote to one another in vacation time but never met out of term. Julia had plans for her future, and clung to them unflinchingly. Ll.B, Ll.M, bar exams, then a high-level position in the legal department of some large organization. When she was twenty-nine, and *not* before, she would think about marriage.

*

Suddenly the summer term and the two-year English-subsidiary course were racing towards an end.

His daily reading tracked and re-tracked through Old- and Middle-English texts and thereafter along a time-line that began with the Elizabethans, moved on through the Interregnum and the Restoration, and stopped short before the Romantics. Spenser, the Metaphysical poets, and Milton in his *Comus* mood enchanted him, as did Chaucer's *Canterbury Tales* and the rhyme royal of his *Troylus and Cryseyde*. But, *Beowulf* and *The Battle of Maldon* excepted, he yawned as he plodded through the Old-English texts.

At the end of a week of afternoons consecrated to re-reading the sixteenth- and seventeenth-century set books, he spent the last evening before Part I finals in his bedroom, boning up on Old English. Along with everyone else in the group, he had pored over the examination questions of the previous five years in the hope of predicting the passages the examiners would have settled on for translation and comment in summer 1952. Now he thumbed back and forth through *Beowulf*, blowing away the cigarette ash that fell on them, mouthing his way again and again through three passages which he had chosen as likeliest to come up.

The coffee-percolator was long cold and the ashtray overflowing, when he switched off the light. Satisfied that he'd done all he could, he lay down and closed his eyes. It was after three o'clock.

Within moments he fell awake into nightmare... *beset by monsters, plunging to the sea's depths hour and hour-long in the grip of a foul sea-troll.*

Ða se eorl on3eat,
þæt he in nið-sele nat-hwylcum wæs
þær him næni3 wæter wihte ne sceþede...

Then he came to himself in a fearsome hall where flowed no water that might work him scathe...

There in the firelight's glare he saw the hag, and struck at her. But now his blade-edge was turned by her flesh, and failed him in his uttermost need. He gripped the hag's hair and flung her down. Swiftly she snatched him in her claws, kneeling upon him and thrusting with her dagger, but she could not pierce his coat of mail.

Then he, breaking free, seized a war-sword from among the treasure, and swung it in fury, in mortal despair, straight at the throat, breaking the bone-rings. Her corpse convulsed, the skull severed…

Whereafter, wonder of wonders, the great broad-sword, rotted by her venomous blood, wilted and dripped away in iron icicles… Of the treasures in that hall he seized but two, the monstrous head and the precious sword-hilt, ablaze with gemstones…

Then he fell truly awake into 1952, and his bedroom in Honey Hill on the day of the Part I English Subsidiary exam. It was now almost four in the morning.

Yes, yes. A phallic dream of detumescence, it went without saying. *Beowulf* and *Jabberwocky*. Though Carroll mentioned no after-battle deliquescence in his hero's snicker-snacking blade. But the bright nightmare seemed to be an omen.

The passage — Beowulf's fight to the death with Grendel's mother — was not one of the pieces he had picked for intense revision. Never mind that. He got up, opened the text and went through the Old-English verses again and again.

When he turned over the question paper in the examination hall the following morning —

Ða se eorl on3eat, þæt he in nið-sele nat-hwylcum wæs —

the nightmare text stared up at him, familiar, hacked and acid-burnt into his brain.

He sailed into the whole of the paper on a great tide of euphoria.

*

'Right-oh, lads. There it is, then,' said Sgt-Major Howell. ''imber. What's left of it. Time to fall out now for a spit and a draw.'

The University Training Corps Infantry Sub-Unit — Tom, Mike 1, Kunle, Bob, Mike 2, and James — halted, stacked their weapons against the eight-foot-high wire fence, and flung themselves down on the turf. Kunle sat up again to groan and rub his shoulder.

'That Bren gun,' he said, catching Bob's eye.

James offered his packet of Player's around. 'Give it a rest, Kunle,' he said.

Behind the wire the graveyard at Imber was a jungle of waist-high grass. The church tower was blistered and chipped. Here and there the roof of the nave had been broken by shrapnel, and there were gaping holes in the window glass. Two hundred paces away at the foot of a slope, the streets of the village were heaped with rubble.

So this was Imber. Post-war Ordnance Survey maps didn't mention the place. The War Office had commandeered it in the 1940s as ideal terrain for D-Day troops to hone their skills in house-to-house fighting. There had been a fuss, Bob vaguely remembered, at the end of the war when the villagers had wanted to return to their homes and had been met with a blank refusal.

Too much unexploded stuff lying around, perhaps. Mortar bombs, shells. Not to speak of rifle ammunition. In the pocket of Bob's battledress there was a live ·303 round that he'd loitered for a moment to prise out of the rabbit-bitten turf. It was corroded with verdigris but outwardly intact.

'Can't we loose off a few mortar shells?' said Mike 2. 'I'm sick of lugging them around.'

'What use is a Bren gun when it won't fire properly? It's killing my arm,' said Kunle.

'You're out of condition, the lot of you,' said Sgt-Major Howell. 'Duw, what's a four-mile bash to an infantryman? I take you all for a leisurely after-breakfast stroll across Salisbury Plain in the sunshine, and you're puffing and blowing like grampuses, isn't it? Yes, yes, all right, then, we'll practise laying down a smoke screen in a while.'

*

After a year of evening parades in the examination halls at South Kensington, the UTC was on summer camp and quartered in Tidworth barracks. For Cadet-Corporal Druce, Tidworth was familiar ground. It was three years since he had sauntered through its lines in hospital blues, every pub put out of bounds by the uniform he wore.

Then he had been a conscript. *Here and now* he was a volunteer, retracing those earlier patterns, contemplating them from an alternative angle. Redeeming the past, in a way.

As a conscript you were under discipline, compelled into submission, in dire trouble if you rebelled. Basic training and its contemptible punishments — shouting back 'I am a sack of shit tied up in the middle, *Sah!*', doubling round the square with your rifle over your head, scrubbing a concrete floor with soap and a toothbrush — all of that was designed to humiliate you, to break your spirit. At *that* time the landscapes beyond the perimeter wire had been for days at a stretch a no-man's land.

Here and now, the whole tenor of life was different. A cadet was his own master. A smart back-answer was laughed at, even on the barrack-square. At the time of his own choosing he could plead 'pressure of examinations' and quit the service. Off-duty he was free to stroll where he cared to and keep his own counsel. When a Military Policeman accosted Mike 1 and Tom in a Salisbury pub and demanded to know what the 'UTC' on their shoulder-flashes stood for, the pair of them looked him in the eye. 'UP THE CREEK', they told him, and turned their backs.

Mounting night-guard at summer camp was a shambolic, unsoldierly affair. With their rifles locked away for the night in the armoury, the UTC cadets patrolled the camp perimeter with pick-handles in their hands. Fifty yards away, inside the main gate of a regular-army barracks, a man on sentry-go marched back and forth along a strip of concrete with his rifle at the slope, brilliantly lit by floodlights. It became a nightly joke for the patrolling UTC guard to lurk in the shadows and challenge the floodlit sentry, 'Halt! Who goes there?' to test his mettle.

*

The sometime village of Imber was lost in a thick cloud of smoke as the infantry sub-unit marched away in the midday sun. Sixty of the seventy-two smoke bombs that they had started the day with had been loaded into their two-inch mortar, and dropped among the rubble of former streets. Now as they marched, there were only two cases left to carry.

Six hundred yards or so ahead, a car had stopped in a hollow and two men were quartering the ground.

'Trespassing on War-Department property, they are. See them? Civilians,' said Sgt-Major Howell. 'What are they up to, then? Let's go look see.'

As the group of territorials drew closer to them, the two civilians hurried to their car and drove away. They halted at the top of a distant rise.

Nearby there was wailing cry, like the scream of a child in terror.

'Hear that?'

Sgt-Major Howell broke into a run.

A moment later he fell to his knees and aimed a savage blow downwards with the edge of his hand. The screaming stopped. 'Bastards,' he said, and stood up. There was a sprung steel trap in his hand, and from it dangled the body of the rabbit he had put out of its agony, still held fast by a mangled and bloody leg.

'This won't be the only one,' he said. 'Scout around and fetch them here. Poor little creature.'

The men in the car were still spying from their safe distance, as eight more traps, three of them sprung and bloody, but all empty, were piled together by Sgt-Major Howell into a hollow in the grass. He draped the dead rabbit over them.

'Against the law these are,' he said. 'Illegal. Vicious bloody things. Wild creatures get caught in them, they'll bite through their own flesh and bone, crazy to free themselves. If I had my way...' His eyes were brimming with tears.

'Now, then. Lesson time. Dealing with a shell that fails to explode. Or a grenade. Now is as good a time as any for you to learn how it's done.'

He reached into his pack and brought out a length of fuse and what looked like three over-sized cotton-reels. He found a cardboard box and took out a piece of copper tubing.

'Fuse, gun-cotton, detonator,' he said. He lined up the cylinders of gun-cotton underneath the pile of traps.

'A yard of slow fuse, that's ample,' he said. 'Watch now. Take hold of one end, leaving half an inch of it sticking out beyond your finger and thumb. See? No more than that, unless you're hoping to blow your hand off. Push it into the open end of the detonator, till it's stopped short by your finger and thumb. You all seen that? Right. Now get yourselves away out of 'yere. Fifty yards to be on the safe side. And lie down when you get there.'

He stooped to slide the detonator through the central holes in the gun-cotton as the others turned to run. He looked round to check on them and stooped again with his petrol lighter flaming. A moment later he flung himself down among them.

There was a distant crash.

'Duw,' he said. 'Always puts the wind up me, having to mess about with detonators. But it's what *you*'ll all find yourselves doing, if you're on duty at the range and there's a misfire...

'Those bastard poachers can kiss goodbye to their rabbit-traps. Scrap metal, they'll be now...

'I hate cruelty to animals. Makes me see red...

'Come on, then. On your feet. We've still a couple of miles to go and a trench to dig.'

'It's all right for you,' said Kunle, hefting the Bren once more. 'Only having rifles to carry. This thing weighs a hundredweight.'

'Twenty-seven pounds, in point of fact...' said James.

'You volunteered, Kunle. Remember?' said Mike 1. 'You insisted on being given the machine-gun. It's not our fault that it won't cock itself with blanks. You can always fire single shots and cock it again by hand. We're on an exercise, remember? We're not firing live rounds at one another.'

'Stop bickering,' said Sgt-Major Howell. 'Or I'll have silence in the ranks.'

'Why did you give me the machine-gun, if it won't work? Why me? Because I'm a black man. O yes. Let the black man do the dirty work. That's the real reason.'

'O, for Christ's sake,' said Bob. 'Grab my rifle, Kunle. *I'll* carry the bloody Bren.'

*

'You'd dig quick enough, boyo, if the enemy was to chuck a few shells over.' Sgt-Major Howell thumped Bob on the shoulder. 'You'd be four foot down through that chalk like a fox terrier.'

Stripped to the waist, the six of them were excavating a slit trench just below the tree-covered top of a ridge. Three inches under the turf, the subsoil was flint-impacted chalk, bone-hard. More than six cubic yards of it had to be hacked out with the pick-end of their trenching-tools, scooped into sandbags with the shovel-end, and dumped out of sight among the trees.

Woodsmoke drifted across from the fire of pine-cones and dead branches where a bucketful of water was coming to the boil. Sgt-Major Howell opened his haversack and emptied a pint of evaporated milk, a pound of sugar and two packets of tea into the bucket. 'Sar'nt Major's tea,' he said. 'She'll be brewed in ten minutes. See how much you can shift before then.'

Kunle groaned and dropped his trenching-tool. He stood up straight to ease his back.

'Right, that man. Give the digging a rest and scout around for a few branches, will you? Enough to roof over the side-arm of the trench…'

'Finding it hard going, that one,' said Sgt-Major Howell, as Kunle vanished among the trees. 'Not used to hard graft…'

'*We* aren't used to hard graft,' said Tom. 'But we don't go on and on about it. Kunle should do his share. That's all we ask. But every time he always turns it round that we're putting on the black man.'

'It's awkward in the mornings,' said James. '*We're* waiting to get the room swept ready for inspection, and *he's* crouching on his gas-cape, banging his head on the floor and praying to Mecca. I mean, I know he's got to pray, but…'

'Give and take, give and take,' said Sgt-Major Howell. 'Back home in Nigeria he's probably a somebody. Not expected to do manual work. Mark of inferiority for him, probably. Then he comes over 'yere and gets nothing but insults thrown at him, isn't it? Being black. But you're his comrades in arms. Fellow students. So give him a bit of leeway. Throw him a good word when he's doing well. Keep him happy. Isn't it?'

The tea, when it was ready, was a muddy orange fluid, almost terra-cotta in colour. It was acrid, cloyingly-sweet. When they'd emptied their scalding-hot mess-tins and trampled out the fire, they found themselves hacking and shovelling with a huge burst of fresh energy.

As soon as the tee-shaped trench was deep enough, they roofed the side-arm with Kunle's branches and a sheet of corrugated iron that Bob and Mike 2 had come across among the trees when they'd gone there for a piss. It was time for every crumb of the chalk that had been piled over the iron, and packed along the downhill side of the trench to form a firestep, to be hidden under sods of turf.

'16.00 hours. Any minute now there'll be umpires across the valley there, doing their best to spot your trench. Get your battledress blouses back on. Try to look tidy, isn't it? Muddy hands, red faces, white boots: you don't look like most people's idea of a soldier,' said Sgt-Major Howell.

'One minute,' said Bob, and fled back into the wood with his trenching-tool. He came back carrying a clump of violets and lovingly positioned it on the firestep, as a four-wheel drive jounced up the slope and stopped a few yards short of them. Major-General Mulliner RAMC and his aide-de-camp stepped out. The infantry sub-unit came to attention.

'Now don't try to tell me you scruffy, feeble-looking lot of scallywags have dug that trench,' said the General. He peered more closely at their work. 'What the hell's that on the firestep?'

'Violets,' said 023 Druce.

'*Violets?*'

'One ought to take pleasure in beauty, sir, even in time of war.'

General Mulliner goggled for a moment. He turned to his aide-de-camp. 'Thunderflashes,' he bawled. 'Get under cover, you lot. You're under fire!'

They scrambled into the trench, packing themselves as far as they could up the side-arm, under the corrugated iron roof. Bob was the last.

'Beauty? I'll show you beauty!' roared the General, lobbing three thunderflashes one after the other at Bob's back. 'Violets!'

Each explosion thumped like a kidney-punch.

*

22.00 hours found them squatting alongside all the other UTC sub-units around a blazing log-fire, swallowing more terra-cotta-coloured tea from one of their mess-tins, and frying pork sausages in their own fat in the other. Kunle, Moslem as he was, ate and drank hungrily, making no comment on the pork.

The three-tonners that had brought up the supplies had all been unloaded, the tents erected, and their floors strewn with a thick layer of bracken from the adjacent wood. Soon there'd be nothing left to do but wipe out their mess-tins, rake over the embers of the fire, spread their gascape-groundsheets over the bracken, and turn in.

The eight-man Intelligence sub-unit had been the last to arrive. Two of its members, separated by some fifty yards, were still playing with their radio receiver/transmitters and still failing to make contact with one another. Suddenly one of the sets began to squawk. After a moment, 'Christ!' said the operator in a voice everyone could hear, and ran, stumbling over sprawling men, to the CO.

The CO blew a whistle. 'Silence! Pay attention! We're striking camp. Now. Get the tents down. Never mind packing up properly. Just get them and yourselves and your equipment back on the trucks as quick as you can. We're pulling out. Sergeant-Major? A word.'

A quarter of an hour later the convoy halted a mile and a half away across the heathland. At the roll-call two men were missing.

Sgt-Major Howell sent back a three-tonner to collect them. 'And drive like the bloody wind,' he told the driver, 'if you want to see tomorrow.'

'Stupid sort of a joke,' said Tom, labouring to untangle a bundled-up tent.

'It's the old man's idea of realism,' somebody answered out of the half-darkness. He put on the throaty drawl of the CO, who on weekdays was a big wheel in the University Admissions office. 'Always expect the unexpected. I do.'

'Nah. It's his idea of a joke.'

'Not this time,' said Sgt-Major Howell, coming across to his infantrymen. 'That radio message was an order to get the hell out of there. Right in the middle of a practice-bombing range, we were. Piece of luck that someone picked up our transmissions and got a bearing on us. The RAF are on their way to give the place a pasting.'

The three-tonner returned with the missing pair. They'd gone off into the wood to relieve themselves and had come back to see a string of tail-lights vanishing. They hadn't got over their panic yet.

As the six men of the infantry sub-unit flung themselves down onto their groundsheets, this time without the benefit of bracken, there was the sound of aircraft engines overhead, and flares began to light up the sky.

'So much for military organization,' someone said.

'SNAFU,' said Tom. 'Typical. Situation Normal: All Fucked Up.'

'Who got the map-reference wrong? That's what I'd like to establish,' said Bob. 'My money's on that Lieutenant Brown who's supposed to be in charge of the I-Corps lot. He took them on a map-reading exercise last week. They all ended up in a field of pigs eighty yards away from the front-door of the pub where he'd gone to wait for them. Fuming and raving that they didn't know how to use a prismatic compass...'

'Yeah, I heard that,' Mike 2 put in. 'Then they found out that he'd done his trial survey wearing a steel helmet.'

'What's wrong with that?' said Kunle.

'Steel. Buggers up the magnetism,' said Mike 2. 'All his readings were miles out. What's the betting the man's a Lecturer in Geography?'

'Bound to be,' said Bob.

'Knock it off, you two,' said Mike 1. 'Get to sleep.'

*

Dawn light. 023 Druce was alone, barely awake but staring cautiously all around him, limping down a broad path between trees with his rifle cocked and at the ready. He and the other five had separated to reconnoitre the wood, aware that an enemy group were somewhere in the offing.

The enemy sentry, when he stumbled across him, was bedded in a heap of leaves, his rifle levelled down the ride along which Druce had been so clumsily creeping.

'Am I dead?' said Druce.

'What?'

'Did you shoot me? You never said "bang!"'

'*Bang?* No.'

'You must have had me in your sights for the last five minutes.'

'Look. Why don't you just take me prisoner? *You* can be dead if you want to. But I've given up playing. I've been lying here for the last bloody half-hour. I'm freezing cold. My leg keeps going to sleep. So sod it. I've had enough of it. It must be getting on for breakfast time. Here, take my rifle. I surrender.'

'Very well. You are my prisoner and will come with me. And you can carry your own bloody rifle.'

*

By 11.00 hours the re-united infantrymen had loosed off the rest of their smoke-bombs at a derelict tank and were holed up in a dry ditch, peering out across the ground ahead for signs of movement, when a runner arrived from the RAMC, asking for a volunteer to be a casualty.

'Me,' said Druce, stumbling to his feet. 'My right heel is chafed raw.'

Two hundred yards back from the front line, one of the dozen medical students who made up the RAMC sub-unit stuck a length of zinc-oxide strapping on the raw flesh of his heel.

'That's not enough,' said the medic. 'You've got to have something more serious than a blistered heel. How about a busted thigh? We can do a busted femur, can't we, chaps?'

'All right,' said Druce. 'You can say I was hit by the blast from a mortar bomb. Will that do you? Or would you like anything else? How about yellow fever?'

'Anyone know the drill for yellow fever? Ah. Sorry, no. Yellow fever's a bit over the top. Especially in Wiltshire. Pick something else.'

'Beri-beri?'

'Nah.'

'Tertiary syphilis?'

'Syph? O, sure. Can do. Right. A million units of penicillin for the syph. And a Thomas splint. Whack in some morphia first, I suppose. You can take that as done. Hah, I've always wanted to get someone into a Thomas. Give us the stirrup, someone.'

'You want to watch him,' said a voice in Druce's ear, as a gang of medics cocooned his leg in bandages and a metal splint. 'We have to make believe about injections. But the bandaging's for real. Give Jumbo his head with that tourniquet and he'll pull your bloody leg off. Yelp if it hurts.'

'So what have we got here? Give us a shufti at yer notes.' Suddenly Major-General Mulliner's face was floating above the patient. 'Mortar wound right femur. Yes, yes. Morphia. Good old Thomas. Sorted out which leg is which, have ya? Well, get on with it, wind it up, put him in traction…'

'Hang on a minute, I know that face. *Violets!* You're the pansy with the violets, ain't ya?'

There was a dutiful titter from the medical students.

General Mulliner peered at the notes again. 'What's this then, hey? Syph? Feller's got *syph*? What are you prescribing for *that*? What? Speak up,' said the Major-General. 'Ah…

'Tell you what. Second opinion,' he said. 'Dig a trench and bury the bugger. Best thing all round. Stick a bunch of violets up his arse. Haw haw.'

*

Life presents a gloomy picture,
Dark and dismal as the tomb…

The four-square Haydn chorale common to 'Glorious things of thee are spoken,' and '*Deutschland, Deutschland über alles*' boomed through a haze of smoke. Pint glass in one hand, cigar in the other, Major-General Mulliner was leading his fellow medical men in raucous song. They'd been at it with barely a pause for the better part of an hour.

> Father's got an anal stricture,
> Mother's got a fallen womb.
> Sister Susie's been aborted
> For the forty-second time…

It was the final night of the summer camp. They were all two weeks' pay plus £48 bounty better off. Time for a farewell party.

Sgt-Major Howell sat smoking his pipe in the midst of his infantrymen. From minute to minute he frowned across at General Mulliner in disapproval. 'Conduct unbecoming, in my opinion,' he said. 'Still, there's officers for you, isn't it?'

It had been a good fortnight all considered. A chance to get out in the fresh air for days at a stretch, to take a holiday from book-learning and quieten the voice of Nadia in his dreams, to forget the final examination papers looming ahead, to look no farther than the physical needs of the moment. Strategy. Tactics. Weapon training every second day. Revolvers, sten guns, mortars and plastic high explosive along with the everyday rifles and brens. The two-day exercise. At the de-briefing he'd tipped four verdigris-corroded rounds out of his pocket.

'Not thinking of firing them, were you?' Sgt-Major Howell had said. 'In that state they could split your rifle barrel. Know what the pressure is at the moment of firing? Nineteen-and-a-half tons per square inch. Open up your barrel like a banana those things could. Give 'em 'yere, I'll hand them over to the armourer to dispose of. Can't have you carrying souvenirs home, isn't it?'

*

But he had other souvenirs. Wandering round Salisbury at the weekend with Tom and Mike 1, he'd bought a Bible for six shillings in a second-hand bookshop. It was bound in heavily-tooled leather with a fretworked brass clasp and brass corners. As he entered the shop, the bookseller eyed him and gestured to a salesgirl, clearly expecting a soldier in uniform to be up to no good. The girl followed him up and down between the rows of bookshelves.

When he set the Bible down and picked up the first volume of a folio edition of Shakespeare, she hovered at his elbow. 'Yes? Can I help you?' she said pointedly.

The twin volumes were bound in red buckram with gold-tooled leather spines and quarterings. They were lavishly illustrated with steel engravings. 'The Imperial Shakespeare, 2-vols: £1,' read the card trapped between the gilt-edged pages.

'Take this,' he said, putting the book into the assistant's hands, 'and come with me. I'll bring the other volume.'

The bookseller was hovering at his desk, staring at him as he as he approached with the girl close at heel.

'Good afternoon,' said 023 Druce. 'Here is six shillings for this Bible. I will take it with me now. And here is a pound for the Shakespeares. I would like you to weigh them and tell me what the cost of sending them on by post will be so that I can pay for that, too. While I am waiting, I will write out my address for you. And you might like to remember that every man in uniform is not necessarily illiterate or a thief.'

*

Twelve days later there was a bang at the door of the Druce's house in Honey Hill. The postman was standing on the step with a folio-sized parcel in his hand.

'Bloody imposition,' he said. 'Having to cart great heavy parcels around in me bag.'

'Where's the other one?' said Robert. 'There should be two. There's only one volume here.'

'Listen, mate,' said the postman in a sudden fury. 'If you think I'm going cart two of 'em in one go, you've got another think coming. You'll get the other one tomorra. Or the day after. *If* you're lucky. You ain't the only customer on me walk, don't think it.'

33

RUE DE SEINE

From the moment that Nadia and he had become lovers, he had stayed away from church. How could you kneel down and beg forgiveness for a sin — the sin of IMPURITY, his tattered *Altar Book for Servers* called it — which you had no intention of giving up? *Almighty and most merciful Father; We have erred, and strayed from thy ways like lost sheep. We have followed too much the devices and desires of our own hearts... And there is no health in us...* What would be the point of an empty and hypocritical recital?

He argued the case with John Robbins. 'The church is for *sinners*,' John insisted, carefully tapping the ash from his cigarette, and squinting upwards so that the whites of his eyes flickered. 'It's where you ought to go to ask for God's aid in avoiding sin. You don't need to tell *me* why you've suddenly stopped going to church.'

But Robert was not to be convinced. Making *use* of someone — exploiting them — yes, of course *that* was a sin. Before or after marriage, with or without a public declaration and benefit of clergy. But, stiff-necked and casuistical as he clearly was in John Robbins' eyes, he saw nothing shameful in his love for Nadia. When they lay in one another's arms, theirs was an act of joy. Not shame. 'She is all states, and all princes, I... Nothing else is.' Nadia saw it, so she insisted, in that way too. 'Sin' it might be from the viewpoint of the church, very well. But they saw no reason to renounce what they shared only for the sake of holding up their heads in church.

But now that their fragile world had broken apart in so bitter a fashion, he was possessed by an aching sadness that Nadia should have come to resent the past. Neither he nor she had ever foreseen such an ending. Yet now... In his own eyes no-one — not God, and least of all he himself — had any power to forgive him from having brought her unhappiness.

But at John Robbins' insistence he returned to All Saints.

Things there had changed. The Reverend Stanford had left to take up a missionary post in Australia, and the parish was now in the charge of the Reverend Ellis. During those immediate post-war years, the River estate had surged across the pasture and ploughland northwards as far as Woodlands Green and south towards the Warrens, doubling the size of the parish. The River estate had its own church now, with its own priest-in-charge. And for the past year the Reverend Ellis's curate, The Reverend Pryke had been busily ingratiating himself with the congregations in both halves of the parish.

Ronald Pryke, BA had acquired a Diploma in Theology after his army service in Germany. He organized parish evenings, brought new blood into the Youth groups, and roped in their members for pilgrimages, tea squashes and woodland picnics. He encouraged prayer and Bible-study meetings in young people's homes. Hail-fellow-well-met, he liked to be called Ron. He was thirty-six years old, engagement and marriage were in the air, and half-a-dozen parish virgins were setting their caps at him.

'You must join our Youth group,' he told Robert.

'I'm off to a TA camp next week for a fortnight,' Robert had answered. 'After that, perhaps. Well yes, why not?'

*

The walnut tree at the bottom of Mr Prentice-Hughes' garden overhung the foot of Black Mutton Hill. Robert lingered in its shade, looking back up at the house. Ron Pryke was waiting by the garden gate, chatting with Mr Prentice-Hughes, and breaking off from time to time to shake hands as another visitor arrived. Every few moments Mr Prentice-Hughes, elderly and fussy, glared at his fob-watch. At last he trotted out through the gate and stood looking up and down the road.

The Reverend Pryke clapped his hands.

Robert switched his gaze to the terrace where girls were setting out plates of food on trestle tables, giggling together. Two of them caught his eye. An olive-skinned brunette, and a girl with a shock of blonde curls. He had noticed them in church the previous Sunday morning.

'Pay attention, everyone. Time to begin, I think. First and foremost...'

As the guests grouped themselves on the terrace, Robert edged across to join them.

'First and foremost, a word of thanks on behalf of us all to our host, and his charming wife…' — a noticeably young woman detached herself from the group and took white-haired Mr Prentice-Hughes' arm — 'for inviting us all to meet together here in their delightful garden.'

There was a spatter of applause.

'We must also thank the young ladies — Joan, and Olive, and Emily in particular, I believe — for providing us with such an inviting spread… And we must give thanks to God for the splendid weather He has provided for us this afternoon. Let us pray. For what we are about to receive…'

Robert looked down at the grass and wondered what was the name of the fair-haired girl.

'Who made these?' he asked a moment later, brushing the crumbs of a bakewell tart from his sleeve. 'They're not bad.'

'Well, thank you, kind sir,' said the girl with the shock of blonde curls, and dropped him a mocking curtsy.

'My name's Robert,' he said. 'And you are — ?'

'Emily. And this is Olive,' she said, as the olive-skinned girl came over to join them. 'Olive made the jam tarts and the rock cakes.'

He smiled at Olive, thinking that given her complexion it wouldn't be hard to remember *her* name. 'Rock cakes?' he said. 'Shall I take my pick?'

'Of course,' she answered. 'Take any one you like.' She hadn't noticed the timeworn joke.

Emily nudged him sharply with her elbow. 'Now don't be naughty,' she said.

He waylaid her later as she was helping to clear the tables. 'Can I see you again?' he said.

'You'll see me in church tomorrow, if you keep your eyes open.'

'No, I meant… O, I don't know, to go for a walk. Or see a film.'

'Hm,' she eyed him closely. 'I don't know. I'll think it over. Now, when we've cleared the tables would you like to help carry the trestles out to the car?'

'Listen,' he said. 'I'll be off to Paris in a fortnight's time for the whole of August. Can I see you before then?'

'Let me help you, my dear.' Mr Prentice-Hughes had bustled across and was putting his arm around Emily's waist.

'Ah. Yes. Thank you. Can you take the tea-urn?' she answered. 'I think they want it in the kitchen...'

'W. H. G.' she said quietly, as Mr Prentice-Hughes hurried away.

'*W.H.G.?*'

'Wandering Hand Gang,' she said. 'He's a dirty old man, for all that he was a missionary.'

'But before I set off for Paris?'

'We'll see... Now go and make yourself useful with those tables.'

*

As they waited side by side to shake his hand after Matins the following morning, the Reverend Pryke glanced at Emily and Robert and narrowed his eyes. He took a keen interest in the lives of the young unwed.

He was not alone in that. During the enforced separations of wartime so many barriers had toppled. Divorce was no longer the public infamy it had been: something that would cost a policeman his job, or get a teacher hounded out of a school staff. Children born into bastardy were no longer openly stigmatized, though tongues still wagged about them behind their backs. But confronted with a world in which the old moralities were being challenged, churchmen proclaimed it their bounden duty to mount a counter-attack. For them, the sexual free-thinking of the young was the first wash of a tide that would, undammed and uncondemned, set the whole sandcastle of the social order crumbling.

It all seemed to come back down to those old, seemingly primeval, tensions. Between head and heart. Between social, and above all, middle-class conventions and the heyday in the blood. Between crabbèd age and impetuous youth.

In his sermons and in the evening Bible-study groups, the Reverend Pryke returned again and again to the theme. Decent lads would not *want* to anticipate their marriage vows. Self-respecting young women *saved* themselves for their future husbands.

How could a young man in his heart of hearts admire a girl who said yes to what he wanted? Why bother to marry her at all when he'd already got what he was after? Could he ever trust her in the future? And how could a girl have any respect for a man who asked her to cast away her most precious treasure?

'I'm sure you all agree with me,' Ron said, smiling round the room in Olive's house where the group had met.

Robert, examining his own conscience and lost in thoughts of Nadia, held his tongue. The cash-and-carry calculatedness of the argument repelled him. If Ron Pryke had talked of marriage as a sacrament, that would have been *more* cogent, a more appropriate argument in the mouth of a priest. But not this vision of virginity as a marketable commodity.

Worse still, its consequences could be appalling. A friend of Nadia's had paid the price of it. Her until then so gentle bridegroom, long repulsed and asserting his seigneurial rights at last, had badly hurt her on their wedding night in an act of drunken rape.

*

'Paris rawly waking, crude sunlight on her lemon streets... In Rodot's Yvonne and Madeleine newmake their tumbled beauties, shattering with gold teeth chaussons of pastry, their mouths yellowed with the pus of flan breton...'

Fragments from Joyce's Ulysses ran on in his head.

Hot August sunlight was beating against the panes. Smells of coffee and the fume of Gauloises bleues drifted in from the stairwell. An Italian couple — he in a ground-floor room, she with the children two floors above — were calling to one another.

'Hé, Maria!...' 'Ecco!' 'Ai dormito bene?' 'Molto bene.' 'E li bambini?' 'Stanchi morti...'

Water gushed and clanked in the pipes, and doors slammed. Seven twenty-five. He swung his feet out of bed and peered at his tarnished reflection in the square of mirror-glass.

Flies buzzed in the window-pane. The street below shone with wetness where a day and night's accumulation of dust and litter had been sluiced away through iron gratings and swept into the Seine.

The lock was broken on the lavatory door. He held it closed with his outstretched left arm while he stood there. Prière de laisser cet endroit tel que vous eussiez voulu le trouver. What existential wag had scrawled that up? 'Pray leave this place as you would have wished to have found it.' A futile injunction. If essence is the consequence of existence.

Back in his gritty shoebox of a room, he stretched out on the bed again. A leisurely cigarette, and then he'd drink coffee and eat a croissant in the bar across the street. He fumbled for the crumpled blue packet under his pillow and thought about Emily and Nadia and the middle-aged woman who had accosted him at the Folies-Bergère.

*

Arriving at the Gare du Nord a few days earlier, he'd encountered two Englishmen of his own age. They were making heavy weather of explaining themselves to a ticket-collector, and he'd offered his help. After that, all three had adjourned to a bar and introduced themselves. They were brothers, Robin and Mark. They'd be in Paris for a week: why didn't he string along with them? In fact, when they'd all settled into wherever they were staying, why not meet up again that evening? They were off to Montmartre and the *Folies-Bergère*. OK?

'Well, why not?' he said.

They met in the foyer, where Robin and Mark left him and went to find their seats. He bought a ticket for the *promenade* and found a suitable spot to stand.

Nudity aside — and wasn't he a man of the world and blasé about naked skin? — the stage machinery and the rainbows of projected light were beyond the beat of his experience. A jewelled casket unfolded itself and became the chess-board for a living game of chess. A couple snarled their way through an apaché dance in a swirl of gunsmoke and iridescence. A bronze naiad at the centre of a fountain came to life, descended somehow through flickering water and emerged in a ballroom to dance with her human lover.

Between the set pieces a chorus line of plumed girls pranced along a catwalk that circled out beyond the orchestra pit into the stalls.

The curtain fell for the interval and he moved around like the other promenaders, stretching his legs. When the curtain rose for the second half, he found a dark-haired woman at his side. 'Tell me,' she whispered, threading her left arm through his as the line of dancers pirouetted onto the catwalk, 'what do you think of their breasts? Do you think they wear veil bras?'

'I'm sorry, I didn't quite… Wear *what*?'

With her American accent, it took him a long second to realise what she had said.

'Veil bras, you know?… Hey, are you *English?*' She hugged his arm more closely. 'I think they should be more, kind of, rounded… To my artistic eye,' she said. And went on whispering.

She'd be in Paris for another four days, she said. She was with a Ladies' Choir from New York. They were touring Europe. She was married. Her children were grown up.

She was still clutching his arm as they walked into the foyer at the end of the show. She looked around for a moment and waved her free hand at a cluster of women. Her rings glittered. 'Hey, ladies!' she called. 'Come and meet my nice young Englishman.'

At that moment he spotted Mark and Robin making their way across the foyer.

'Excuse me,' he said, freeing himself, 'but I must join my friends… Goodnight. I hope you enjoy your tour.'

He pushed his way towards the other two.

'OK. Let's get out of here,' said Robin. 'Scrumdown!'

Mark and Robert linked their arms around Robin's shoulders and they butted their way through the press of people and out onto the streets of Montmartre.

*

The following day he had met Mark and Robin for lunch at *Chez Jean*, a couple of blocks away from his hotel. Since then he gone on eating there almost every day, staying his hunger until evening on an omelette, a ficelle of bread, and handful of *gauloises*.

Chez Jean was crowded on weekdays from before noon until after two o'clock, its air cloudy with cigarette smoke and the fumes of frying. The place was cursed with a singing accordionist. She was short-skirted, plump, and fortyish, and her peroxided hair was black at the roots. Between songs she cocked her ear for an English-speaking voice or accent. When she heard one, she would mark down the speaker, break off short her repertoire of Edith Piaf imitations, and put on a simpering smile.

Tra-la-la-tveedle-ee-deedee, eet geefs mee a sreel…

She bucketed her way through the sprawl of tables and chairs, thrusting her accordion ahead of her, wheezing its bellows open and shut and clattering its keys:

To vake up een zee mornink to zee mockink bird's treel...

She lingered beside her victim's chair with her hip nudging his shoulder until he laid a coin beside his plate.

*

He enjoyed the company of Mark and Robin. Once they had gone back home to Hertfordshire, he was lonely, left to his own devices. Alone, he still could not shake off the habit of talking to Nadia in his mind.

Once or twice he went to an indoor swimming pool at Denfert Rochereau. Once or twice he clambered up and down the stone staircases that led to Montmartre and Sacré Coeur. For a week or so he passed the time in cafes with fellow students, in windy and barely-informed disputes about existentialism and the work of Sartre and Karl Jaspers. At the height of a discussion he once quoted, 'Isn't existentialism nothing more than *excrementialism*?' The dispute threatened to become a brawl, and he and three others were ordered outside by the café proprietor.

The few relationships he made were transient. Passing encounters, not to be renewed.

Nine years earlier, he had committed to memory Don Marquis's *ballade* of a Parisian alley-cat into which the soul of François Villon had metempsychosed. Now as he patrolled the streets and the quais — conversing with many strangers, or sitting on a bench with a book — he recalled the images of Don Marquis's poem, confronting a Paris he had first glimpsed through the eyes of Maupassant and Villon, and had momentarily found again in Joyce. Villon's avatar thumbed his feline nose at bourgeois values, flaunting convention in his rejection of capital letters and punctuation.

tame cats on a web of the persian woof
may lick their coats and purr for cream
but i am a tougher kind of goof

scheming a freer kind of scheme
daily i climb where the pigeons gleam
over the gargoyles of notre dame
i rob their nests to hear them scream
for i am a cat of the devil i am

When he strolled after dark through the streets of the *quartier latin* and under the bridges of the Seine he silently rolled the words on his tongue and they matched his mood —

when the ribald moon leers over the roof
and the mist reeks up from the chuckling stream
i pad the quais on a silent hoof
dreaming the vagabond s ancient dream

— until he reached the closing images, and laughed aloud —

my rival i rip and his guts unseam
for i am a cat of the devil i am

*

One morning, close to the Madeleine, he loitered on the pavement looking down in amazement at the fencers in the basement hall of the *Ecole d'Escrime*.

Their play was utterly unlike the swordsmanship he'd revelled in on the stage or in the cinema: gymnastic feats that swept the duellists up and down flights of stairs, through doorways, across balconies. At the Ecole d'Escrime that morning, each bout lasted no longer than a heartbeat. No more than the time it took two men to sideways-spring along a cat-walk and clash in a single thrust and parry.

It was all over in the flicker of a second. Someone called out the score. The duellists strode back to their places. For an instant they stood immobile, their eyes invisible behind the gauze of their masks. Then again there was a sudden sideways leap and a single clash of foils.

He was reminded of the time he had watched a chameleon. The creature had frozen into stillness, with only the cone of its eye fractionally swivelling… Suddenly there was a splash of movement too fast to follow, and a patch of spittle on a nearby leaf where a fly had loitered. Then only the chameleon's throat working as it laboured to swallow its tongue.

In the basement hall the fencers paced apart and froze and sprang again. '*Bonjour, chéri.*'

He turned to find a young woman standing behind him. She wore an elegant business suit, and her blonde hair was combed back into a pony tail. She looked him in the eye, smiling, as she hitched up her short skirt and adjusted her suspender — '*Ça vous plaise, ce que vous voyez?* You like what you see?' Then she glanced at her watch and invited him to accompany her to an *hôtel de passe* nearby.

And who should I see but the Spanish lady?
Hissing her petticoats over her knee…

O! Whack to my tooral looral laddy!
Whack to my tooral looral lee…

*

After the Reverend Stanford's rambling and exclamatory performances in the pulpit, and the Reverend Ellis's brisk expositions of doctrine, Ron Pryke's first sermon had come as a surprise, like those which followed it. He aimed them at the fledgling adults in his congregation and spiced them with anecdotes, for the most part of his own doings. That first Sunday at Evensong, Ron recalled his own months of soldiering in post-war Germany, where sex was to be bought for a handful of cigarettes or a bar of chocolate and where young men, like the hero of the tale he had to tell, were faced with temptation at every street corner…

Separated from his mates, lonely and far from home, a young soldier had been picked up at the close of an evening's drinking. Now the woman was leading him — staggering, and half-eager half-afraid — to her back-street home. She unlatched the door…

The story silenced the usual coughs and fidgetings in the church. Robert could hardly have been the only listener waiting for a conclusive: 'How do I know all this? I WAS THAT MAN'…

But — a larger matter of conjecture and suspense — how soon and *where* would Ron Pryke's tale reach its climax? In a soiled and creaking bed? In remorse? With cold stone under his knees and hands clasped in prayer? Would the hero of Ron's tale emerge as victor or victim of his own lust?

None of these, it transpired.

The woman lit a lamp and the young soldier saw her clearly for the first time. She was old enough to be his mother, whose accusing face now rose before him. Desire ebbed away on a flood of shame, and he stumbled out into the street. The Reverend Pryke's tale broke off short, and the members of the congregation shifted in their pews in the sudden silence.

Was that *it*? Nothing more? No moral? No conclusion to be drawn? No point to be made? No. That was *it*.

Well, be damned to it for an unsatisfactory text! If that *was* how the soldier's night had come truly to an end, then why *was* there no final, 'I WAS THAT MAN'? As it ran to its peroration the tale rang out of true, like a cracked bell. For every tone of the Reverend Pryke's voice and every line of his body had proclaimed that he *was* that man.

Robert's thoughts slid unbidden into an *explication de texte*. Why tell the story at all if he wasn't going to go through with it? Did the sudden silence mark a failure of honesty? A failure of narrative nerve? Or was Ron's incomplete confession only a baited hook to draw out other confessions?

You could only guess. For, gathering innocence about himself along with his books and papers, Ron had launched into his doxology...

... and now unto God the Father, God the Son, and God the Holy Ghost be ascribed as is most justly due, all might, majesty, dominion and power, henceforth and for ever more...

and there he was, bright-eyed and smiling about him, descending the pulpit stair.

*

O! Whack to my tooral looral laddy!
Whack to my tooral looral lee...

410

Her business suit neatly folded and hung on a hanger, '*Ô chéri, tes os me font mal,*' the young woman told him later, spreadeagled, naked. 'Darling, your bones are hurting me.'

O, here was a tale that would have come as grist to Ron Pryke's professional, confessional mill, he told himself, hastening away at last into the sunlit street, leaving her.

Ex nihilo nihil fit. An expense of spirit in a waste of shame. Nothing from nothing. *The flies in the window pane buzzed and stuck…*

James Joyce's image. An objective correlative.

Nothing from nothing. *Rien de rien.* Only his loneliness intensified, and laced with disgust. Only the sour emptiness of satisfied curiosity.

Thirteen years earlier hadn't Mrs Nightingale handed him a prize 'For Diligence in Finding Out'?

If he had thought to crush Nadia's remembered image into silence, he had proved himself bitterly wrong.

He lingered outside the Ecole d'Escrime, and gazed at the swordsmen for a moment or two, then made his way to Saint Sulpice and a shimmer of candles.

*

It was high time he found the paid job in Paris that he'd hoped for.

He picked the names of American and English-sounding companies out of *Le Bottin*, and telephoned them, asking if there might be a place for him: 'Just as a summertime fill-in, perhaps? While someone is on holiday?' 'Sure, of course. You have a work permit?' 'No, not yet.' 'Pick one up, and give us another call. OK?'

But whenever he applied for a work permit, he was told to re-apply *after* he had found a job.

He took himself in person to the offices he had telephoned. Perhaps if they *saw* him, they'd be more helpful. 'Certify that you'll take me on, and I can get a work permit,' he told them in turn. 'Sorry. That's not the way it works. *Until* we've seen your permit, there's really nothing we can do to help you.'

Impossible to break into the charmed circle. What skills he might have were not wanted. More and more he began to feel again as he had felt that

411

last hideous weekend at Pargetting when all the doors seemed barred against *him*, the unwanted visitor. His own hangdog discouragement counted against him.

One morning near the Pont Neuf, he came face to face with a fur-coated woman wrenching a leopard cub along the street on a scarlet lead. The animal cringed into the gutter, pressing its flank against the kerb, seeking the comfort of a stone wall at least at one side. He felt a fellow-feeling with it.

Earlier on he had spent his cash in hand too freely in the company of Mark and Robin, fondly banking on finding work. He had seduced himself into buying far too many books at the bouquinistes' stalls. Now he began to count out the little money he had left, reining in his appetite for food with another cigarette, making his savings last until the end of the month.

His hunger took no account of niceties. In a backstreet off the rue de Seine an Algerian had sawn an oil-drum in half to make a multi-purpose fryer out of it. Every afternoon the man dragged his contraption across the pavement. Coke smoked and glittered in the bottom section. Above it a flotilla of saveloys, fish-cakes, turd-balls of mince, herrings, andouillettes, and collops of flesh rose and sank in a tankful of murky oil.

Evening by evening as his last days in Paris dragged by, he sampled them all, washing them down with a sour vin rouge which cost less than the empty bottle he had bought to carry it home in. Its acridity partly countered the greasy fetor of the meat while, by the time he had drained the last tumblerful, his spirits had lifted a little.

In a bid to give it a sparkle one bored and hungry evening, he shot into his wine a spoonful of the Eno's Fruit Salts that his mother had tucked into his suitcase. The cup brimmed over in froth, and he watched the crimson fade away into a clear greyish fluid with a black dust drifting down.

It tasted foul. He had made a Satanic miracle of turning wine into soot and water.

*

At the Gare du Nord a middle-aged couple had already spread themselves and their cases over one side of the compartment when he pushed through the doorway and pitched his suitcase up onto the luggage rack. He went to stand in the corridor, and lit a cigarette.

'Which way does this goddam train pull outa here, hey?'

The man had joined him at the corridor window, and was prodding him with a blunt forefinger.

'Does it go *this* way? Or *that* way?' said the man, gesturing left and right.

'Well, I sincerely hope it goes *that* way, since you ask. Because if it goes the other way, there'll be an almighty bang...'

'So,' said the man. 'You a limey, huh?' and went back into the compartment to rearrange his wife and himself to face the engine.

The couple nagged one another all the way to Dieppe, trying to draw him into their dispute.

On the deck of the ferry a Catholic priest accosted him.

'Good evenin' to you, Professor,' he said. 'So you're on your way to England. Now tell me this: can we look forward to a quiet crossing, in your considered opinion?'

Together they turned to look up at a moon almost at the full.

'Ach, tell me this, now. Would'ye be travellin' *wid* someone or by yerself?' the priest asked, his Irish brogue growing stronger.

'Alone.'

'Then I've a little favour to beg, if *you* think you're up to ut. Tell me now: what wouldya name be?... Is that right? Would'ye step this way, Robert the Druce? There's a young lady I'd like ya to meet. She's asked me if I'd look after her on the trip. But it's my opinion that you're the *better* man for the job.'

She was pale and slender, hunched on a slatted bench. She looked ill.

'Now this is Mister Robert Druce. And *this* is Miss Barbara Bruce Satterthwaite. Who is under the weather and needs nothing more than a handsome young fella as it might be yerself to take care of her. Willya do that for me? Sure an' an ould fella like meself is poor sort of company for a smart young lady. So I'd best make meself scarce.'

He turned on his heel, but returned after a few paces.

'Hm,' he said, 'Barbara Bruce Druce... Now that has a *ring* to ut. What d'ya think? eh? Barbara — Bruce — Druce.' And he bustled away.

Robert looked at Barbara and raised his eyebrows. She gave him the ghost of a grin. 'He shouldn't have bothered you,' she said. 'But he saw that I was feeling rotten, and offered to help. I've been feeling pretty dreadful for the past week.'

413

They stayed on deck during the crossing, chatting in the moonlight. She was in her final year of reading French and engaged to be married. She was going to train as a teacher.

'... Miss Barbara Satterthwaite,' a voice was calling over the public address system as he lugged her case and his own into the Customs hall.

'That'll be a message waiting for me,' she said. 'My father's a customs officer...' She walked past the queue and up to the man at the counter. 'I'm Barbara Satterthwaite,' she told him.

'Ah. That's fine. Could you come this way? Is this young man with you? Anything to declare, have you, sir?... Fine. Mr Vine wants a word.'

'Your father rang through,' said Mr Vine. 'You're to take a taxi from Victoria to King's Cross. You're not to worry about the cost; he's asked me to give you this.' And he handed Barbara a ten-pound note.

'Hello there!' cried Father Whoever-he-was, as Robert carried both cases along the corridor of the train. 'Is that young fella lookin' after ya nicely?'

The holy father was ensconced with three fellow-priests in a compartment to themselves. They were seated opposite one another, playing bridge. A suitcase was balanced across their four pairs of knees and one of them was laying out dummy. 'Will ya excuse us now? We're doubled up and vulnerable.'

At Victoria he found her a taxi. 'Could you come as far as King's Cross with me,' Barbara said. 'Please.'

At King's Cross he bought Barbara her ticket to Cumberland, and carried her case to the platform.

'Safe journey home,' he said. 'Get well soon... And good luck with your Finals.' Briefly, he kissed her cheek.

He journeyed on to Liverpool Street and the Village, with his head filled with moonlight and the echoes of her voice and the wash of the sea.

34

FINALS

'That boy there!'

The music master was gazing at him.

'Yes, you! Now then tell me, boy, what in your opinion has been the greatest invention of the human intellect?...

'WHAT? The internal combustion engine, my backside!' — this was heady stuff for form 2A — *It's the symphony orchestra! And one day you'll all thank me for telling you.'*

He remembered that occasion eleven years later, trudging along the forest paths a little below Hangboy Wood, with a group of friends from the youth club in Joslin Road. They were taking turns to lug a portable gramophone. It housed a heavy clockwork motor, and a handful of shellac records were stacked under the lid. It was made of cloth-covered plywood and it clouted their legs as they swung it past the brambles.

They spread themselves out under the willows in the central hollow of Maze Hill, wound up the spring, set the needle on the record, and lay back to listen.

Ever since his childhood visits to the clunch-pits above Rectory Farm, he'd thought about what it would be like to lie there at twilight among the hawthorns and the glimmering clunch, listening to music. The quarry-like hollow of Maze Hill, site of a former gravel-pit, was the next best thing.

The day's grown old; the fainting sun
Has but a little way to run...

The shadows now so long do grow
That brambles like tall cedars show...

Benjamin Britten's *Serenade*. Charles Cotton's verses brought the shadowy landscape and their mood into sharper resonance.

They took turns to squat on their heels and change the needle, wind up the motor, and slide the records in and out of their brown-paper sleeves. With every playing the steel needle wore away at the tip, scratching the shellac grooves a little deeper, gritting away the finer subtleties of sound.

Music at twilight.

After a bit they stopped to munch their sandwiches, washing them down with swigs of cherryade from the bottle.

There was a recording which listeners often asked the BBC to play over the air. A nightingale singing in a Surrey wood, while a woman sawed away at her cello nearby, striving to turn the nightingale's recital into a dialogue. An absurd idea. A nightingale's song alone had been enough for John Keats. A poet in a Hampstead garden, his life smouldering towards its end. *Darkling I listen…*

Lights had long come on in houses beyond the dark sweep of the forest beeches. Here they were in a hollow among the thornbrakes of Maze Hill, alone and at the centre of a tiny, magical lake of sound.

When the gramophone handle had been cranked around for the last time, it was Keats' sonnet 'To Sleep' that brought the *Serenade* to a close…

> *Then save me, or the passèd day will shine*
> *Upon my pillow, breeding many woes. —*
> *Save me from curious Conscience, that still lords*
> *Its strength for darkness, burrowing like a mole;*
> *Turn the key deftly in the oilèd wards,*
> *And seal the hushèd casket of my soul.*

Alone with the thoughts of a poet long dead, he was not easy in his mind in the glimmering dark

*

Mrs Druce seemed welcoming enough when she met Emily on the doorstep in Honey Hill for the first time, and led her into the front room.

'What a horrible day. Come in,' she said. 'I've lit the fire.'

She went off into the kitchen and returned with the tea-things and a plate of biscuits.

'So you're Emily,' she said, pouring out the tea. 'Tell me about yourself. Milk and sugar?'

Ten minutes later Emily was still explaining how she had moved away from Suffolk to live with an aunt and uncle in the Village, when the front gate clicked, and a shadow passed across the net curtains.

'O dear!' said Mrs Druce. 'There's your father, home early for once. He'll be wanting his dinner. You'd better drink up your tea and make yourselves scarce, the pair of you.'

As she bustled them out into the hall, they could hear the back door rattling open, and Mr Druce's voice.

'Dorothy? Dorothy!'

His mother shut the front door behind them, and they went out through the gate and down Honey Hill.

'Well!' said Emily, while Robert tried to explain about his father.

When he returned from escorting Emily home to her uncle's house in High Garth Close, his mother greeted him with a tight-lipped smile.

'She's the wrong woman for you.'

'What? You've only spoken to her for five minutes.'

'Keep your voice down. Your father's asleep… Phhhh! She's not a patch on Nadia. And why you had to…'

He didn't stay to hear the rest of it.

'A secretary, is she, this Emily? A short-hand typist?' said his father the next day. 'The Uncle and the Aunt, now. What kind of people are they? A toffee-nosed pair are they, up there in High Garth Close? And what about the Father and the Mother? What have they got to say for themselves?'

'He's only met the Aunt and the Uncle,' put in his mother. 'The Mother and Father live in Suffolk.'

'*You* come from Suffolk, mother,' he said.

'That's as may be. What I don't understand is, why does she have to live away from home in the first place. What are the Mother and the Father thinking of, that's what I'd like to know. Isn't her home good enough for her? Why you and Nadia ever had to… Still, that's none of my business, I suppose…'

'Exactly.'

'Watch your tongue,' said his father. 'Or you can get upstairs and pack your bags now. Double-quick.'

*

The Aunt. The Uncle. The Mother. The Father. His parents never spoke of Emily's family in any other way. When 'She' and 'Her' were not enough and they were forced to mention Emily by name, they pursed their lips.

Emily was utterly unlike Nadia. But that didn't seem cause enough to take against her so swiftly and so bitterly.

Half-Polish as she was, Nadia physically resembled his mother: even to sharing her left-handedness along with her blue eyes and dark hair. In their upbringing and their ways of thought they were not the least bit alike.

Fair-haired and grey-eyed Emily, on the other hand, looked nothing like his mother, but echoed her closely in temperament, rooted as she was in the same Suffolk background and Suffolk ways.

Should a mother be flattered or repelled, when her son casts his eyes on a woman who resembles her?

But then again, who resembles her in what way? In flesh or in spirit? Like attracting like? Or repelling her, thrusting away a rival, after the fashion of like magnetic poles?

If his mother had encountered Emily in any other circumstances, would she have set out so single-mindedly to dislike her? It was a rankling question the relevance of which he refused to admit.

Not then, nor for another thirteen years.

It couldn't be a matter of her regarding every other woman as a rival for his love and attention. Despite the shock of finding Nadia half-naked in his bed, she had somehow accepted the implications of that night, and had only for a brief while failed to make Nadia welcome. Now, despite having cast every photograph and letter he possessed into the flames, now she seemed to imagine that only by marrying could the pair of them set all the broken equations right.

'Nadia was the right woman for you,' she sighed, and would go on sighing for many months. 'If only...'

Too bitter to accept into his waking thoughts, it was an awareness that would not vanish from the edge of his dreams.

But the enmity of the Druces towards Emily served only to harden his, and Emily's, defiance.

Not that the conversations they shared remotely resembled the oceans of talk that Nadia and he had launched themselves upon whenever they were together. Nadia was volatile, outspoken, quick to weave fantasies, quick to seize upon an ill-considered image or a second's illogic, and tease out its implications. Their minds chimed.

Whereas Emily and he were both single children. Unfamiliar with the need to adjust to siblings. Unable to tease or be teased without feeling threatened. Clumsy-tongued when it came to a declaration of how they felt. Incapable of being the first to break the ice.

If he can't see how I feel, it's not up to me to tell him!... Well, I'm damned if I'll plead with her to understand... And vice-versa.

Did he love Emily? Physically, yes, *yes*...

But not in the way that things had been with Nadia. There was no swoop of blood through his veins at the simple thought of her. No sense of balancing on a sea of bubbles when she was at his side.

But how could you require such joy to recur? Once in a lifetime was magical enough, an unrepeatable, fairy-godmother's gift. It could never come a second time, he told himself.

And if there were no-go areas with Emily, quicksands which a glint in her eye or the set of her mouth would warn him to sheer away from, still he felt himself largely at ease with her, comfortable, affectionate. As on her side she also seemed to feel.

Enough. It would be enough.

And safer far than the crazy roller-coaster ride which Nadia and he had known, plunging them from indescribable joy to a wrenching sense of loss when they were apart and alone.

His parents would just have to get accustomed to the fact of Emily's being around.

*

South Kensington. A hot and airless day, the first of a fortnight-long heatwave.

Hundreds of school desks had been arranged in rows in the Examination Halls. The inter-connecting rooms were as broad and cavernous as the transepts of a church. Light flooded in through high windows and, after dark, fell from the ranks of hanging thousand-watt lamps. Months earlier, demonstrating with a tennis ball how to lob a hand grenade, he'd shattered one. For an instant shards of white-flashed glass glittered in his memory. But months had slipped by since his final parade with the UTC.

He found his place, disentangled his fountain pens from an inside pocket, and laid them in the groove of the desk-lid. Newcomers brushed past him, searching for the desks with their examination numbers pinned to them. On a dais at the front of the room, a black-gowned invigilator and his assistant were leaning towards one another, talking and glancing at their watches.

He stripped off his jacket, draped it around the back of his chair, and checked once more that the bottle of ink, foam-rubber cushioned inside its bakelite case, was still safe and sound in an outside pocket.

'Good luck,' muttered a familiar voice from the desk behind him. Steve Durston, in his own year at UCL.

He looked around for other members of the French department, but they were elsewhere, scattered through the adjacent halls, mingled in the alphabetical order of their surnames with candidates from other disciplines and other colleges.

'You may turn over your question papers now,' said the Invigilator, and the room rustled.

'Hm, *hm!*' It was Steve, affecting to clear his throat. He sounded pleased.

Robert nodded in acknowledgement, in case Steve was watching the back of his head for an answer. He took a couple of deep breaths, and studied the questions.

Voltaire et la politique…?

Get that essay over first. Not what he'd hoped for, but he could cannibalise the greater part of what he'd prepared on Voltaire's relations with the Catholic church. He scribbled down a ragbag of phrases as they spilled out of his memory.

Two hours into the paper, and with two essays written, he held up his hand. The invigilator dispatched a porter to him.

'Toilet?' said the porter.

'Yes.' He stood up and turned to wink at Steve. The man escorted him to the lavatories, and prepared to wait beside the open cubicle door. Guarding against any attempt to cheat, of course.

'Well, since I'm here,' he said. 'But in fact it's a smoke I'm dying for.'

The man took the cigarette he offered him, and back in the lobby they stood a while smoking and chatting. Then, 'O, well,' he said, treading the cigarette-butt under his heel. 'Back to French literature.'

'Rather you than me, sir,' said his escort, tugging open the door of the examination hall and waving him through.

The few minutes of relaxation in the everyday world paid off, along with the nicotine-triggered rush of adrenaline. Back in eighteenth-century France, he spotted half a dozen errors in spelling and phrasing that a first read-through had failed to detect. He marched on into the third essay with renewed energy.

The heatwave continued unbroken as day after day after day the three-hour-long papers raced past. His friend the porter kept a look-out for him, nodding and smiling as he went in to take his place. At a convenient point half-way or so through every paper, 91783 Druce R. held up his hand, the porter hurried over and they stood together in the lobby, smoking. The air was cooler there.

On his third afternoon a girl arrived at the until then empty desk across the gangway from him. She stood staring around her for a long moment, sniffing noisily and curling her lip. The next morning she wrenched an air-freshener bottle out of her mackintosh pocket, thumped it down onto her desk, and jerked up the chlorophyll-soaked wick. He told his friend the porter about it.

'Well, sir, it's understandable, innit? I mean, what with the 'eatwave, it '*as* been getting a bit ripe in there…' The man came closer, and lowered his voice to a whisper: 'You see, sir, it's the ladies. They can't help theirselves, but when they gets nervous they all starts to pong.'

*

When the ten or more scattered days of finals had ground to an end, he felt empty and dispirited. Pages of lecture notes, prepared texts, critical opinions thumbed through over and over again for half the night before each paper. Declensions of Old French nouns, verb paradigms, word-lists, essential dates. A catalogue of slippery mnemonics chivied into memory. Everything you had absorbed of the entire Honours course sloshed out onto the page in a final splurge. Nothing left to do now but wait for the verdict.

He envied Frank O'Connor, who had the move to a new flat, and the birth of a child to occupy his mind. Frank had sat a Civil Service examination a few weeks earlier, and his sights were set on the Foreign Office. Already the prospect of a career as a civil servant and life as a paterfamilias were claiming Frank.

As for himself, he felt disaffected. Dissatisfied. Drained of words. Marriage to Emily, day by day impending, was still a long way ahead. The months and years of work intended to prepare him for a career as a medievalist were losing what significance they had had.

During the nights of revision his mind had often wandered away to the thought of making a lathe and working in wood. Of labouring no longer with abstractions, but with honed steel and woodgrain under his finger tips, breathing in the sweet tang of sawdust and wood shavings. Vinegary oak, resinous pine.

He bought an electric motor, and brackets and bearing blocks of cast aluminium. He bolted them onto lengths of angle-iron that had once formed the sides of a bed-frame, and ferretted around Dawson's timberyard in the village for offcuts of pine and oak, beechwood and sycamore.

His lathe was a ramshackle contraption, rigged up on the concrete outside the back door, and powered by a cable strung through the open window. To work at it he had to squat with his back against the coal-shed door. But it served well enough for making a table lamp and wooden platters and dishes.

One by one, he handed them over to Emily for safe keeping.

*

When the envelope tumbled onto the doormat, he carried it upstairs and left it lying on his bed. It was three in the afternoon before he mustered the courage to go up and slit it open.

Class 2B: a lower second. Not what he had dared to aspire to, but better than what he dreaded. So that was that. He stuffed the letter into his pocket and walked down the road to telephone Frank O'Connor.

'Well?'

'2B,' said Frank. 'You?'

'Me too.'

They had never discussed it, but both knew that had either outshone the other, envy would have put an end to their jostling friendship.

Back at UCL, Brian Woledge, the Professor of Medieval French, took him through his exam results with his usual unfailing courtesy. They were wildly inconsistent, high marks starring the literary exercises that had caught his delighted interest, low marks rewarding his lack of enthusiasm for topics that he had found pedestrian. There was a dazzlingly high score and a special mention for the Petrarchan sonnet he'd produced in translation of a sonnet by Hérédia. There was a middle-of-the-road score for translation *into* French. The English text had been a technically-slanted piece about goods-wagons in a shunting yard: buffers clanking, while sparrows chirped in the eaves of a signal-box.

For historical linguistics there was a mark weak enough to make him hot with shame.

Despite which, Professor Woledge assured him, there was no good reason why he should not proceed to a research degree and, in the fullness of time, take his place as a medievalist. He agreed to think the matter over, but with little inward enthusiasm. Three or four further years as a raggèd-arsed student — he could hear his father's phrase — — living on his parents' backs? Yes, perhaps — had Nadia's voice been there to encourage him. But he couldn't envision Emily rejoicing at the prospect.

Meanwhile John Robbins, rejected by the Institute of Education despite a first in Geography, had at this point come to the end of his teacher-training course at Westminster College. No harm in trying like John for a place at both places, thought Robert Druce, writing away for application forms. A Postgraduate Certificate in Education wouldn't come amiss, whatever career he ended up in, in or out of school or university. What's more he'd get a grant and a year's respite before being forced to decide on a career.

The tutor who interviewed him at Westminster was friendly and welcoming. Yes, they'd be pleased to accept him in the autumn. And, yes, they quite understood that if meanwhile the Institute of Education accepted him for a place, it would be in his own interest for him to take it up. After that first dummy run, a more searching interview at the Institute in Malet Street passed off in smiles and handshakes and the offer of a place.

There was one proviso: students were expected to make their own arrangements to spend a fortnight teaching in a secondary school somewhere convenient for them. Straightaway. Before the current school term ended. Nobody from the Institute would be coming around to supervise what they did. It was just so that they could dip their toes in the water as it were, and test out what skills and enthusiasm they might have, before they were faced with the demands of a supervised teaching practice.

For a fortnight he filled the pages of a fat, hard-backed exercise-book with his daily doings in front of the classes at Joslin Road, a bare hundred yards from Bren Slaney's front door. And that was that. There it was, he had done what was asked, it was all set down, ready to be gone over in detail with his tutor when the Institute term began. Time enough to think about it then.

Far more central to his existence at the moment was the need to earn some money. On the 17th July, he caught the train to King's Cross, talked to a man in a tiny office smelling of soot, and got himself signed on as a goods-porter for the rest of the summer.

*

After Liverpool Street and the night mail, the routine was familiar enough. Sacks and packages to be unwedged from the guards' vans, hefted onto barrows and trundled along the platforms to a high-arched hall. There to be sorted and manhandled onto the chest-high platforms of the loading bays — the 'windows' — and piled up in the inter-station motor-vans. A contra-flow of packages and parcels brought by road from the other London termini, to be chalked with a destination code, hefted across to the appropriate barrows, wheeled to the platforms and loaded into the guards' vans. The code-numbers, station by station, were painted on the wall, twenty or thirty in sequence, above each archway.

All day long and throughout the night, newspaper vans drove up with successive editions of every national newspaper. The drivers and their mates were paid by the load and always in a fury to get away for another cargo. If the porters didn't grab the bundles of newsprint from the tailboard nimbly enough for their liking, they hurled them out onto the roadway, making it twice as hard to hoist them onto the barrows. The sisal string around the bundles scarred your gloves and left splinters in the flesh of your fingers.

From time to time a van drew up, loaded with a stack of magazines. Their art-paper pages were stiff with glue and china-clay and they were strung together in piles three times as weighty as a bundle of newsprint twice their size.

Each vanload was dispatched to catch the train that would get it to the farflung newsagents in good time. The Inverness express steamed out in the early evening, and as the night-hours passed, the destinations drew closer to home: the Scottish lowlands, the north, the midlands, and at last, at five-thirty in the morning, the local line to Enfield Chase, Hertford and Hitchin. As the daylight hours progressed, midday, evening and late-night final editions were trundled out to the platforms.

He preferred night-work, and not only because you got paid double-time for it. At night the public concourse was clear of passengers; and greenbat drivers — who steered the battery-powered tractors with their trains of barrows — had a clear run along the platforms. You could take turns with a mate to nip away for a smoke. The single fly in the ointment was Wenya.

'Who or what is Wenya?' he asked.

'You'll know all right when you meet 'im,' they told him.

He found out on his first night. The regular porter had left him to finish unloading a barrow on platform 9. When only four packages were left, a weasely voice from nowhere spoke in his ear.

'Whenya done that, get down to platform 16 for the 5.30.'

*

The 5.30 stopping train to Hertford was a curse and, inevitably, it fell on him, the newcomer to the night-shift.

By five in the morning, the goods-porters had knocked off work and sat upstairs smoking and playing cards. Most of them were waiting for 6 a.m. to pile into the back of an inter-station van whose driver would drop them off at Covent Garden in time for the market pubs to open. But there would be no taking it easy for the unlucky one, whose job it was to plod down the steep ramp to platform 16 with a barrow-load of newspapers and magazines.

'Oy, Student! Watch it wiv ya barrer on the ramp,' somebody called out in a last-minute warning. 'Get it front of it, see? And walk dahn backwards, uvverwise it'll drag ya orf ya feet an' the whole fuckin' lot will end up on the track. Yerself included.'

In the roadway above, he would find a lorry parked. Inside it the perishables — sausages, confectioner's synthetic cream, hothouse blooms from Holland, boxes of frozen fish that had come down overnight from the north — were stacked near the tailboard. They all had to be wheeled down the ramp and hefted, along with the newsprint, into the goods van of the waiting train.

Half-asleep on his feet one morning, he almost forgot the perishables.

In a last-minute panic he piled boxes of fish and ice alongside and on top of the newspapers, flung a cardboard carton of cut flowers in among them, and ran along the platform slamming the door as the signal light turned green, the driver opened the regulator, and the 5.30 clunked away in a cloud of smoke and steam.

When he reported for work on the following night shift, 'Oi! Watch out for Bullock. He's after your guts, mate,' someone called across to him.

All along the line from Enfield Chase to Hertford, people had been ringing up their newsagents to complain about sodden newspapers that stank of fish. When he trudged off to the Hertford train in the early hours, Bullock and Wenya were waiting for him with a galvanized tank of sawdust on a barrow.

'Oh dear, oh dear, Stooood'nt. Whatever is it keeps your ear'oles apart?' said Bullock, nudging Wenya with his elbow. 'Can't be brains, can it?'

The pair stood on the platform grunting commands while he stacked the newspapers and magazines in one corner of the van, the fish-boxes in the opposite corner, and the remainder of the perishables in another. Under their guidance he built walls of sawdust six inches high around each corner and from side to side across the centre of the van.

They put him through the same performance every morning for the rest of the week. 'Here, woss all this caper with the sawdust?' a regular porter asked him. 'The carriage cleaners are doin' their bleedin' nuts.'

For the rest of his summer season at King's Cross, Bullock ambushed him from time to time, springing out of doorways if there was a likely audience for his wit, asking him what kept his ears apart.

Bullock's sense of humour was less tolerable when he turned upon his favoured victim, a fifty-year-old porter who was twisted with arthritis and terrified of being thrown out of work. 'Hobbling again, Charlie?' Bullock would taunt him. 'O dear, O dear, how long can British Rail afford to pay your wages, I wonder. No, I think we're goin' to have to let you go.'

*

On the day-shift there was no chance of overtime or double-time pay, but at peak passenger hours the goods-porters supplemented their wages by weaselling. It didn't do to let Wenya or Bullock catch you at it.

Weaselling was what the uniformed passenger-porters did officially all the time, waiting along the platform with their two-wheeled luggage trolleys when an express was due, or opening taxi-cab doors in the hope of earning a tip. They didn't object if at rush-hours pairs of goods-porters joined in the game unofficially; one to do the full-time work of both, the other to shuffle along the taxi-rank as the cab-drivers dropped off their passengers.

'Follow?' you had to shout as you joined the waiting throng of porters.

Then you cocked your ear and looked around as the previous last man identified himself.

'You foller me, mate, I foller 'im.'

A moment later, you'd be pointing to your predecessor, passing the succession on, 'You follow me, I follow *him*.'

When you reached the head of the queue, you sprang to open the door of the next cab to draw up: 'Porter, sir? Porter, madam?'

If your luck was in, you lugged the travellers' bags and baggages to wherever they asked, and hoped to trouser a respectable tip. A shilling was good; half-a-crown — an agricultural labourer's hourly wage — a windfall. Five bob was a king's ransom.

When the answer was 'No,' as it usually was, you shouted 'Follow?' and went to the back of the queue again.

When you'd had enough of it, you split the cash with the mate who'd been standing in for you. On a bad day, you'd have to shell out money of your own, so that he wouldn't think you were trying to put one across him. On a red-letter day you might end up with a quid or more apiece.

*

In the middle of Bob's second week Neil, a third-year student of dentistry, arrived to join the gang. 'What are those numbers in aid of?' he asked, pointing to the wall above the arches. 'What's Leeds 112?'

'That's the code-number of the mainline station at Leeds. When anything comes in labelled for Leeds, the leading porter chalks the number on the crate. Then *we* know which barrow to load it on, and the greenbat driver knows which barrows to couple up and take to the next train to Leeds.'

'So they all know the numbers by heart?'

'No. The leading porters *say* they do: that's why they are leading porters. And they can always sneak a quick look at the wall if a number slips their memory… Tell you what. See how many you can learn by heart in three minutes. I'll time you. Then I'll try.'

It was as good a way of any of passing the time. By the end of that week Neil and he had almost all codes by heart between them.

The day came when a leading porter was not to be found. Tom, the only regular porter on the window with Neil and Bob, shrugged his shoulders.

'Come on, *come on*,' shouted the van-driver. 'I can't hang about all bloody day.'

'*I'll* take the chalks,' said Neil.

'You *what?*' said Tom. 'You ain't bin on the job five minutes.'

'Try me,' said Neil; and with Bob to supply an occasional number, the van was unloaded before the missing man arrived.

'How come you two know all them numbers? I bin porterin' 'ere three years an' I only know nine or ten of 'em be heart,' said Tom.

'We learned them off the wall,' Neil told him.

'What d'ya wanna do *that* for? You're only 'ere tempory. Wass the point?'

'It passes the time,' said Bob.

'Students,' said Tom, shaking his head. 'Blimey, I dunno. Don't reckon I'll ever get to the bottom of students an' their ways of goin' on.'

*

Travelling into London each evening against the rush-hour flow of city workers was a pleasure in itself in contrast with the swaying, standing-room-only crush you glimpsed as home-bound trains clattered past your own half-empty carriage. For you there was space to stretch out your legs and read a book. Leisure enough to nod to your fellow night-workers and study the eccentrics among them. Like the self-declared pimp who accosted him one evening on the underground platform at Liverpool Street, as he waited for his Circle-line train.

'Am Ah right for King's Cross, standin' here?' said the man, breathing beer-fumes into his face.

'Yes.'

'Sure of that, are ya?'

'I'm going there myself.'

'Prawns,' the man announced to the world at large, and took a step nearer. He was heavily built, well over six feet tall. He was clutching a fat, damp, brown-paper bag in his right hand. He fumbled in it with his left and drew out a boiled prawn. He wore chunky signet rings on the middle fingers of both his hands. There was a scar on his cheek.

'Aye,' he said in his great booming voice, 'Ah'm a right boogger for prawns.' He bit off the head of his prawn, blurted it down onto the track, dropped the remains into his mouth, champed, swallowed, belched and fished out another. He went through the performance a second and a third time. People standing nearby stared at him and drew away.

'Where are ya goin?' he suddenly boomed, as Bob began to edge further down the platform. 'Coom back 'ere! Ah'm talkin' to thee.'

Better humour him, thought Bob, peering along the tunnel in the hope of seeing a train. His ears were burning.

'What day is it, then? Friday?' said the man, looking around him. 'Aye, Friday it is. Saturday tomorrow.' He blurted the heads of more prawns over the edge of the platform, filling his mouth again. 'Ah'll mek the most of it. Monday, happen Ah'll be in prison,' he said, raising his voice. He fumbled more prawns out of his paper bag, stretching his eyes at his companion. He seemed to expect an answer.

'Prison?' Bob murmured, hoping the man would drop his voice too.

'Aye,' roared the man. 'Livin' on immoral earnings.' He bit the head off another prawn and spat it onto the track. 'Mah wife's on the game, ya see… Ah say, she's on the *game*. She's a *prostitute*… Coom 'ere, listen. D'ya play cards?'

By now other travellers on the platform had left a space around them.

'Contract bridge, yes.'

'Can ya tell the fall of the cards? Keep track in ya mind of what's been played and what's to coom?' He laid his free hand on Bob's shoulder.

'Well, yes,' said Bob, red in the face and glancing around at a distant and staring audience. At least the man's talk had moved on to safer ground. 'That's what bridge is all about.'

The man belched and went back to gulping down his prawns and spitting out their heads in silence for a while. Then he blew into the empty paper bag, burst it noisily, and laughed. 'That made yon booggers joomp,' he said, leering at the onlookers.

When the train came in at last, he clutched Bob by the arm and pushed him down onto the seat beside him.

'Ah mek mah livin' on the trains,' he said. 'Long distance. Playin' cards. Apart from what the wife brings in, that is… 'Ow do you mek *your* livin'?.. Oh aye, a student, are ya? University? What d'ya stoody? French, eh? Parlez-voo?… Ee, put yourself into my 'ands, lad, and ah'll mek your fortune. Train you oop, put you wise, teach you all 't tricks of the trade. Three card trick. Poker… There'd be no stoppin' ya, once ya got goin', a likely lad like thee.'

'King's Cross?' he said, when Bob stood up and told him they'd arrived. As they walked together along the tunnels towards the main-line station, he stopped and grasped his companion's arm. 'All right f'ra ticket, are ya?' he said, pulling a bunch of green privilege tickets out of his coat pocket. 'Nah then, King's Cross…' He fumbled for a pen, and wrote the words in the blank space on a ticket.

'Listen,' he said, groping once more through his pockets. 'Wait on till Ah find a piece of paper. Write down your address where you live. Put yeself in my 'ands, lad, an' I'll mek ya fortune.'

Bob seized his chance to escape through the barrier, and hastened away into the bustle of the main-line station. From a safe distance he turned to watch his would-be mentor hand over the forged ticket with a flourish, and pass through on his way to the north of England and a vaunted spell in jail.

Living on immoral earnings. *Proxénétisme.* The French term hovered in his memory.

But, with his ringed knuckles and stolen tickets and his breath laden with the reek of alcohol and shellfish, loudly informing every one around him of secrets better left unspoken, the man was only one of a series of grotesques encountered in the weeks at King's Cross, who seemed to seek Bob out to confide in him.

There was the ageing and peroxided barmaid in the station buffet who, in the intervals between serving other customers, returned to him to continue the intimate, blow-by-blow account of her husband's violence and the break-up of her marriage.

There was the forty-year-old Irish porter who reeled towards him one night through the shadows at the end of a platform. 'Willya watch dis now,' he said, and spanged the metal tops off a couple of bottles of Guinness by hooking them in turn against an iron stanchion and clouting them with the heel of his hand. The neck of the second bottle splintered, but he put his lips around it and drained it as he had done the first.

'Ana… Anaesthetic,' he said, pointing unsteadily towards his open mouth.

His teeth were stained and broken, pitched across one another like headstones in a derelict graveyard. He reached into a pocket, drew out a pair of pliers, thrust their open jaws into his mouth and began to rock the handles back and forth. A moment later he was waving the bloody stump of a molar under Bob's nose.

'Grinders,' he said, steadying himself with an arm across Bob's shoulder, and gobbing out a bloody clot of mucus. 'Rotten. Forty years old I am. And I'm not goin' ta let dem bastards get de better of *me*, Mister.' He reached inside his coat and slammed the cap off another bottle.

Bob wondered what it was that seemed to draw strangers to confess themselves so openly to him — a sense of his unthreatening acceptance? His willingness to go on listening? Or an apparent man-of-the-worldliness? An aura of authority?

'Don't kid yourself,' said his father, when he put the question to him. 'One look at you, my son, and any tomfool can see that you're as green as grass.'

35

SIR JOHN TEMPEST'S CHARITY

'*A Critical Survey of My Education*. Write it down.'

Mrs Franks bestrode her swivel chair back-to-front. Her skirt was hitched half-way up her thighs, and her hands were in her jacket pockets. A cigarette hung in her mouth, and her left eye was clenched shut against the smoke. The room was cramped and misshapen, at the top of a steep staircase that led up to the attics behind a Georgian facade in Woburn Square. A strip of sunlight faintly glowed on the gloss-painted plaster wall.

Four women and three men, strangers to one another, rummaged in their bags and briefcases. It was their first meeting with the tutor who would supervise their postgraduate year.

'I expect to find your essays in my pigeonhole in ten days' time. At the very latest. "Education" is to be interpreted in the broadest sense. Fifteen hundred words is an absolute minimum. Yes, Mr Er — ?'

'Druce. The notes we made on our teaching practice in July. When would you like to see them?'

Mrs Franks ran her eye around the half-circle of aspiring teachers.

'I don't *want* to see them. That preliminary practice is there so that you people can find out just how committed you are. The time-wasters can weed themselves out in advance. I'm not the least bit interested in what you did in July. *My* concern is with how you spend your time from now on. Assuming, that is, that you last the course.'

She swung round to the ashtray on her desk, stubbed out her cigarette and lit another.

'Are there any questions about the essay? No? Very well then. We'll get down to business… You're sitting here today because you've applied to train as teachers of French. You know who *I* am. Now I want each of you in turn to tell us who you are.'

Mrs Franks fastened her gaze on the blonde girl on her immediate left…

*

Despite the vow he swore in 1945 never — not in a thousand years — to become a teacher, Tuesday 10th of July 1953 had found R. Druce BA loitering in a classroom less than half a mile away from Honey Hill.

Joslin Road Secondary Modern.

He was familiar with the building. But until now only after school hours when it had transmogrified itself into a youth club, and wafts of scent and hair-oil joined the fumes of chalk-dust and the reek of school-dinners in its corridors and classrooms.

Girls. Since 1940 he'd not had to face a class with girls in it. In 1945, Cavendish Street Juniors had been a boys' school. R. Druce hoped that he knew more or less where he stood with a roomful of boys. But coping with *girls*? The prospect was disturbing.

Two-thirty. *Nouns.* Form 2B for a double period of English. A whole ninety minutes of it. He looked at his watch.

Minutes after the school bell had stopped snarling, knots of thirteen-year-olds were still drifting into the room. The girls for the most part glanced at him incuriously and continued their conversations. One or two boys stopped short, affecting to be amazed.

Are you a *student*, sir?' one boy asked, and turned to grin at a couple of mates. 'Are you going to *teach* us?'

He got up and closed the door behind the few last stragglers.

He cleared his throat.

'Now hurry up and settle down, all of you,' he said. 'Monitors, hand out the textbooks. Exercise books and pens as well… You, yes *you*, the boy in the corner! Will you be so good as to open a window?'

He waited, fastening his unseeing gaze on the poster pinned to the wall at the back of the room, avoiding the thirty-seven pairs of eyes in front of him. When the chatter and the slap and rustle of books had subsided, he looked down at his lesson plan.

FORM: 2B. *DURATION*: *Double Period* — *90 mins.*
DATE: *Tuesday, 7 July.*   *TIME*: *2.30 p.m.*
TOPIC: *Nouns, common, proper, abstract.*
AIM: *To teach classification of nouns.*
KNOWLEDGE: *Nouns.*
INTRODUCTION: *(10 mins.)*:
1. Revision of definition of Noun.
2. Statement of Aim…

'Where's Mister Rippingale?' somebody asked loudly.

'Be quiet,' he said, clearing his throat and staring down at his lesson plan once more, in a last-minute shudder of panic.

Richard Rippingale was the Senior English Master at Joslin Road. This was his classroom.

*

'Take a crack at it tomorrow afternoon, dear boy. Last double period of the day,' Rippingale had told him, sucking a flame into the bowl of his pipe, and leaning back in his armchair in the staffroom.

'Room 10, class 2B. Far end of the bottom corridor. You'll find a pile of textbooks in the cupboard: *First Aid in English*… Help yourself to a copy before you stagger home this afternoon. Exercise books should be in there, too. Keys in the top drawer of my desk. Do the chapter on Nouns, can't recall the page-number offhand…

'Nouns, anyway. Common, Proper, Abstract: you know the rigmarole…'

The Senior English Master unclenched his jaw and exhaled a mouthful of smoke.

'Ask a few questions round the class first. Then find the passage in *First Aid*, copy it up on the board, and get the kids to call out which are the nouns as you go, while you underline 'em. When they've had a good squint at it, rub it out: are you with me? Time for the kids to make their own fair copy from the book, while they put the underlines back in again. When they've finished that, they can answer the rest of the questions on their own. Plenty for them to get on with. They know the drill…

'Wander around while they're at it, collect up the books at the end,

I'll drop in for a look-see at knocking-off time. All right? Don't stand any nonsense…'

Mr Rippingale thrust the mouthpiece of his briar once more between his teeth, and turned his matinée-idol profile, with its clipped moustache and jutting jaw, away towards the window.

*

Form 2B. *Nouns…*

Mr R. Druce glared at the faces in front of him, taking a deep breath and hoping that he looked like a man prepared to stand no nonsense.

'All right,' he said, and cleared his throat again. 'All right. Who can tell me what a Noun is?'

To a man-jack and a girl-jill, form 2B gazed around at one another, sighing noisily. 'We've *done* Nouns,' somebody said. 'Twice.'

'Never mind that. Now you can do them again,' he said. 'Open your books. If you've done them before you'll know the right page without being told.'

He ignored the rebellious murmurs.

'Get on with it,' he said. 'Start copying the passage. You haven't got time to gossip…'

He picked up a piece of chalk and turned to the blackboard. Slowly the room filled with the scratch of pen-nibs and a dejected muttering…

*

At three minutes to four, the Senior English Master put his head round the door. The exercise books had all been passed along the rows and piled up on the teacher's desk. The pen-monitor was prodding pens into the holes in his wooden block. The blotting-paper monitor was wandering up and down the rows, assembling her heap of grubby pink sheets.

'Have you had quiet guard? Nothing untoward?' enquired Mr Rippingale, coming into the room and peering into his cupboard.

'Harvest safely gathered in? O, come *along*, Linda. Do hurry up with the blotch… Books all present and correct? Pens? No empty sockets in the block? Splendid.'

Mr Rippingale glanced at his wrist-watch.

'Very well, 2B… Stand. Good afternoon. Girls first, lead on.'

As the classroom emptied, the bell snarled.

'Ah,' said the Senior English Master, turning towards the door. 'Forgive me, dear boy. Must dash. Busy evening ahead. First read-through of *Quiet Weekend* scheduled for eight pip emma. Know the play, do you? Rip-roaring stuff! Next Village Players production.'

The Village Players. Amateur dramatics… Of course! 'Producer: Dick Rippingale': *he'd been reading that name on their posters for the past couple of years.*

'I'll leave you to it, then,' said Mr Rippingale. 'Stack the books on my desk when you've finished marking 'em, there's a good chap. Muchas gracias.'

Moments later his scarlet MG two-seater was accelerating out of the school gates and along Joslin Road.

*

2B: *First Aid in English* — Nouns, Adjectives, Verbs. 2A2: *First Aid in English* — Rules of Concord, Direct Speech. 3A2: *First Aid in English* — Personal Pronoun (Objective Case), Relative Pronouns, Indirect Speech…

Day after day, class after class, through nine double-periods a week for the space of a fortnight, the dreary litany had continued — 'Boring, I know, but stick at it; you're getting them under your thumb,' said Dick Rippingale. 'You can't afford to let up, old man. It all has to be hammered into their tiny grey cells' — before R. Druce BA could swap his decent suit for an old sports jacket and trousers, and sign on as a porter at King's Cross. Evening after evening he had listened as the scarlet two-seater growled past the staff-room window before the clangour of the final bell had died away.

It was just as well that Mrs Franks had no wish to read about it. Teaching French — and he pictured Walter Mason's classroom — was never going to be like that. Nor was teaching English if he ever came to have a classroom of his own.

*

His 'Critical Survey' essay, revealing as it might be here and there, was incomplete, he learned, when his turn came to discuss it with Mrs Franks.

'You haven't said a word about sex… I can't see why,' she told him. 'Education doesn't stop at the school gates, does it?'

'What I'm prepared to say about it *does*,' he said.

'If that's going to be your general attitude, don't expect high marks,' said Mrs Franks, stalking to the door and holding it open.

But he was too involved, too close to the emotional tangles in his life to want to discuss them. Or to contemplate them even, in cool blood. And absolutely not at Mrs Franks' behest.

Emily. Nadia.

Nadia — already eighteen years old — whose ghostly presence continued to haunt him as the fancy took her. Emily, older than Nadia by as many years as he was. Emily, whose physical self at his side could banish Nadia's ghost into the lurking shadows of his mind. But not for long.

*

With money in his wallet after the days and nights at King's Cross, he had bought an academic gown, everyday garb for a grammar-school teacher. Along with it he acquired a BA hood, silk-lined with russet and the white border of Convocation, to flaunt around his neck on Speech Days and parents' evenings. Spending money on the necessary trappings helped to anchor his thoughts on a career as a teacher.

His father was delighted.

'Be guided by me,' Robert Druce Senior had long insisted. 'Forget journalism, forget a so-called career as a writer. That won't put a roof over your head. That won't put bread and butter on the table. Dorothy, am I right?…

'Teachers have got a job for life. A *career*. With a decent pension waiting at the end… The country is always crying out for teachers. Always will be…

'If you *must* write, you can always make it your hobby.'

When he donned his robes in the kitchen in Honey Lane, his father circled round him, plucking at the sleeves of the gown and straightening the hood on his shoulders as if he were posing a mannequin. Mrs Druce ran upstairs to fetch her camera.

When she'd snapped him from varying angles enough, 'Here, take it off and let me have a go,' said his father, glancing at himself in the mirror. 'Come on, Dorothy. You might as well finish up the film.'

The camera shutter clacked while Robert Kitchener Druce peacocked up and down the kitchen and struck poses in the doorway.

*

Two days later his son stood in the jeweller's shop in the High Road and watched Emily slide a sapphire-and-diamond ring along her finger.

'It's a perfect fit,' smiled the assistant. 'Now you must take it off again and let the gentleman slip it back on your finger… There we are. Doesn't it look lovely? And now you can make a wish.'

Like his BA hood and gown, Emily's engagement ring was a symbol of the decisiveness of mind that he so much wanted to feel but somehow could not quite screw into focus. An attempt at forging a date-stamp to the end of his despair over Nadia. Of compelling himself to confront the looming commitments of marriage and a career.

If his parents kicked up a fuss, so what? Wasn't Frank O'Connor, married to his Audrey in the teeth of a father's fury, an example to follow?

His parents' embittered silences and the shouts of rage when they saw the ring on Emily's finger dragged on for days. 'Is this the reward we get for supporting you all these years?' said his father. 'No. You just can't *wait* to get out of this house, can you?' said his mother. 'After all I've done for you.'

Along with the sniffs and mutterings of Emily's aunt and uncle, the Druce's recriminations only case-hardened the happy pair in their resolve, uniting them in setting aside anxieties which they both felt.

*

'Complete this sentence,' Mrs Franks announced at the start of her third tutorial in the attic room at the top of the stairs. '*Mother began to form…* No, I don't want you to say anything. Write your answers down.'

'Mother began to form an opinion… an opinion… an opinion… an opinion…'

As the first four read out their answers, Mrs Franks smiled like a cream-fed cat.

'Opinion,' she said. 'Precisely what I expected… And now let me tell you *my* sentence: *Mother began to form in the test-tube…*'

She reached for a cigarette.

'Mother began to form in the test-tube,' she said again, blowing smoke towards them.

'We are all imprisoned by our language background. That is my point. Biologists will understand my sentence, because they know that "mother" is the name of a mould. The sort of mould that sours wine into vinegar. But as non-scientists the only expression any of *you* can come up with is, "form an opinion".'

'Fours,' said Robert Druce. 'Mother began to form fours. *I* didn't write down "opinion". *Mother began to form fours.* A parade-ground manoeuvre. Standard drill in 1914 to '18. Nowadays, of course, you move into columns of three.'

'I am acquainted with the term,' snapped Mrs Franks. She sucked her cigarette and exhaled a lungful of smoke. 'And in any case, your sentence is utterly ridiculous. How could your mother form *fours*?'

'You don't know my mother,' he said, expecting her to laugh.

Mrs Franks sniffed and changed the subject. She had no patience with frivolity.

*

Three blocks of teaching practice were scheduled for students at the Institute of Education, one in each term of their post-graduate year. Druce R. found himself assigned to a hundred-year-old grant-aided grammar school in the East End of London. It was a ten-minute bus-ride through the surging Stepney streets from the underground station at Aldgate East.

Sir John Tempest's Charity School was a rambling edifice four storeys high, the mid-Victorian gift of a local brewer and churchman. The building itself was split down the middle: female pupils in the northern half, boys to the south. Only on the topmost floor was there a door through which staff and sixth-formers might move from one domain to the other.

On the boys' side of the flat roof there was a prefabricated classroom perched on stilts like a lake-dwelling. It was out of bounds to girls. Through its window panes you could peer out across half a mile of tenement roofs and factory chimneys to where the lanes and courts below were threaded by alleyways that led down to the wharves and the river.

Limehouse, Ratcliff, Shadwell, Wapping…

Nightmare settings of his youthful reading, the place-names alone were a litany, heavy with the imagined stench of opium-dens, piracy, and torture. Blood soaking into floorboards. Corpses slid through trapdoors into the slopping waters of the Thames. Oily mudflats and foul tidal pools haunted by Rogue Riderhood, Daniel Quilp, and the yellow-skinned servants of the green-eyed devil doctor Fu-Manchu.

*

On the mid-October afternoon of his first visit, the Headmaster conducted him to the Senior French Master's room and rapped on the wired-glass window in the door.

'Wait!' bawled a voice. 'Resume your seats, you mutinous dogs.'

There was a long drawn-out scrape and clatter of desk-lids. Through the pane of glass in the door, Druce and the Head watched Alan Allworthy clutch his MA gown about him with his right hand, and clamber down from his own desk.

'In!' Mr Allworthy shouted, flinging the door wide open. In his left hand he clutched an eight-foot pole ferruled with a hook for opening high windows. 'Ah, Headmaster,' he said, red-faced and out of breath but unruffled. 'Got my student there, have you? *Comment vous nommez-vous, mon gars?'*

'Druce. Robert Druce. I — '

'*Très bien. Formidable.* Trot him along to the staff common-room, would you, Headmaster? I'll be free after break and I'll put him wise to everything he needs to know then. *D'accord?'* He gave his new student a friendly punch on the shoulder, and turned back to the Headmaster. 'You must excuse me, now,' he said. 'I've a bone to pick with this rabble about their latest excremental piece of so-called homework…'

As the Head led Mr Druce away to the empty staffroom, they heard the Senior French Master resume his diatribe. 'Mutiny, is it, eh?' he roared. 'Up on your desks again! The first of you to make one false move, I'll spit him in the gizzard with this window-pole, so help me God!'

'A first-class teacher, Mr Allworthy. Outstanding examination results,' said the Head, hitching his gown around his shoulders. 'His methods are eccentric at times, one must admit. But we all have our oddities. And it doesn't do to forget that Alan Allworthy was a wartime hero: parachuted into France and fought alongside the French resistance. Decorated for it. *Chevalier de la Légion d'Honneur*.'

*

Mr Allworthy — 'Alan to you,' he insisted, before sending R. Druce to sit at the back of the class and observe — conducted lessons the forty-five minutes of which — along with those moments when he resumed his Long John Silver act to the huge delight of the class — raced past in a surge of hilarity and fluent French.

'The man's a clown,' said Mrs Franks, dismissing Mr Druce's attempt at praise. 'Don't ever get any ideas into your head of modelling yourself on *him*.'

There were two other teachers on Alan Allworthy's French-department staff: Bill Harrogate, and Dr Woodman.

With doctorates from Louvain and Brussels, Dr Woodman intoned his French — when he ventured to speak in that tongue — in a cooing and ponderous Scots accent, oblivious of the paper pellets and chalk that flew through the air from one instant to the next.

'This is Misterr Drroooos, and Misterr Drroooos is a furrst-class teacherr, and he has a degrree in Frrench, and he knows a grreat deal of Frrench…' — Dr Woodman's well-intended introduction threatened to be the kiss of death.

'Mr Drroooos… Eh, now sit down Jaanus, why are you out of yourr place? Pentecost, go back to yourr seat. I'll not warrn you a second time… Pentecost!'

Even the names of the denizens of 4C were freakish enough to be ominous.

'*Qu'est-ce que c'est que ça?*' Dr Woodman asked 4C, glancing at Druce and making a fleeting concession to the Direct Method. He tapped the blackboard where he had drawn what looked like an unravelling skein of wool. Possibly it was meant to be a lobster, Druce decided, looking at the 'afternoon on the beach' text in the French coursebook. '*C'est un sanglant mess, Monsieur*,' Jaanus answered, then obligingly whispered to his mates, 'Well, it *is* a bloody mess.'

441

'Noo, noo,' cooed Dr Woodman, 'it's a lobsterr. *C'est un homard…*'

Bill Harrogate, sandy-haired and sinewy, was the most recent appointment to the school staff and lowest in the graduate pecking order. Lower yet were the PE and woodwork and technical-drawing masters, of course, since neither of them were graduates. But they kept to their own hidey-holes, store-rooms adjacent to the woodwork-room and the gym, and only ventured into the staff common-room if they were invited to attend a meeting.

Bill Harrogate B.A., a bare eighteen months older than Druce, was in his probationary year and still learning to find his feet. Out of classroom hours he helped to coach the school rugby team. That, and his swift irascibility, put an edge on his efforts to maintain discipline in his French classes.

Discipline and how to keep it was a topic that Mrs Franks' students brooded over endlessly. In private, that is, for she cut short any talk of it. 'Bore the children and they'll misbehave,' she would point out with her feline smile. 'Interest them and they won't.' True. Yes, absolutely. But her gnomic assertions, take them or leave them, were cold comfort in the early weeks when you were floundering to find yourself.

*

'Thursday 3 December 1953. 2.25 p.m. 1C. French. . .'
Traffic noise from the Stepney streets outside beat against the window panes. Inside the classroom walls and within R. Druce's skull, the prospect of a forty-five-minute lesson with Bill Harrogate's 1C seemed to stretch ahead to the last syllable of eternity. Steam clanged along the heating pipes. The air smelt rancid.

R. Druce settled his BA gown around his shoulders, playing for time.

'If you'd care to begin?' said Mrs Franks.

Heads and bodies swivelled round to look at her.

'*Très bien. Alors, qu'est-ce que c'est que ça?*' said R. Druce BA, waving a pencil in the air and crying out in a high-pitched gabble. '*C'est un crayon, n'est-ce pas?*' he instantly replied, ignoring the raised hands, in a sudden panic that nobody in the class would give him the right answer. '*C'est un crayon. Qu'est-ce que c'est? C'est un crayon. Oui, c'est un crayon. Est-ce que c'est un stylo? Non, pas du tout! C'est un crayon. Très bien.*'

He inhaled a second lungful of breath, threw down the pencil and snatched up a ruler.

'*Et qu'est-ce que c'est que ça? C'est un règle. Un règle.*'

The pencil rolled off the edge of the desk. Three boys plunged out of their seats to pick it up.

Mr Druce stared the front desk's twin occupants in the eye. His left hand was locked in a spasm on the metal edge of the desk-lid. He knew that he ought to be chalking the words up, but he flinched away from what to his fevered brain seemed like endless furlongs of glass-slippery floor stretching between him and the blackboard wall six feet away at his back.

He rapped out his questions faster and faster, answering them the instant he had uttered them. At the edge of his vision his tutor, a cartoon figure pinioned into a school desk by her swollen mauve flesh, appeared to bulge and grow more purple instant by instant.

At times of stress, the nightmare of that afternoon was going to unfold itself in dreams for the rest of his life. And not only in his dreams, but in future classrooms where he, himself now the visitor and judge, would watch other teachers gabble through everything they had to say in the first few instants of a lesson. And then, drained of the power to move, stand tongue-tied and hollow-brained, staring out across endless space into eternity.

Each time his heart would pound and his nerves shrivel in empathy with his remembered twenty-three-year-old self, and them.

At this point my tutor took over the lesson...

His final comment rounds off the sorry tale of that desperate three quarters of an hour: the last and grimmest of three lessons observed by Mrs Franks in the course of a single day. His words lie here now, under my hand.

As 1C trailed away along the corridor, his tutor turned to look at him.

'I was a bit worried by that,' he said, as she drew breath.

Mrs Franks' lungs emptied in a rush like a knifed bladder. 'My God, so you should be.'

Alone with her in the staff-room moments later, 'Look,' he said. 'If you think I'm not up to it, just fail me now,' — after all, she'd already sent John Aumonier packing, a bi-lingual member of her tutorial group — 'then neither of us will waste any more time. There can't be any point in letting things drag on till June, only to fail me then...'

*

And now it was December already, and here they all were in a lecture-theatre in Malet Street.

Philosophy of Education. The final seminar of the autumn term.

Each time his cigarette burned down to his fingers, a stab of pain jarred him awake. He prodded Steve Durston, slumping open-mouthed beside him, and slid the cigarette along a further half-inch. When there was nothing of it left but the filter-tip, it would be Steve's turn to mount guard and set *his* cigarette like a time-fuse between his fingers. Meanwhile, both of them glassy-eyed with lack of sleep, they glared at the lecturer once again, jerking their heads up and assuming expressions of frenzied interest.

Unloading Christmas mail at Liverpool Street throughout the past eight nights, Steve and he had snatched barely two hours of sleep in every twenty-four, spreadeagling themselves in a corner of the Student Union from half-five to half-past seven. In previous years there had been no difficulty in catching up on sleep during the day, but the Institute of Education term continued for a further week beyond the autumn term at UCL. From Monday to Friday Steve and he had worked and slept in their clothes, yawning their way to Malet Street in time for a 9 a.m. tutorial, after a quick wash and shave in the Gents' at Liverpool Street station.

'Fuckin' students!' snarled the washroom attendant every morning, as they stood at the basins, stripped to the waist. 'Come on now, clear orf out of it! Get ya bleedin' clothes back on, an' stop runnin' orf all my fuckin' 'ot water. Make way for *genuine* people!'

As the Christmas term fizzled down to its end, Steve was having increasing doubts about a career in teaching. In the New Year he would not return to the Institute.

But almost as disaffected as Steve was, Druce R. was reluctant to throw his hand in yet awhile. His jejune efforts at teaching French fell far short of his Mrs Franks' standards and his own. But teaching English to Mr Silver's classes — poetry, above all — was another matter. Meanwhile for the two schooldays of each week, the raucous, polyglot tangle of Stepney had not stopped dragging at his senses, while back in Malet Street the Psychology course was luring its followers into enticing byways.

Most compelling of all, for half a term now whenever he could snatch the chance, he had fled along the corridors of the Institute to sit in on James Britton's and Nancy Martin's English seminars, tingling with excitement as he waited for them to begin.

36

SPITALFIELDS

In the autumn term, observation and practice teaching had been compressed into fifteen lesson-crowded Tuesdays and Thursdays, while lectures and tutorials in Malet Street and Woburn Square made up the rest of the week. In February 1954, Robert found himself back at Sir John Tempest's Charity in Stepney for a further three-week stint. But now the classroom sessions would last from Monday to Thursday, with Fridays alone the occasion for tutorials in Woburn Square.

Classes as yet unknown to confront. New faces and fresh lists of names to memorise. Among them the denizens of Bill Harrogate's 3C, whose dwelling-place was the prefabricated classroom perched on its steel stilts on the roof. 3C was a notorious and disruptive bunch, now enduring their eighth term in the school. Over the years French lessons had become a standing joke in their eyes, and Bill was the twelfth French master to wrestle with them.

'You'll be number thirteen. Not superstitious, are you?' he asked Robert. 'I'll let you introduce yourself to 3C,' he said. 'Better if they don't get the idea that I had to come along as your minder.'

In the event, it was the velocity of R. Druce's arrival in 3C's midst that preserved him from rage and disaster.

At 2.25, when his first rooftop session was scheduled to start, he was still winding up an English lesson with 2A in the school basement, in a hot and airless classroom next-door to the boiler-room. At the first jangle of the bell, he snatched up his pile of books and ran for the stairs.

Five flights later he emerged into the windy spaces of the roof, with a hammering pulse and aching knees. He was out of breath and already minutes late.

"Ere 'e *comes!*' yelled a voice, and a door four feet above his head slammed shut.

He flung himself up the iron staircase, twisted the door-handle, and hurled the door open with all his force. He intended it to crash back against the wall, and so once and forever signal the arrival of Druce, The Demon Disciplinarian. A Man Who Would Stand No Nonsense.

Failing to notice the four-inch-high step, he launched himself across the threshold.

With his feet hooked from under him, his own momentum swept him across the front of the class to the opposite wall, where he collapsed in a shower of books with his BA gown and the sleeves of his jacket tangled together around his shoulders. 3C roared with delight. As he got to his feet, they erupted from their desks, clutching their sides and shrieking with laughter.

He realised that he was laughing too.

Opéra bouffe. Slapstick comedy. He couldn't have produced a more clownish pratfall if he'd tried.

'Very well,' he said. 'Très bien... My name is Druce. And now you know who *I* am, shall we begin? *Alors, on commence, n'est-ce pas?*'

At the end of the forty-five minutes, they were still grinning. And not quite, perhaps, but almost eating out of his hand.

It was undeserved good luck. Had the Grand Entrance he had planned been less supremely idiotic, had there been a few rags of dignity left for him to gather about him, he might have been goaded into losing his temper, and that would have been fatal. Worse still, he might have cast around for a scapegoat: 'You, boy. Yes, *you!* Just who do you think you're laughing at?' But as it was, he'd hit the right nerve. He had laughed at himself.

It was an invaluable lesson. It explained Alan Allworthy's success as a teacher. And confirmed his own unease about his tutor's chillier classroom stance.

*

Within a week he contrived to annoy her again.

A few days after the start of their first term, the four tutorial groups of the French department had been brought together for a Polish lesson. The object was to remind them of what it felt like to be an absolute beginner in a foreign language.

'*Moje nazwisko jest* Williams,' said the visitor, pointing to his own chest and announcing himself. '*Moje imi_ jest* Alan.' Surname. First name. When his class had recited their own names to him and then to one another, he fished an apple out of his briefcase. '*Ko to jest?*' he asked. And answered himself: '*To jest jab_ko.*' Fixing his gaze on a girl in the front row, 'Ko to jest?' he asked again.

An oral lesson. The Direct Method. Everything, barring personal names, in the foreign language itself. Nothing written down at this point. Remember that. Above all, no translation. Not a single syllable.

Mrs Franks' right eye glinted — her left was once again squinted shut against the smoke of her cigarette — as afterwards she bestrode her chair and questioned her tutorial group on what they ought to have gleaned from the demonstration. They'd seen an example of the Direct Method. Never mind how they had been taught French themselves: from now on they would be using the Direct Method, was that understood?

Yes. O yes.

The Polish words for first name and surname had been swiftly and safely scribbled down in phonetic script in Robert Robert's notebook the moment he had got outside the demonstration room. He hadn't bothered to transcribe *jab_ko*, that was easy to remember.

Now, three months later in tutorial, Mrs Franks sprang her entirely predictable trap. '*Ko to jest?*' she said, thrusting an apple towards R. Robert's face.

'*To jest jab_ko,*' he replied.

'*How* do you know *that?*' It seemed to irritate, not please her, that he knew the answer.

'We had a lesson in Polish. At the start of the course. You were there,' he said, feigning innocence. 'And the Polish for "apple" is easy to remember: *jab_ko* sounds a bit like "apple core", doesn't it?'

Her irritation turned to sudden fury. 'You're *translating*, you're *TRANSLATING!*' she cried. 'You must *NOT* do it.'

But if you found the right word on your tongue when you needed it, did it *matter* what hook you hung your information on? More cogently, perhaps, how could you forbid anyone's brain to make its own connections?

Thirty years on he was to recite his few words of Polish for the second time in his life. '*Moje nazwisko jest Druce,*' he told the girl behind the desk in a Warsaw hotel who had questioned him in English, asking his name; '*Moje imi_ jest Robert.* I, er, I haven't got an apple in my pocket, I'm afraid, or I could also tell you, "*To jest jab_ko.*"' For an instant they were both convulsed with laughter.

But that afternoon in 1954 Mrs Franks narrowed her gaze. She knew perfectly well what subversive thoughts he was thinking.

Nor did his second essay, the evaluation of a textbook, come up to scratch either.

*

He spent that Easter vacation in the area between Brick Lane and Vallance Road in the slums of Stepney.

He had chosen a Child-Psychology option as part of the Postgraduate Certificate in Education programme and the coursework involved making a detailed case-study of a teen-age boy or girl. Inviting the cooperation of a neighbours' child back in the Village didn't seem to offer much in the way of a challenge. But there was material infinitely more exacting close at hand in the East-End slums. And there, for what he took, he might perhaps be able to give back a little.

Don Best had been his friend since their junior-school days at Consort Road. In 1952 Don had married Barbara, the same frizzy-haired Barbara whose tray of pencils Bobby Robert had kicked into the air, and who later had lingered by the front gate in Auckland Drive while he strummed his way through piano practice. Don and Barbara lived in Whitechapel, and both were case-workers in the slums of Spitalfields and Stepney. Barbara had been off work with a bout of jaundice since early April, so it was officially agreed that Robert could take over her visits to two or three of her problem families while she convalesced, and make his case-study at the same time.

His choice fell on 'David', the twelve-year-old son of 'Betsy', a former prostitute. 'Betsy', like 'David', was a pseudonym he chose for his case-study, in order to maintain a correct professional anonymity.

He ferreted through a French dictionary for a word plausible enough and not too distant from the true one, to use as the family surname. He settled on 'Bastide'.

In three months' time that name, to his amazement, would irrupt and lift his spirits in the Methodology exam.

*

The details of David's life, as they accumulated in Robert's notes, were grim.

'Betsy', now 34 years old, was the third child and only daughter of Russian Jews whose own parents had fled from the pogroms and settled in Whitechapel. At sixteen Betsy began to run wild. Her family — all but a younger brother — washed their hands of her, and she absconded to Liverpool with her Nigerian-born pimp and lover, the father of David. In Liverpool, and later back in their East-End haunts, Betsy earned the couple's keep for twelve years or more by picking men up on the street and in bars. By the time she was thirty, she had grown so fat that few potential clients would look at her. She was pregnant with 'Queenie', her second child. The Nigerian beat her up and threw her out onto the street.

Soon after Queenie's birth, Betsy was accosted at an all-night coffee-stall by Oscar Bastide, a 62-year-old Mauritian who was 'on the lookout for a wife' at the time. He married her — it later transpired that a wife in New York was still alive and undivorced — and Betsy's children assumed her new surname. Since then she had given birth to two more children who, with straight hair and milk-chocolate-coloured skin, were quite unlike David and Queenie, with their sepia flesh and woolly curls.

A seaman by trade, Oscar Bastide had long been diabetic and unemployable. The gangrenous toes of his right foot, crushed in an accident, had been amputated, and he staggered around with a stick. He regularly thrashed David with it, and occasionally Queenie, too: explaining that he was 'beating the bad black blood out of them.'

He could speak English when he chose, but preferred to invite his Mauritian cronies around to gossip with him in Mauritian-French patois. He snarled at officials and case-workers in the same tongue. Betsy spoke no French, but her brother regularly dropped by; and then they turned the tables on her husband by chattering in Yiddish.

The Bastides occupied two rooms on the first floor of a tenement building in the labyrinth of courtyards and alleyways between Old Montague Street and Brick Lane. The family's sole source of income was the old man's disability pension supplemented by welfare payments. Out of it Mr Bastide paid a token rent to the local council to secure their right to live where they did: the landlord had long been an absentee. Below them the ground-floor rooms stank of the litter piled high inside their walls, and the shattered windows had been boarded up. The floor above them was lined with work-tables where six — and, at seasonal rush-times, ten or more — women sat stitching leather gloves on sweated piece-work, treadling machines that throbbed and clattered from early morning till late at night.

In the back-yard, an out-house door opened onto a single toilet-pan. Rarely flushed and never cleaned, it was the sole lavatory available to everyone who lived or worked in the building.

The Bastides made use of a single room as living-room and kitchen. It was criss-crossed from wall to wall with lines of grey rinsed-out nappies. Saucepans for food and laundry stood on the coal-stove, and food was kept in a cupboard or on the table. The room was lit by a single naked bulb. A second frayed length of flex looped down from the ceiling socket and passed through a gaping hole in the wall and out to the landing, where it vanished through another hole into the Bastide's bedroom.

Betsy and her husband slept there on a double bed, sharing it with the four-year-old who regularly wetted it. The eighteen-month-old baby lay in his pram at night, while David and Queenie slept side by side on a mattress on the floor. Both were frequent bed-wetters. In both rooms and on the landing, colonies of bed-bugs lodged under the wall-paper, crawling out along with the cockroaches after dark.

*

Almost every day, David was forced to run the gauntlet of his natural father. The man lived in a nearby street and amused himself by calling out, 'Who your daddy, hey?' after his son. It was only one of many humiliations. At school, along with his sister and stepsister, David was entitled to free dinners. They were despised by the children who paid for their own. At holiday times, they ate at a soup-kitchen run by the Jewish Board of Guardians, and were looked down on. Clad as they were in second-hand and usually ill-fitting clothing, not always clean, the Bastide children were jeered at on the street and in school.

The polyglot, multi-racial microcosm of the East-End slums, it soon became apparent, was split and split again by tribal hatreds, bitterly intensified by the propinquity in which so many families were condemned to live. As a Jew, David was resented by the non-Jews; as a black, he was victimised by the whites.

When Robert rang Emily from a call-box one afternoon, David asked if he could speak to her, and chattered happily while Robert went on pushing coins into the slot. Afterwards, in the street, David said musingly, 'Course, I s'pose she don't know I'm black, does she?'

He had a criminal record. A year earlier, a seventeen-year-old mentally-subnormal lad had broken into a lockup, stolen a box of biscuits, and handed them out among the younger children who had gathered outside to watch. David had been brought before the juvenile court, charged with 'receiving one chocolate biscuit, knowing it to have been stolen'.

Playing in the tenement yard one day, he had gashed his right eye on a broken bottle. Betsy had insisted on hauling him home before the wound was healed, claiming that she had herself been mishandled and abused by nurses in this hospital where she had been treated for syphilis as an eighteen-year-old, and later diagnosed as an incurable schizophrenic. David was now permanently blind in that eye, and the cornea was white and disfigured. Despite which and despite the doctors' prognoses, Betsy had carried him off to a faith-healing Christian Evangelist who promised publicly and in the name of God that the boy would regain his sight.

There were extracts from David's and his mother's medical records among the casework files. Three times Betsy had been remanded in custody and examined by psychiatrists, both in Liverpool and London. Their comments were conflicting and dismissive. A 'typical manic-depressive' in one account, she was a 'severe schizophrenic' in another. According to the third, she was 'what she will always remain, an unstable, vicious psychopath'.

Yet, endlessly voluble, bustling her great bulk to and fro, ducking under the lines of nappies in her kitchen, spooning potato mashed with gravy into the baby in his pram, wiping the toddler's nose, breaking off to press a cracked and weeping cup of sugary tea on her visitor, trying to drag a comb through Queenie's frizz of hair, resting her hand for a moment on David's shoulder, Betsy could glow with energy and affection. It was impossible not to warm to her vitality.

The first time that Robert called, Betsy's crippled husband sat hunched in his corner, slamming his stick on the floor, and snarling at the intrusion. Robert, who grasped the general drift of what he was saying, answered him in French. Well then, why, Mr Bastide asked in more careful French, couldn't something be done about his money? The clerks at the Assistance were robbing him.

Robert had already heard from Barbara that Mr Bastide had run amuck at the National Assistance office, hammering with his stick on the counter and shouting. Twice he had been ejected onto the pavement and forbidden to return. 'Well, let me see if *I* can do anything,' Robert said. He collected information from the casework files, talked it over with Barbara, and went to stand in a queue at the National Assistance office. It appeared that the Bastides were entitled to seven pounds a week more than they had been getting. Oscar Bastide struggled to his feet to welcome him after that, while Betsy insisted on sugaring him a cup of tea and standing over him while he gulped it down.

He loathed the taste of tea, above all when it was sugared, and hadn't touched it since his days of Army service. But it was out of the question to refuse it.

*

At the heart of the case-study lay the need to put David through an intelligence test. But, like his mother when the mood took her, in company David was a whirl of over-excited activity, flaring up and changing direction from instant to instant. Impossible for him to sit still for an extended interview. He jigged up and down in his chair, ran away across the room, dragged things out of his pockets, fiddled with them for a moment and threw them across the table, sat down and got up again all in the space of a minute.

In desperation Robert escorted him on the bus to Victoria Park, hired a boat for three-quarters of an hour, rowed half-way out across the lake, and shipped oars. Marooned there in the lee of an island, with escape cut off by water, Robert defied the hostile stares of people in other boats while David submitted to answering the questions in the Terman-Merrill revision of the

Stanford-Binet test. When their number was called, they got back to the landing-stage with no time to spare.

At school David had been dumped in the backward class, among the illiterates, a long way below his potential level. But forced to concentrate, he was far from stupid. And to Robert's amazement — given the broken English, Yiddish, Mauritian French, street-slang, and the quotidian obscenities that beat about David's ears, — at twelve years old he reached the Average Adult score in the English-language test.

Anxious about what might become of him, for a year or so Robert hovered in the background of David's life. The boy left school and found a job with an upholsterer in Spitalfields from whom he could learn the trade. He claimed to enjoy the work, and seemed to be settling down. Some years later, a chance meeting with a teacher at the school the Bastide children had attended told Robert more. Oscar Bastide was dead. David was still living at home, and earning his living as an upholsterer. His sister Queenie, inevitably perhaps, was in trouble. Despite Betsy's tigerish efforts, the chance seemed remote that Queenie and her half-sister Caroline would escape their mother's fate.

Back in his bedroom in Honey Lane at the end of that Easter month, he pieced together his notes and memories, handing the drafts a page or so at a time to Emily who typed them out in her office lunch-break. The final version ran to sixteen pages: some five thousand words. He left it with his Psychology tutor, and slid a carbon copy into Mrs Franks' pigeonhole in Woburn Square.

*

Daily in Stepney he was coming into close contact with people in places for the reality of which neither Dickens' vivid reportage nor the twopence-coloured horrors of Sax Rohmer's tales of Fu Manchu had prepared him. Bomb-sites, littered with weeds and festering rubbish. Building sites behind ramshackle walls of plywood and corrugated iron, where the wartime rubble had been bulldozed aside and trenches dug and concrete poured. Boarded-up tenements, leaning together, shored up by baulks of timber.

So many rotting streets and courtyards to explore, so many families that, unaided, were even less capable of survival than the Bastides. Men, women, and children sinking under appalling handicaps. Sad grotesques who were kept alive but, finally, imprisoned by their own daydreams of escape.

In the case-work unit's files he found a group of letters in which 'Hannah' told her story. She had been born, a few years after Robert's own mother, a virtual hermaphrodite, with both male and female sexual characteristics. She had been baptised and brought up as a girl. That was how she had always seen herself: as a female. But with the onset of puberty maleness had begun to take her body over; her voice broke and her beard sprouted.

Since then Hannah's life had been an unending sequence of humiliations. She longed for babies of her own and, although she accepted that marriage and bearing children could never be her lot, she still wanted people to see her as a woman. To dress as a man — the ruthlessly logical advice which every consultant, lay or medical, gave her — would, in her eyes, have been a senseless and wicked masquerade.

She had a weak bladder, and that made matters worse. On several occasions women had reported finding her in a women's lavatory, and she had been arrested and forcibly stripped. Inevitably, when the shameful episode and the embarrassed apologies were over, she was asked the same hateful question, however well-intentioned: 'If you want to stay out of trouble, why don't you just dress as a man?'

Unhappy as she was, Hannah did not seem to be bitter about her fate, and contrived to accept it with humility. She wasn't writing her letters to ask for help from the agency, but to offer her own help as a case-worker.

Her ever becoming one, it seemed apparent to everyone but her, was out of the question.

*

A stone's throw away from the Bastides lived the 'Abdullahs'. They, too, were on Barbara's case-list. Many pages of notes had accumulated over the months on Mr Abdullah, and on 'Pansy', his 20-year-old common-law wife, and their three children, all under school age.

The whole family gathered in the kitchen when Robert paid his first call.

Mr 'Abdullah' was in his early thirties, a strikingly handsome man. He lolled in an armchair, staring and saying nothing when Robert explained that Barbara was ill, and they would be seeing him instead for a week or so. Pansy remained standing. She was tiny, slim, pale-skinned, dark-eyed, wide-mouthed: strikingly pretty in a louche way. The two- and three-year-olds stood around her, leaning against her and clutching her skirt.

After a moment, Mr Abdullah unbuttoned his fly and began to masturbate, still glaring at the visitor and saying nothing. When he had finished, he wiped himself on a dirty handkerchief and put his penis away.

It was a habit of his, Robert was to learn, a gesture of defiance, a public assertion of his mastery in his own home. At other times he had been said to push Pansy down onto the floor or across the table, pull up her skirt and couple with her while the children looked on.

Mr Abdullah was able-bodied enough to work, but preferred to sit indoors for most of the day, drowsing in his armchair or filling out football pools and betting slips on the kitchen table. When cash ran short he sent Pansy out onto the streets. Pansy had boasted to Barbara several times about the money she'd made during Festival of Britain Year doing the business in Hyde Park and Kensington Gardens.

Mr Abdullah frequently wetted and sometimes soiled his bed. From time to time Pansy would bring a shit-smeared blanket round to the agency for a case-worker to wash.

The family could not have survived on Pansy's casual earnings as a prostitute, and where the Abdullahs' income came from was a puzzle. There were questions and conflicting comments in the case-notes. Mr Abdullah could be voluble when he wanted to, and when the mood took him he boasted at great length about his 'private' income. In the course of his few visits, Robert heard several versions of the tale, embroidered and re-embroidered in the telling.

Mr Abdullah's mother was an English 'society lady' whose name he had never been allowed to learn. She was rich and titled. She was still alive. She had died tragically. She sat in the House of Lords. Mr Abdullah's father was the young Egyptian with whom she had fallen madly in love, and who had seduced her. He was an air-force officer. He was an army doctor. In some versions of the story her lover had abandoned her. In others her family had hunted the man down and had him murdered or deported. Abdullah, despite the blue blood in his veins and all that it entitled him to, had been given away as a baby and adopted.

His sprawling Arabian Night's fantasy of a tale, as it sprang from the lips of a man in semen-stained clothes in a squalid and verminous room, provided Mr Abdullah with ample justification for his public behaviour. It was not entirely fictitious. An investigation by the case-work agency revealed that money was paid every month by a firm of solicitors into a bank account in Mr Abdullah's name. Any further attempts to identify its source, the agency was advised, would be countered by legal action.

*

Don pointed 'Mary' out to him one day across the street. A lank-haired, middle-aged woman, she was shuffling along in a overcoat and bedroom slippers. She looked harassed and ill.

'O dear. Mary's back in dreamland,' Don said. 'She's got a new lot of magazines, I expect. I'll have to arrange a visit.'

Mary was capable of looking after herself, but before long she would be in trouble again, hooked on her own kind of drug, and a group of case-workers and helpers would come round and knock on her street door. The same scene always met them.

Mary, shuffling along the passage in her slippers, still clutching the 'True Love' story she had been lost in. Her greasy old outdoor coat pulled on over a nightdress. A smell of sweat like the smell of an unwashed dog. Her hair tangled. In the kitchen a stack of magazines borrowed from a local book-and-magazine exchange spilling over the floor around her armchair and across the table, and a lingering stink of saucepans boiled dry and burnt. Dirty pots and pans on the gas-stove and in the sink, stale food and filthy cups and plates on the table and the floor. Soiled clothing heaped in a corner.

'O, Mary,' someone would say, 'not *again.*'

Mary's eyes would fill with tears as she looked from the face of one visitor to another.

The immediate remedy was simple enough. They would sweep the floor, boil kettle after kettleful of water, wipe down the walls, clean out the cupboards, wash up the crockery and pots and pans. Someone would carry Mary's soiled clothing and bed-linen round to the laundrette. When hours later the flat was tidy, Mary would gaze around and exclaim, as she always did, 'O, it looks lovely. O, it's like Buckingham Palace. O, if only my Alf was still here to see it.'

Smartened up, and out in the streets again, Mary would call across the road to anyone from the agency and hurry over to invite them round for a cup of tea. For a while the novelettes which beckoned her to escape from the world around her might seem to have lost their hold. But they were as hard for her to break free from as any addictive drug. It wouldn't be long before she lost heart and began to neglect herself, turning back to her dream worlds. Then within a week or two, word would come again that Mary needed help.

*

He was at the casework agency late one afternoon when a call came from the maternity ward. They'd allowed Mrs Leonard to take her new-born baby home, but his navel wasn't quite healed up yet: the hospital staff were run off their feet; could somebody pop round and check?

'I'll go,' said Don. 'It's more in Barbara's line, but she's still not well. D'you want to come with me? I might need a hand.'

Vera Leonard lived in a ground-floor bedsit in Flower-and-Dean Street. 'You'd better come in,' she said, and stood around helplessly while Don unswaddled her baby boy. She looked about seventeen.

'The hospital say they've given you a supply of fresh dressings,' Don said. 'Can you find me one? And a saucepan. I have to boil up a new dressing and let it cool.'

Mrs Leonard unearthed a bagful of dressings from under the tiny sink. Each was sealed in its own plastic wrapper.

'And a saucepan.'

'I 'ain't got a saucepan,' she said. 'Won't the kettle do?'

'No. All right, look, I'll go and buy a saucepan,' Don said. 'There's still just about time. Can you hang on here, Bob?' The street door closed behind him.

The baby started to wail and Vera Leonard gave it a breast. 'Sit down,' she said. 'You 'ave the chair, I'll manage on the bed. 'Ere, d'ya like my cocktail cabinet? Posh, ainnit?'

It was a flashy monstrosity of veneer and glass, blocking up the remaining floor space.

Still nursing the baby, she reached across with her free hand and pulled open the drop-down door. The glass shelves were empty.

'There's a light comes on when ya open the door,' she said, 'but I ain't got a electric point. It's lovely, ainnit, looks a picture. We got a tallyman comes round the streets.'

When the dressing had been boiled up in the new saucepan, allowed to cool, and bandaged in place over the baby's red and swollen navel, he walked back through the streets with Don, clenching and unclenching his fists. Tears of rage brimmed his eyes.

*

Abdullah, Mary, Hannah, the Bastides; and all the others whose faces he had glimpsed in passing and whose stories he had been told. All only a tiny fraction of that self-renewing *submerged tenth* of society whose plight had been brought to the public gaze half a century earlier by William Booth. Human flotsam adrift in currents and whirlpools too powerful for them. Gasping air at the surface but repeatedly sucked down by poverty and sickness; drowning in the fantasies that might seem for a while to buoy them up.

A vision of 'Vera Leonard' possessed him. A teenage girl in a rented room with the baby she was not competent enough to cope with. A bed, a chair, a sink, and a gas-ring. Not even a saucepan until Don went out and bought her one. But, triumphantly caressed, as she gave a breast to the baby, the veneered cocktail cabinet, with its empty glass shelves and a light that she could never switch on. It was a symbol of her dreams of what life might offer.

What smooth-tongued swine could have blarneyed her into spending her shillings on it week by week?

'If I could get that bastard alone,' he said, imagining the sweep of his own arm as he smashed an unknown tallyman's face against the wall. 'No, I'm serious…'

'Look. Hang on a minute. I must make a quick call to the hospital to let them know we've changed the dressing,' Don said. 'Then we'll settle down somewhere and relax over a quiet drink, eh?'

Halfway through his first teaching stint in Stepney, Robert had dropped into a pub early one evening and found a corner on his own, planning to sit there unobserved, watching East End life go by. A woman had caught his eye and smiled at him. Moments later she came over to his table. She hitched up her skirt, settled herself on the bench at his side, and laid her hand on his thigh.

'Looking for a nice time, love?' she asked.

He had been off-limits. His appearance marked him out. Wearing a suit and tie, carrying a briefcase, what else could he have been doing there but looking for a pick-up?

Tonight, as Don and he carried their pints of beer across to the table furthest from the juke-box, they still stood out from among the other drinkers, were still outsiders. But for a different reason. Outsiders they might be, but they were *known*. Faces he faintly remembered nodded across at them through the haze of smoke, then turned away to mutter among themselves.

A woman with jet-black hair that was white at the roots threaded her way across the room and leaned down over them.

"'Ere, you're from the agency, ain't ya? You got any spare coal there? I ain't 'ad no bleedin' coal to burn fer a week.'

'That's the Gawd's truth, mate. So, wot ya goin' ta do abaht it?' added another woman, joining her.

37

ARABINS

He met Bill Harrogate's 1A at the station in the village, waiting and watching as they spilled down the stairs from the platform.

Bill shook his hand. 'Looks as if the weather's on our side.'

1A followed in a straggling crocodile as Bill and he set off along Station Road.

A quarter of a mile to Consort Road School. Then across the road and on through the trees to the open glade at the edge of Abbot's Wood.

'Here?' Bill said. He pulled his referee's Acme Thunderer out of his pocket, and blew a long, screeching blast. The boys of 1A huddled around him. 'Mr Druce?' he said, turning to Robert.

'Right,' said Mr Druce. 'Welcome to the woods. If you've never climbed a tree before, it's high time you learned how. That's what they're there for. Keepers? Forget it. You're not in Victoria Park now. I'll give you all thirty seconds to find a tree and scramble up it, feet off the ground. Go!'

Unbelieving faces turned from him to look at Bill.

'Pile your satchels on the grass,' said Bill. 'Well, what are you waiting for?' and he looked around as 1A scattered to the trees. 'Come on, feet off the ground, Green; you heard Mr Druce!...

'East end kids. *Climb the trees*, sir?' Bill nudged him and laughed. 'They couldn't believe their ears... We'll give 'em fifteen minutes: what do you reckon?' he said. 'Then I'll whistle them back for a game of rounders.'

'It's just after ten,' said Robert. 'We could let them have half an hour's tree-climbing. Then the rounders. We're not due at Kate's Cellar until around twelve. It'll take us half an hour or so to get there. So if we give them, say, twenty minutes of rounders, there'll be plenty of time in hand for jumping the brook on the way up to the pub and the Retreat.'

'Jumping the brook?'

'Ah. You'll see. It was a daily pastime for Roy Shotley and me, jumping backwards and forwards across the brook on our way to school and home again… Don't hang about, Collins! Jump for the branch, sling your legs over, and swivel yourself round.'

'That's it, Collins. Good lad!' said Bill. 'Keep 'em on the move, eh? Get rid of some of that surplus energy. Hoy, Fielding, what's that horrible racket in aid of?'

'Please sir, Tarzan sir,' replied a boy astride the low branch of a beech. He put his finger back into his mouth and wobbled it again in an undulating howl. The rest of 1A who had a hand to spare from clutching the branches began to join in.

*

Bases marked out with satchels. Half an hour of clouting a tennis ball and scampering across the grass from base to base, and they looked as if they'd had enough of rounders. Bill plucked out his Acme Thunderer again and marshalled 1A into a noisy swarm. 'Stage two,' he said. 'The route march. Keep together, you lot, we don't want any stragglers…

'Lead on, MacDuff,' he added, for Mr Druce's benefit.

Off they set into the leaf-drifts under the pollard hornbeams, down the slopes towards Sandpit Plain, skirting the edge of the Hollow Ponds where sixteen years back in time Kenny Woods had run to Bobby Druce in a panic, reckoning he'd seen a jack-pike smacking its lips over little Janey's corpse. Onwards, along to Roy's and Bobby's old jumping-place, just downstream from where its tributary joined the brook.

The spot, if this was it, was unrecognisable. Over the years its high cliff of clay and impacted flints had been undermined and toppled by floods, and a dark sludge of rotting leaves had buried the banks of pebbles where their boots had crunched down with a shock that jarred their spines.

But already there were shouts and steely crashes from thirty yards upstream. Outriders from 1A had sniffed out a corner where the waters had carved another precipice and laid bare another pebble-bank below and opposite.

*

Across the grass from the pub at Arabins Green there was an airy wooden barn. In its heyday it had been one of half a dozen 'Retreats': places built by charities where East-end children could spend a day or two romping among the forest trees and filling their lungs with fresh air. Now it served as a breezy annex to the cramped bar-parlours of Kate's Cellar, long reputed to be the lurking place of an eighteenth-century highway-man's moll.

'Did you all hear what Mr Druce was saying about highwaymen?' said Bill, as 1A scrambled among the benches and tables and unpacked their sandwiches. 'Now, pay attention. Change of subject. Who'll volunteer to give us both a hand to fetch the lemonade?'

As he watched the twelve-year-olds of 1A, for Mr Druce it was a day spent in the hovering company of his own multiple childhood selves. Bunching together and looking over their shoulders when the tree-trunks crowded close and shadows grew thicker; whistling and shouting to keep their spirits up. Clambering, uncertain of whether they dared, among the lowest branches; racing away through sedgy grass and kicking over ant-hills. Peering down into running water. Loitering to finger the velvety moss in Dead Man's Slade.

A day, too, of a kind of atonement for the times at Consort Road when he had joined his fellow-pupils and lain in ambush for the East-End children who spilled out from Staple's Charity and into the forest slopes, and he had stood and jeered along with them.

*

SUBJECT: FRENCH
TOPIC: The Partitive Article.
FORM: 1B
DURATION: 45 minutes.
DATE: 25-5-.54   TIME: 2-.25
AIM: 1. Revision and consolidation of the masculine form of the partitive
2. Introduction of new material in the shape of the feminine form…

Back in Alan Aldridge's classroom at Sir John Tempest's Charity, Mr Druce picked up the brown-paper parcel on his desk and held it aloft. 'Alors, qu'est-ce que c'est?'

A spinney of hands waved above their owners' heads.

'Eh bien, Marcel?'

'C'est un paquet, Monsieur.'

'Bien. J'ouvre le paquet… Et… Qu'est-ce que c'est que je trouve là-dedans?' He tore the paper open and revealed a chocolate bar.

'Chocolate,' said thirty voices.

'Non, non, non…' He flashed a glance at the grid of names on his desk. JEAN-JACQUES. *Second desk in the left-hand row.* 'Jean-Jacques, dîtes-moi: qu'est-ce que c'est?'

'C'est *du* chocolat, monsieur.'

It was Mr Druce's demonstration lesson, the final battle with live ammunition, the basket all his eggs were piled in.

God bless Alan Aldridge and 1B. 'Don't worry, they'll see you alright,' he'd said; 'if the going gets sticky there's always Marcel, Alain, Michel — don't forget to bring yer grid of names, eh? Those three'll know their stuff. Pierre, too… Jean-Jacques.'

Wedged in a back-row desk Mr Parker, the external examiner, nodded his approval and encouragement. In the far right corner Mrs Franks gave no sign.

Mr Druce took a deep breath. *Go steady, now. Take things slowly. Get 'em all to practise it.*

'*DU* chocolat, oui; c'est *DU* chocolat. Et maintenant, tout le monde?'

'C'est du chocolat, monsieur,' 1B dutifully chorused.

Mr Druce looked at his watch. 2.26. Forty-four minutes to go before the end-of-lesson bell. He grasped the wine-bottle and hoisted it above his head. 'Et dans la bouteille? Est-ce qu'il y a du chocolat dans la bouteille?… Jean-Jacques?'

'Non, monsieur.'

'Evidemment, non. Non, c'est du –?'

'Du vin, monsieur.'

Et patati. Et patata. Uncle Tom Cobleigh and all. And how long have I got now?

But he didn't dare to glance at his watch again so soon.

A glass inkwell half-full of ink. Chalk rattling in a box. A staffroom cup awash with the dregs of four or five tea-cups. A plate of biscuits. Water in a glass. *Du… De la… Des…* Masculine, Feminine, Plural. *Du chocolat. Du thé. De la craie. Des biscuits.*

Time passing.

He was striding back and forth to the blackboard now, writing his phrases up. Venturing along the open lanes between the lines of desks, addressing individuals near at hand or across the room.

The inkwell. The glass. Contents the name of which began with a vowel. *Dans l'encrier, DE L'encre. Dans le verre, DE L'eau.*

Repondez-moi. Pierre? Tout le monde? Alain?

Time passing. Time passing.

(What's in the inkwell: tea? Water? No! Is there any ink in the cup? What IS in the cup?…)

Suddenly it was *FIVE TO THREE*. The red-inked time-check cried out at him from the margin of his notes. *Voilà. Très bien.* It was time to clean the blackboard and write up the questions he'd prepared.

(So tell me my little ones. En Français, bien sur! What's in the box? Where's the water? In the bottle, there's … what? And in the packet? Where's the tea?)

Nine minutes past three, and the second hand of his watch was flickering towards XII. 1B were passing their pieces of paper to the front. A monitor moved across the rows, collecting them. The bell rang. They stood.

'Au revoir, la classe.'

'Au revoir, Monsieur Druce… Et au revoir, Monsieur… Au revoir, Madame.'

Wonderful! They'd remembered to take their leave of the visitors.

He waited while Mrs Franks and Mr Parker finished muttering together at the back of the room.

'Had you thought perhaps, of making the whole lesson into a kind of tea-party? Lemonade, cakes, biscuits and so on? When they'd got the answer right they could take a swig of lemonade, or munch a biscuit or a bit of chocolate,' said Mr Parker, growing more and more enthusiastic as the three walked side by side along the corridor. 'You could pick things that would practise all your partitives: masculine, feminine, singulars, plurals. Might be fun: what d'you think?'

At the far side of Mr Parker, Mrs Franks pursed her lips.

*

'By the way,' she said, when they'd both walked with Mr Parker to his car and shaken hands, 'I've a bone to pick with you... I've read your study of the Bastide boy. Who wrote it? *You?* Is it all your own work?... Then why on earth couldn't you write as interestingly as that in the essays you wrote for me?...

'And another thing. *Bastide.* Where did you get that name from?

'It's not his real name.'

'I know it's not his real name. But what inspired you to choose *Bastide?*'

'I picked it out of the dictionary. Why?'

She narrowed her eyes at him. 'Purely by chance? Hm... Very well.'

Now what's bitten her? he thought.

'My lesson, though. Was it all right?'

'You did reasonably well. It was adequate.'

*

Freed from the treadmill, the next day he flung himself into a drama lesson with 2A. They clattered on ahead of him down to the basement, and into a classroom harsh with the tang of dust and heated iron from the adjacent boiler-room.

A marvellous convenient place for our rehearsal.
This green plot shall be our stage, this hawthorn-brake our tiring house...

Thisbe stand forth!
Mum's old dress. Trouser legs rolled up and falling down.
This beauteous lady Thisby is certain.

Moon muttering, fretting about the props he ought to have.
'But, Sir! I haven't got a dog, nor a lantern neither.'
'Never mind. *Mime* it. Make pretend.'

Well shone, Moon. Truly the moon shines with a good grace...
But silence! Here comes Thisby...

Lion, ramping across the gritty floorboards on all fours.
Well moused, Lion!

And then came Pyramus...

A cardboard breastplate and a wooden sword, silvered with aluminium paint.

A summer midnight's play within a play come suddenly alive, and 2A's hempen homespuns transcending time and their thirteen-year-old selves.

His own nerves tingling.

Come blade, my breast imbue
And farewell, friends.
Thus Thisbe ends.
Adieu, adieu, adieu...

The end-of-lesson bell ringing, dead on cue.

Bless thee, Robert. Thou art translated.

*

Relaxing in the staffroom in his last week at Sir John Tempest's Charity, it was high time to ask himself how he foresaw his future.

Consider Alan Allworthy, then, planning the day's lessons on the back of an envelope between Liverpool Street station and Aldgate East. Alan aloft and brandishing his window-pole. A brilliant, natural teacher, secure in his idiosyncrasies.

Doubly-Doctored Woodman entuning Glaswegian French in his nose full fetisly while the air hissed with flying chalk.

Bill Harrogate. Tense and irascible in the classroom. A daily malcontent, who out on the leafy slopes of Arabins and the Warrens had become a man transformed.

Teachers and occasions more grotesque, encountered in Sir John Tempest's rooms and corridors. The Latin master who day in day out nodded off at the front of the class, behind his barricade of books. The two-hour-long handiwork lesson Druce had been sent to observe, with its hoarse-voiced instructor repeatedly lashing at a sheet of iron with a t-square for silence. That same elderly man carefully closing the Headmaster's door behind him and brushing away tears.

The Deputy Head, whose reedy warble of *Non nobis, Domine, non nobis* sanctified the start and finish of each school lunch… Who had stumbled across Druce — dispatched to the empty staffroom on his first morning to wait until the Head was free — and greeted him with a petulant snarl: 'You are sitting in *my* chair.'

The master who every morning and afternoon break spooned bismuth powder into a mug of water, and swilled it down to neutralise the nervous acid in his stomach.

The Head of English — 'Just sit yourself down at the back of the room and watch me' — preening himself on how to approach Robert Bridges' poem: 'Whither, O splendid ship, Thy white sails crowding?'

Question round the class, test their comprehension, that was the way, he insisted. And then, 'Now I wonder, 3A, who can tell me what the second verse of the poem makes me think of?'

What kind of daft question was *that*?

The mustachio'd, seventeen-year-old Head Prefect whose official side-line it was to cane the malefactors. Ah, but that was tradition, you see. Time-honoured. Like being required to repeat, 'May I go forth?' if you wanted to empty your bladder.

All that — apart from Alan Allworthy — on the minus side.

And on the plus?

Well, he still had a few summer weeks — assuming he passed the Theory papers — in which to make up his mind.

*

But he didn't know what he wanted, walking again with Emily that long summer evening, up along the forest paths towards Kate's Cellar, distracting his attention from his misgivings by telling her at length about Bill Harrogate's 1A.

In the bar he recognised two faces that he'd not seen for nine years.

'It's Drucey,' they said, accosting him and eying Emily. 'Well, well.'

'Lou. Dogger. How are you getting on?' he said.

Lou's hair was thinning fast. There was a bald patch over his fontanelle. Dogger hardly seemed to have changed at all. But at least his steel-framed goggles were free of insulating tape.

'I'm in the oil biz,' Lou said.

'Baltic Exchange, me,' said Dogger. 'You?'

'Teaching practice year. What brings you over to Arabins Green? Bit out of your way, isn't it?'

'Yerss, well,' said Dogger. He hadn't lost the Cockney speech that had got on Alwyn Black's nerves.

'Crumpet,' said Lou. 'So what's the local talent like? You seem to be doing all right for yourself.'

'Who are *they*?' asked Emily when he carried her crème de menthe across to her a moment later. 'I don't care for the look of *them*.'

'Marsh and Bone. They were at Monkswood. In my class. The last time I saw them was in 1945.'

'So you're going to be a teacher, Drucey, eh? What a surprise!' said Dogger a moment later, sitting down at their table. He grinned at Emily. 'Can't fink what you see in '*im*, darlin'…

'O, well, well! Excuse *I*,' he said, as Emily silently held up her engagement hand with its sapphire and diamond ring.

*

'Going to be a teacher. Is it *that* obvious?' he said, as Emily and he threaded their way home along the forest paths through the fading twilight. 'Bone may think so but I'm not so sure. Not so sure at all.'

He glanced at Emily. She was looking at him but said nothing.

'I just don't want to find myself turning into a caricature, like some of them at Sir John Tempest's. Or keeping going only by dint of swilling down stomach-powder twice a day. Too much like my father. That's no future.'

'You've left it late to start having doubts. What *do* you want to do with yourself?'

'I don't know. Psychology. I'd like to read for a degree in psychology.' He walked on, gazing straight ahead into the dark.

'And how long is *that* going to take? And where does it leave *us*?' she said. 'You can't just chop and change. And I can't see your parents going on keeping you year in and year out. How can we even *think* about getting married if you're not earning?'

'Perhaps we shouldn't,' he said, staring grimly ahead.

She came to a standstill, clutching his arm.

'Are you saying you want to break off our engagement?'

'No… No, no. I'm not saying *that*…'

Emily was weeping.

'Tell me you don't mean it.'

He turned and faced her in the shadows. 'No, no. Of course I don't mean *that*,' he said.

But his own voice inside his skull was crying out, *Yes. You do. You do,* and he shouted it down. He couldn't bear to hear Emily's weeping.

'Your parents will be pleased, at any rate,' she said. 'I know they can't stand the sight of me.'

'Don't be silly. That's just not true.' But he could see their faces. *She's no catch, that one. I don't know what you see in her, I really don't.*

'Of course I want to marry you. It's just that… O, I'll apply somewhere. A Sec Mod, perhaps. No pressure there and — listen — I could apply to Birkbeck for a BA in psychology. Evening lectures. I'll drop by and pick up a prospectus next time I'm in Malet Street. That way I can eat my cake and have it. Eh?'

He put his arms her. 'Come on, darling.

'Come on.' He kissed her. '*Come* on… Before your aunt and uncle start complaining about the time… Listen, I haven't told you about 2A doing *A Midsummer Night's Dream* yet, have I?'

Talking. Talking. Shouting down the voice in his head.

Walking back with her, hands linked, through the moonlit summer midnight.

*

Within a month Emily's father took to his bed. 'Never had a day's sickness in his life before. He's as fit as a fiddle. He'll pull through,' Emily's aunt assured her, 'no need to worry.'

But suddenly he was seriously ill, and they were travelling together up to Suffolk.

He put his arm round her. '*I'm* here with you, darling,' he said.

'*Are* you? *Are* you?'

*

And now here it was. The last hurdle. Nothing in the first batch of theory papers — History of Education, Philosophy, and the rest — had caused a sense of panic and a sudden plunging upward of his pulse. Moreover, given his case-study of 'David Bastide', Child Psychology ought to be in the bag. But this afternoon it was the turn of the paper in Methodology, barbed-wired and booby-trapped, no doubt, by Mrs Franks. If he fell on his face here... He turned over the question paper.

'Study the following passage and explain in detail how and at what point in a secondary-school French course you might base a series of lessons on it...

Monsieur Bastide ouvrait la porte et...'

He couldn't believe his eyes.

'Monsieur Bastide'.

The name that he'd picked at random from the thirty thousand head-words in his French-English compact dictionary. With only the faint echo of 'David's' true surname to influence his choice.

In 1952 there had been his foreshadowing dream of the *Beowulf* passage in Part 1 finals. And now *this*. It seemed to be beyond coincidence.

As it must have seemed to Mrs Franks, ferreting her way through the carbon-copy of the case-study that he'd tucked into her pigeon-hole unasked the previous month. Could she suspect him of having got his hands on a copy of her question paper? Of rifling her desk? Suborning the printer? Of *mocking* her with his fore-knowledge?

No wonder she'd narrowed her eyes.

But time was ticking past. *Bastide.* A blockhouse; a fortified farmhouse. That was the meaning of the word. Forget the look on his tutor's face. Accept the name and what it meant as an omen, and get on with it.

As he began to dissect the text, sorting its elements into a possible teaching sequence, he couldn't shake off the faint impression that some One, some Presence somewhere, was peering over his shoulder.

38

STEPNEY GREEN

It was high time to think about a finding a school and a job. Time, too, for Emily and Robert to put some distance between themselves and the Village, his parents and her aunt and uncle.

He bought a copy of *The Times Educational Supplement*, and thumbed through it, circling the advertisements for teaching posts on the far side of London. A County Secondary Modern School for Boys in Surrey was looking for a master to take charge of French. He searched the *London A to Z,* and found the school, on a road that ran in a looping curve alongside the Thames.

'Secondary Modern?' said Mrs Franks. 'Well, if that's your choice, you can say goodbye to your career before it even begins. After that sort of start, no grammar school will even consider taking you onto the staff. Why a Sec. Mod., for heaven's sake?'

'It will allow me the time I need to read for a degree in psychology.'

But that was not the only reason.

He thought of Bill Harrogate and Bill's frustrated ambitions and forthcoming marriage and anxieties about money. Bill, at the start of his career as a full-time member of the language staff, teaching both French and German — and already waiting for dead-men's shoes; condemned for years ahead to playing follow-my-leader at the bottom of the pecking order.

Offering only French and English as Robert did, his *own* position in a grammar school would be even more restricted, with minimal hope of promotion to head of a language department for a very long time. If ever. It was not an inviting prospect.

But all that was his own affair, and nothing to do with Mrs Franks.

'In the coming year or two, *your* responsibility is to settle down to teaching French — very well, English too, if it matters so much to you. But certainly not to go haring off after another degree...'

Mrs Franks sniffed noisily. 'But if you won't be told, you won't be told.'

*

Mr. Druce has taken his teaching practice at the Sir John Tempest School where he has taught French up to the sixth form and some English. He speaks French with a good accent and his command of idiom is adequate.

Mrs Frank's testimonial, when it arrived, began promisingly enough: although 'adequate' stuck in his craw...

... a clear voice which carries well... manner in the classroom confident... has given much thought during the year to the problems involved in successful language teaching... gradually working out a technique suitable to his personality... ready to experiment with new ideas... class management has been satisfactory... could give help with dramatic work and with games...

Reasonable. Nothing to be ashamed of there. Faint praise, even. The twist of the knife was lurking in the final sentence:

with further experience both of life and of the classroom he should become a useful member of a school staff.

'... *should* become... *useful*... further experience of life...' Mrs Franks had not swerved from the truth. Admit it. But then, the greater the truth the greater the damage.

He thrust the testimonial back into its envelope, and flung it aside. How could he send out *that* sort of commentary along with an application for an interview? After a fortnight of angrily unfolding it and creasing it flat again, he consigned it to a drawer.

Where it still lies, severed by those time-worn creases into six yellowing rectangles.

Meanwhile, back in July 1954, he sent off his application to the Thames-side Secondary Modern, enclosing the testimonials that Brian Woledge and Walter Mason had given him. Walter, now a headmaster himself, knew exactly what a headmaster looked for. His 'Mr Druce will be a martinet for discipline' proved to be a clincher. As was his 'I should at all times be pleased to answer questions on his behalf.'

*

'A labouring job? You?' said the man behind the counter at the Stepney Labour Exchange.'You wouldn't last two minutes, son. Naow, what *you* want is an office-job. Clerical. *Pushing a pen.*' He started shuffling through the file-cards in his tray.

'No, I want to work on a building site.'

'I tell you, you'll be wasting your time just asking, mate...'

'I mean, there's rebuilding going on all around this area.'

'Well, if you won't be told what's good for you...' The man sighed. 'No point in sending you to a union site. I s'pose you *could* try Horsebitt's. Globe Road. Just across the street from Stepney Green tube. Non-union site. They're looking for a couple of general labourers, but — '

'I'll go there now.'

'I'm tellin' you, you won't last two minutes. They're all bog-trotters on that site. Irishmen to you... Paddies. Born with a pick in one hand and a shovel in the other. One look at you...' But already he was speaking to the empty air.

The Globe-Road site was a wasteland of open trenches, stacked door-frames and window-frames, mud-heaps and random pyramids of bricks and breeze-blocks.

'Can you handle a pick and shovel, now?' said the foreman.

'Yeah,' he answered.

He'd done spade-work enough at Scott's nursery three years earlier. He'd even swung a pick-axe once or twice.

'Let's see your hands.'

Ah, he was prepared for that, hardening the skin by rubbing methylated spirit into it night and morning for the past week.

'Tomorrow morning then. Half-seven sharp. Bring your cards.'

*

A rubble of demolished tenements and uprooted streets had been bulldozed away from Horsebitt's site and already the half-built shell of an apartment block ran north-to-south across the area. Alongside it the concrete foundations of another had been poured, and a dozen labourers were digging the trenches for a third.

The site foreman set him to 'back-filling'. Shovelling earth and rubble into trenches where concrete had been poured and the first dozen or more courses of a foundation-wall had been laid. When he'd scooped and flung the muck back in to the depth of a couple of feet, he had to flood it with a hose and thump it down with a baulk of timber to compact it.

On his fourth day he was told off to join the gang who were excavating new foundations. The double row of trenches stretched for thirty yards. Each trench was five feet wide, and both were already over a yard and a half deep.

'Dahn ya go, Stoodent,' the ganger-man, Old Peter, told him, nudging him towards the ladder. 'The last coupla yards is yourn. Keep on at it till ya git dahn ta solid gravel.'

Old Peter seemed to be the only man around the place without an Irish accent.

Across the whole site the layer of impacted gravel was a good six feet down. By the time your pick jarred against the gravel, you could look up and see the walls of the trench looming more than two feet high above your head, what with the muck piled up behind the mould-boards that were wedged there to stop it slithering back.

He spat on his hands for a tighter grip on the sweat-polished haft of the pick, then swung it up and raked it down the end wall of the trench, scarring a groove through the mass of blue clay and blitz-shattered tar-macadam and Victorian brick. It promised to be a back-aching struggle to keep the trench-walls straight.

When his pick lodged in a sudden layer of mud-black earth he grabbed up a handful and sniffed it. It stank like the sludge at the bottom of a drain.

But foul as it was, it was earth all right. Earth! Memory flung him back across twenty years to his childish notion that all the earth in London must have been dug up in the fields and gardens of Cambridgeshire and poured into holes made ready for it in the bricks and concrete and tar of London.

'Ach, come on now, Student!' growled twenty-year-old Pat at his back, who for the previous ten minutes had been flinging shovelfuls of rubble up into the daylight with the single-mindedness of a dog in a rabbit burrow. He looked round to find Pat's carroty hair level with his own waist.

'Get a move on now, willya? I'll be havin' the feet from onder ya in a minut.'

There was a knack to flinging a shovelful of muck upwards so that it dropped behind the mould-board, and didn't cascade back down and clout you on the back of the neck as you bent to scoop up another. It took him several minutes to perfect the jerk of the wrists that sent it vanishing upwards and away, never to return. By the time he'd mastered it, a voice had been shouting off and on for a while somewhere near at hand.

The cries grew suddenly wilder and a figure loomed on the skyline above him, brandishing a shovel. It was the Irishman from the adjacent trench.

'Sure now, an' ya can have the fockin' lot back again,' he roared, pitching half a dozen shovelfuls of spoil back over the mould-board and down onto Student's head and shoulders.

Student's efforts had been all too successful. Half the muck he threw upwards had been crossing the narrow gap between the trenches and raining down on his neighbour. 'Sorry,' he said. 'I'm sorry.'

'Yah, fockin' students,' said the man, and kicked over a parting bootful.

'Skibbereen is ut, ya granny come from? D'ya tell me that? Ach well, you'll do,' said the same man in the public bar of the Globe that evening, as they buried the hatchet under a glass of Guinness apiece.

*

Old Peter the ganger-man, with his tattoo-inked body sunburnt to the waist, his beer gut and hairless head and white-bristled chin, was at first sight a Magwitch caricature, a ticket-of-leave man from a Victorian nightmare. Four or five times a day he wandered up to Student's end of the trench to light up a dog-end and run his eye over Student. When his dog-end had fizzled down to a tiny saliva-soaked cone, he would flick it into the trench and grunt and spit and shuffle away.

At the start of Student's second week, 'Yus,' he said, approvingly, suddenly laying his lean brown hand for a moment on Student's shoulder. 'I reckon we'll make a navvy of ya, Stoodent, if ya keep this up.'

It was an accolade, not to be taken lightly. Robert felt himself tingling with a sudden blushing pleasure.

'So wot colledge d'ya go to, Stoodent?'

'I've finished now. But I used to be at University College.'

'University College dahn Gower Street? I woz there a year or two back. On the war damage. Gawd, there woz some prime-lookin' bits of 'ows-ya-father knockin' abaht there.'

He turned to the group of Irishmen who had downed tools to join him in a quick smoke.

'Lovely-looking gels they woz. Free with their langwidge, an' all. Ya wouldn't credit it. One of 'em give me a long look, an' sez to 'er mate, she sez, "Oo look, that man's got bigger tits than wot I got," she sez. Straight up. "He's got bigger tits than I got," she sez. No word of a lie.'

There was a disbelieving laugh.

Old Peter turned back to him. 'Wass ya name, son?'

'Bob.'

'Bop?' That was how it sounded on Old Peter's lips. 'Good-looker she was an' all, Bop. Yeah. "'E's got bigger tits than wot I got," she sez.'

His fellow-labourers took Old Peter's cue. The roughly vertical walls of Student's trench and the tale of the tits had served as a rite of passage, a passport into the gang. From then on, cack-handed or not, Student was never 'Student' again, but 'Bob'.

*

Essential as it was for him that Horsebitt's was a non-union site — he'd not have been taken on otherwise — the place had its drawbacks. Corners were cut and safety measures ignored to an extent that no shop-steward would have countenanced. There were mould-boards, yes, you couldn't do without them. But nowhere was there a proper shuttering of planks to brace the sides of a trench against a cave-in. Long before you hit the layer of impacted gravel that you'd been looking for, tons of clay and a rubble of ancient bricks and tiles — Victorian, Georgian, mediaeval, Roman — were looming up alongside and above you, unsupported and a lingering threat. Three or four feet below the surface, an ancient network of gas-mains and water-mains and electricity cables criss-crossed the site. Pools of stagnant water and condensed gas-tar still loitered along the bottom of the cast-iron mains, but at least the five-hundred volt cables were dead. All of them had been cut off and sealed outside the site area, Horsebitt's site-manager had been assured.

Greenhorn as he was, Bob didn't recognise the meaning of the chain of interlocking stoneware tiles that he uncovered in his end-section of trench, and he happily set about smashing them with the blade-end of his pick. It was only when he shovelled the shards away that he found the steel-wrapped cable lying under them.

In a flash he was flung back into a recurrent nightmare of his childhood. Of losing balance and falling against a naked electric cable and finding it backboned with death. He thanked God that the electrodes here beneath his boots were quiescent, the venom drawn from their fangs.

'Here Pat, what d'you make of this?' he said.

'Ah, good on ya, Bob, dat's great,' said Pat. 'Dat's bloody marvellous. Dat'll be worth a few bob. We'll have ut out and flog ut for the copper and the bluey in ut... Hey, but hang on a minut. Keep ut covered up till the clerk of works has done his rounds. An' sling some muck over dose bits of tile dere. The man has eyes in the back of his head like a weasel.'

As long as the clerk of works was in the offing, Bob hacked and shovelled all along the bottom of his trench everywhere but where the cable ran. As soon as the man was safely away, Pat and the others gathered round and Bob scraped the dirt off a seven-foot length of tarred-canvas and steel-wrapped cable.

It ended in a swollen, lead-sealed head. Pat seized it and wrenched it out of the groove it nestled in. Close to the far end where the cable emerged from the wall, Pat wedged the head of his pick underneath it to form an anvil.

'Give ut a crack now wid ya pick...'

As Bob hesitated, 'Come on, willya?' said Pat; 'Ach, gimme ya pick and I'll do ut.'

The flash vaporised the final half-inch of the blade as the pick split through the tarred cloth and rusty steel sleeving and short-circuited the copper electrodes.

Pat staggered and fell over backwards. But it was a dry day and the shock was to his self-respect, not to his flesh and bones.

'Jaysus Christ,' somebody said. 'The fockin' ting's alive.'

The cable lay malignant, almost blown apart but for the ribbon of steel wrapping that still bridged the break.

'Ah, no,' said somebody else. 'Not now, it's not. De fuses will have blown.'

Fuses? In a power-line?

'Dat's right, now. Give it a twist and it'll snap off.'

He drew away against the side-wall of the trench as Pat, raging to square accounts, bent down and grabbed the length of cable still not quite free. The second flash, when the steel wrapping twisted across the naked copper rods, flung Pat onto his back. This time he *had* received a swift electric shock, and he picked himself up in a raging fury.

'Ah, ya focker! Wouldya? I'll fockin' *killya!*' he yelled.

He snatched up handfuls of muck and began to pelt the live end of the cable, now completely severed and flaring like a candle as the wax-impregnated insulation burned away.

Images of Lawrence's 'Snake' slithered through Bob's brain, as Pat went on hurling muck. Turn by turn the cable flamed quietly for a moment, then roared again into incandescence the instant the waxed-paper insulation was charred enough for the current to arc across.

At last the flare reached and was smothered in the end-wall of the trench.

Old Peter spat a gob of mucus down beside his boot. 'Nah we're gunna 'aveta bring in the clerk of works. That fing's a menace,' he said. 'Can't be left in *that* state. But we'll chop orf the end coupla inches of the bit we 'ave got first. Tell 'im thass all wot woz stickin' aht. 'E'll 'aveta content 'is bleedin', fievin' self wiv that. We'll 'ang onta the resta the bluey, n' flog it rahnd the corner later.'

'Bluey?' said Bob.

'Bluey? Thass *lead* to you, Bop,' said Peter. 'Lead. And we'll drink it's 'ealth ta-night.'

*

A week later Death mistimed its move a second time on the Globe Road site.

In a follow-on trench the gang uncovered a 13-inch disused water-main, a bare couple of feet above the gravel layer, bulging out from the unshuttered side-wall along half the length of the trench. It invaded the space by less than a hand's breadth. But no, it would have to come out, the clerk of works decreed, you knew what awkward bastards brickies could be. They'd play hell if they thought they were cramped for space laying the foundation brickwork. Any bloody excuse was good enough for that lot.

So the pipe was shattered along its length with a sledge hammer, and they shovelled the cast-iron shards and flung them up beyond the mould-board. When the gang clambered out for the mid-morning tea-break, there was a foot-deep hollow all along the trench-wall where the water-main had run.

'I don't fancy the look of that,' Old Peter muttered.

There was a fleeting shower of rain during the break. As they plodded back to the unfinished trench the ground was glistening underfoot.

All along the trench where the water-main had been, the wedge of back-filled earth above it had parted and caved in. Tons of clay and rubble had slumped down, carrying the ladder and the mould-boards and the piled up muck along with them. Five men or more, Pat and Bob among them, might have choked to death under the earth-fall, if the rain had begun a minute or two earlier.

*

His innocent eyes were opened in other ways at Horsebitt's site.

There was an afternoon when his gang was ordered out of their trench by the site clerk. Two hundred concrete-breeze blocks had been stacked on the wrong spot and would have to be moved from one side of a half-built apartment-building to the other. Old Peter organized a human chain to pass them along the shortest route.

The first man had to grab a block from the stack and lob it through an open doorway to the second man, who was inside the building. *He* had to turn around and throw it to the third man. The third man lobbed it sideways through an inner doorway to the fourth man. Who then lobbed it to the fifth man who was waiting seven feet away, beside the window-gap in the far wall. The fifth man threw it out to the sixth man whose job it was to build the new stack.

The rest of the gang were left to wait around and be ready to take over when the first team wanted a break.

The blocks, made of concrete slurry and gasworks coke, were sharp-edged but not unduly heavy. You'd be alright if you were wearing gloves, but on Horsebitt's site there were no gloves to be had. And however circumspectly approached, the harsh surfaces could draw blood. If you caught them cack-handedly you could kiss a strip of your skin goodbye. Better to let them drop, and skip your feet out of the way as they fell.

Within five minutes there were fragments of breeze-blocks lying in the doorways and below all the window-openings. The wrongly-sited stack was shrinking at a snail's pace; and the empty shell of the apartment building rang with curses.

Bob, still waiting to take his turn, thought a bit of initiative was called for. So he nipped off to the site-clerk's office and asked if he could borrow the petrol-driven dumpy truck. Its hopper was big enough for the whole stack to be ferried from one side of the apartments to the other in five or six loads.

When he returned in triumph with the dumpy, the scowl on Old Peter's face told him that he was in trouble...

'Wos *your* game, then? 'Oo said you could 'elp yeself to *that* fing?'

'I asked the site-clerk.'

'You bloody *wot*? 'Oo d'ya fink you *are* to go talkin' to the site-clerk? Gettin' above yerself, ain't ya?'

'I thought it would save time using the dumpy... anyway one in every five or six breeze-blocks is getting broken.'

'Wos that to you? You don't 'aveta pay aht fa breakages, do ya?'

'And anyway, they're bastards to handle. They can slice the skin off your fingers... I thought — '

'Yerss, well don't go finkin' again. It don't do to start finkin'; it ain't your place to fink, my son. If this was a union site, which it ain't, doin' what you done, the 'ole place'd be out on strike be now.'

Old Peter inhaled smoke and spat out his spittle-soaked dog-end. 'Nah, well alright Bop, ya wasn't ta know, I s'pose. But it ain't your job to *fink*... "Yes sir, no sir, free bags full, sir." That's the way to answer to the likes of site-clerks an' clerksa works. Ya got that, son?'

*

A day or two later, the whole gang had gathered round for a spit and a draw at one end of the trench. Earlier on, someone had spotted a nurse at the hospital opposite washing herself at an uncurtained window, and now Michael, a usually staid and quiet-spoken man, was holding them spellbound with his talk about his landlady's daughter he'd known in Lancashire.

'Mother-naked, she was, not much older than twenty-two or three and a fine-lookin' woman. Fair-haired. Ah, an' I could look down and see for meself she was a real blonde. An' she steps up to me and she sez, "How do you like me?" she sez…'

Michael's listeners shuffled their feet and held their breaths, while Sir Thomas Wyatt's lines unreeled in Bob's skull and he felt his blood surge:

… In thin array, after a pleasant guise,
When her loose gown from her shoulders did fall,
And she me caught in her arms long and small,
And therewith all sweetly did me kiss,
And softly said, 'Dear heart, how like you this?'

'O, Jaysus,' somebody said into the silence…

'Did you marry her?' asked Bob, after a moment.

'I did *not*,' snarled Michael, turning on him. 'Christ in Heaven, I'd not marry a whore like that! I've never seen me own wife naked. Nor she me, I'll have ya know!'

There were murmurs of approval from all around the group.

*

The public bar of the Globe was an ideal place for contemplating East-End social life unnoticed and unchallenged.

On teaching practice and wandering alone into an Whitechapel pub still dressed for the classroom, Bob had stood out among the other drinkers, an obvious mark for prostitutes. As a temporary case-worker he'd been equally visible, and there had always seemed to be someone near at hand who recognised him and begged for advice or a handout. But among his Irish mates, with the glasses of Guinness lining up in front of them, he was anonymous, unknown, of little interest to prostitutes or scroungers. His old wire-framed Army spectacles dug out of the back of a drawer, his stained hands, his black unshaven stubble, the concrete splashes on his boots, all lent him a cloak of invisibility as he slouched through the courts and alleyways down towards the Thames. He could look around him with all his senses stretched, docketting images, savouring alien smells, tuning in to the clamour of the streets.

Only once was his cover nearly blown. Late one afternoon, sensing that he was being watched, he straightened up from stacking bricks near the entrance to Horsebitt's site. A pair of faces from Mr Silver's sixth-form class were gazing in his direction.

'No, look again. It *is* him,' one said to the other. 'It *is* you, sir, isn't it?'

'Ach, get away outa that,' Bob shouted in a crude approximation to a Dublin accent, and bent to claw up a handful of muck and fling it in their direction.

'There you are. *Told* you it wasn't,' said the second boy as they skipped away out of range.

*

The state of his appearance that summer long was more than his father could bear.

'I'm known in the Village! People know you're my son. Just take a look at yourself in the mirror! If you've got no self-respect, think of *my* position for once in a blue moon. Anyone would think you were a down-and-out by the sight of you! And what does that make *me* in people's eyes? Answer me that! Scrape the filth out from under your nails. And for God's sake get your hair cut. You look like a bloody chrysanthemum! If you imagine you can pass an interview for a teaching job in that state, you're in for a sad awakening, my son… My *God*, you're going to have to buck your ideas up.'

Driven to counter-measures, the former PC Druce made it his business to stroll round to the railway station and chat with the ticket-collectors. There he sang a different tune.

Oh yes, the boy had done very well, got his BA. And this was his idea of seeing life, putting in a couple of months on a building-site before he started teaching. That's why he trailed home looking like a scarecrow. Talking about writing a book. Youngsters of today, eh? I dunno. You had to smile.

One of the ticket-collectors button-holed Bob one evening, and told him about it.

Meanwhile in the house in Honey Hill the family rows still went on.

'What does *she*, this Emily or whatever her name is,' his mother asked him, 'what does *she* think of the way you look, eh? Ashamed to be seen in your company, I should hope, if she's got any sense at all in her head.'

*

'PERFECTION IS IN SMALL THINGS. BUT PERFECTION IS NO
SMALL THING.'

The elaborately hand-lettered admonition, on a six-inch wide strip of card, was pinned to the blackboard wall in Room 4 of Lowther Secondary Boys' school. It was signed at the bottom: 'A. E. Pierce'.

The walls of the room, high-windowed along the sides that faced inward into the school hall and out to the roadway and the Thames embankment, were naked of any other decoration.

So this was the classroom of Mr Pierce. French and English.

'Now this is the textbook,' said Mr Pierce, fumbling in the open cupboard and handing his visitor a disintegrating copy of a French reader. With its flapping spine, dog-eared and ink-decorated pages, it had been published in the nineteen-twenties.

'Ah. Yes, I see.'

'Good, reliable stuff,' said Mr Pierce. 'Plenty of exercises for them to get their teeth into. You might as well hang on to that copy, I suppose.'

'Right.' As he fanned through the pages, Mr Druce's eye lit on a full-page illustration. A gaggle of mustachioed and goatee-bearded French officials gesticulating wildly, besieged by a mob of farmyard animals on a railway platform. He slid the book into his brief-case.

First priority: order a set of up-to-date course-books.

A two-foot strip of tan-coloured cowhide lay on Mr Pierce's otherwise empty desk. Lines had been ruled across it in indian ink at one-inch intervals.

'Aha, I see you've noticed my little persuader,' said Mr Pierce, picking it up and flexing it. 'Finest teaching aid in the world, bar none. Two strips of boot-leather, see? Flesh-sides stuck together with rubber glue. Marked out like a ruler. School Inspector opens the door, sniffs around, sees it lying there, it's a ruler, isn't it? O, yes,' said Mr Pierce, stretching his narrow lips into a grin. 'Inspector leaves. Right! The next boy to play the fool gets a cracking good wallop on the backside. *Doesn't* he, McCloughlin?'

'Sir,' agreed a lad in the front row.

Mr Pierce gazed around his first-year French class, before bringing his little persuader down onto McCloughlin's desk-lid with a thwack. He was a hissing little turkey-cock of a man, on the point of taking early retirement. Druce R., BA, his interview over, was going to replace him when the new term began.

1A were staring at the intruder. Summing him up.

So I'll pin up a few French Railways posters around the room, and a map of France; something to make the place look a bit more cheerful. And Mr A. E.Pierce's nagging little diktat on perfection can go straight into the bin for a start... Yes...

William Blake knew what he was talking about — The errors of a wise man make your rule; rather than the perfections of a fool'.

'I'm sorry?' He woke up to the fact that Mr Pierce was still addressing him.

'Yerss... As I was saying, I suppose you'll want to change everything around, eh? New broom. Get rid of everything I've achieved here over the years... Discipline...' Mr Pierce made a lengthy performance of sighing.

'But then, of course, I'm just an old-fashioned, practical teacher. Came up the hard way. The great University of Life, as they say. Not a *graduate*, like you...

'Well, I've got to get on. Work won't do itself. I can't stand around here gossiping all day.'

Mr Pierce led his visitor to the door. 'Still, I'm going to be very interested in hearing just how you get on. What sort of fist you manage to make of things,' he said, ignoring Mr Druce's outstretched hand.

As 1A's French teacher-to-be glanced back into the classroom, Master McCloughlin caught his eye and winked.

*

'Well?' said his father. 'How'd you get on? Did they offer you the job? Come on, spit it out.'

'Yes.'

'You don't look very pleased,' said his mother.

'It's not that... No, of course I'm pleased. But it was a queer sort of interview... There were four of us up for the job. I was the last on the list. The first three were in and out, in and out, twenty minutes at a time, while the rest of us sat around in the staffroom. Then it was *my* turn and the interview barely lasted ten minutes. It all seemed a foregone conclusion somehow.'

'Well, with your qualifications…' said his father.

'That's just it. There was an old boy on the committee, Mr Prentice, a school governor. Owns a big department store in Twickenham, he told me.

'When it was all over he came up to me and shook my hand. "Lovely qualifications," he said; "Lovely qualifications…"

'He told me he'd said as much to the Headmaster over the phone yesterday evening: "O yers, beautiful qualifications: we shall have to run an eye over the lad of course but, like you said, Headmaster, I reckon he's our man." That's what he told me.'

'Well, there you are then,' said his father. 'Stick to teaching, and you've got a job for life. Haven't I always said that? If only I had had the chances you have. I wouldn't have found myself out of a job at forty. I wouldn't have had to go cap in hand, and kowtow to a lot of jumped-up nobodies before I could settle down to a position I can take a pride in, would I?'

Six weeks earlier Bob's father's run of bad luck had changed with his being taken on as a security guard at St Luke's Printing Works, part of the Bank of England

'Well, you're happily settled now, said Bob's mother. 'And there's no need to go on and on about the past. That's all over and done with, so just give it a rest for all our sakes.'

She turned back to her son. 'What else did they say to you?'

'O, general stuff. Would I help with taking games? Would I help teach swimming? I said no, not really, to that: I wasn't qualified…

'I had a quick word afterwards with the current French teacher. Mr Pierce. A miserable sod. He'd got no time for the likes of me, he made that clear enough…

'Anyway, O, I don't know… I had the feeling that the whole thing was a put-up job. Decided in advance.'

'Don't look a gift horse in the mouth, my son,' said his father.

'It's a lot of travelling,' said his mother. 'Backwards and forwards to the other side of London. And it won't be long now before the nights start drawing in. Soon it's going to be pitch dark before you get home of an evening. So what is Her Ladyship going to say to *that*?'

39

ROSEBANK GARDENS

'*December*?' His mother said. 'You plan to get married in *December,* the pair of you? Phhh! That's not three months away. *When* in December?'

'The eighteenth. Saturday the eighteenth.'

`And whose preposterous idea is that, then? *Her Ladyship's,* I suppose? Phhh!'

His mother flung herself across the room and stood by the front window, peering out through the net curtains, blowing out a whole fistful of invisible matches. 'Phhh!'

'And what are you proposing to live on? *You've* got no savings. And I can't for the life of me see *her* having anything much put by... Where d'you imagine you're going to live? You can't live in *this* house, if that's your big idea. Your father would have forty fits just at the thought of it. And I certainly can't see The Aunt or The Uncle taking kindly to the idea of the pair of you living with *them*, either. From what you say, they're not made of money, any more than we are.'

'Don't worry, we'll find somewhere.'

'Phhh! And *this* is all the thanks we get for feeding you and clothing you and keeping you at school and all through university. The moment you start earning, you're itching to be off. No thought of paying back a little of what you've had from us over the years. No, you just can't wait to shake the dust of your home off your feet, can you?'

'I'm twenty-four, mother...'

'Phhh! Your father and I waited until he was twenty-seven before we even *thought* about standing up in church. *And* he'd been taking money home and paying his parents for his keep ever since he was fourteen...'

'That was then. Things have changed since the 1920s...'

'For the worse, if you ask me… And so Her Ladyship has decided to get married in December!'

His mother narrowed her gaze. 'Why December? O, my God, she's not expecting a baby, is she? If I thought you'd got that girl pregnant, after all that business with Nadia — which your father has yet to be told about, I might add — Nadia's the one you ought to marry, you know that as well as I do — if I thought that your and Her Ladyship, I'd… You haven't, have you?… Look me in the eye!

'Well, I daren't imagine what your father's going to say about this when I tell him. I wouldn't want to be in your shoes for all the tea in China when he hears the news.'

*

'Now, listen darling. There's so still so much we need to talk about,' Emily said, 'Now that the date's more or less settled, we need to think about making a firm booking for the church at Cornard. The banns will have to be read at St Andrews and at All Saints here in the Village, don't forget — '

'Ha! That'll make *some* people sit up and take notice,' he said.

'Very likely. The banns have to be read out for three Sundays in a row, so they'll have to start — pass me that slip of paper — they'll have to start, erm… at the absolute latest on Sunday 26th November. And here we are already halfway through October. Can I trust you to sort it out with Mr Stanford? I'll ask mummy to talk to the Reverend Thomas at Cornard…

'Then there's my wedding-dress to be thought about. Joan has always promised to make it when the time came and she's going to be my bridesmaid, in any case. So that's under control. We must book an organist. And you will have to find someone to be best man.'

'Brendan.'

'Not John, then?'

'John *who*?'

'John Robbins.'

'No! No, no. He'd trip over his own feet and lose the ring. No, Brendan. Yes, I *know* he's a Catholic, but he'll not let *that* stand in his way.'

'And we must make plans about where we're going to hold the reception,' said Emily. 'How many guests do you think there will be from your side?'

Mr Rotkin's large body was surmounted by a puddingy, veal-coloured face, with dead-haddock eyes. As he opened the door, his lips drew away from his brown-stained teeth.

Welcoming little fishes in, with gently smiling jaws.

'Ah. Mr Bruce, is it? No? O, I see. Anyhow, come along in. You found it then… This is my next-door neighbour, Mrs Frisk.'

Mr Rotkin turned to wait while a thin blonde woman swung an inner door shut behind her and scampered along to join him…

'Well, up we go, then. I'll lead the way,' said Mr Rotkin, ushering Emily and Robert into the hall and setting his foot on the first tread of the stair.

1 Rosebank Gardens: the address was on a slip of paper in Emily's handbag

The walls were covered to shoulder height with embossed wallpaper, gloss-enamelled dark brown. Above that they had been painted cabbage-water green. There was a lingering smell of stewed soup and unwashed dog about the place.

Mr Rotkin came to a halt on the half-landing.

'Bathroom here to the right. Toilet next door to it. You'll be sharing them with me,' said Mr Rotkin.

'You'll have to come to an agreement with Mr Rotkin about when you can make use of the bathroom,' said Mrs Frisk. 'Excuse me…' As she edged past them, a shaft of weak October sunlight from the landing window made it quite clear that she was naked under her sleeveless nylon blouse.

'It should be simple enough to draw up a timetable,' she said.

'This will be your kitchen then,' said Mr Rotkin, rattling a china door-handle and shouldering open the door of a room some twelve feet square. The soup-smell was replaced by a stink of soot. At the centre of the room, between two padded bedroom chairs, stood a rickety-looking table draped with oil-cloth. There was a minuscule cast-iron grate; and a hand-basin in an alcove by the window. Twenty yards away, an embanked railway platform loomed up beyond the crab-apple trees in the garden. There were signboards along its length.

'That's the down platform,' said Mr Rotkin, pointing.

'You could hardly be more convenient for the railway, could you?' said

Mrs Frisk, laying her hand on Mr Rotkin's shirt-sleeved arm, as he dragged the room door shut.

'I'll leave it to you to get your own gas-stove installed,' he said. 'No objection to that. You'll have your own shilling-in-the-slot-meter...

'Yes? On we go, then, up to the next landing. Now then. The door straight ahead is the door to my bedroom. *Your* bedroom is in here, to the left. It was the bedroom of I and my wife, before she passed away. It's a very nice room.'

'*Very* nice,' said Mrs Frisk.

'Well, you can see for yourselves,' said Mr Rotkin, thrusting open the door.

It was a large room with its own musty smell — but that was probably nothing that a coat of polish on the floorboards wouldn't deal with. A double bed. A wardrobe. A mirror-winged dressing-table blocking most of the light in the window bay. Net curtains. Fraying bedside carpets.

Robert and Emily glanced at one another and then out at the six-story block of flats across the road.

'That's Rosebank Mansions,' said Mrs Frisk. 'Foreign embassy people, most of them. Well, I expect you noticed the cars and all the CD plates. *Corps diplomatique*. Dr Frisk and I have always got on well enough with them, I must say; once they've got it firmly into their heads that they are *not* entitled to park across other peoples' driveways. Come along and see your sitting-room.'

'That's right. Now, this is what will be your lounge,' said Mr Rotkin, ushering them into the adjoining room. A threadbare sofa, a table and three chairs. And another net-curtained sash window looking out onto Rosebank Mansions.

'So there you are,' said Mr Rotkin. 'The rent is sixteen pounds a month.'

'Payable in advance,' put in Mrs Frisk.

'Payable in advance, of course,' smiled Mr Rotkin. 'As from the first of November. You realize, don't you, that if it's a self-contained flat that you are looking for, you can expect to fork out double what I'm asking.'

'O, at least double,' said Mrs Frisk, 'A great deal more than that, I should imagine... Well, there you are. You look like a respectable enough couple. You've seen it. So what do you think?'

'Emily?' said Robert, turning to her.

Three Saturdays later he was staggering along the embankment road, hefting a wobbling six-foot sheet of hardboard and a fistful of wooden beading. Emily was at his side, clutching a brown-paper bag of nails and a can of paint. Every few moments a gust of wind from off the river caught the hardboard sheet and swung him off balance, sending him lurching into Emily while the strips of beading went sprawling, trying to twist away from his grasp.

George Rotkin had given his blessing to his tenant's plan to fix painted hardboard panels to the walls behind and alongside where the gas-stove was going to go: 'You understand, I hope, that all and any permanent fixtures a tenant is permitted to install remain the property of the landlord if and when the tenant leaves,' he said. 'Just so that there's no misunderstanding in the future...'

'Yes. Yes, of course.'

Only three more weeks and he would be fifty miles away, standing in front of the Rector of St Andrews, and sliding a wedding ring along Emily's finger.

As they rounded the corner by the chemist's, Moggy McCloughlin came out of the paper-shop and hurried to confront them.

'Hallo, sir,' he said. 'Is this your wife?'

'Nearly, but not quite. Three weeks from now she will be.'

He paused to take a firmer grip on the spilling strips of beading, and turned to Emily.

'This is Mister Moggy McCloughlin,' he said, 'my self-appointed guide, philosopher and helpmeet since term began.'

'Here, give us that, sir,' said McCloughlin, prising the beading out of his hand. 'I'll carry it for ya.

Far to go, is it? What, here in Rosebank Gardens? Well, thass gonna be convenient for school, innit?. 'ere! 'Ang on a minute! What daily paper d'ya read? Cos it's me what delivers the papers round 'ere...'

The trio stopped outside number 1 for a moment while Emily unlocked the front door and went on in. Moggy handed over the bundle of wooden strips. 'Be OK with these now, sir, willya? Need any more help with anything? You sure? Alright then.'

He walked away to the front gate, and turned, sticking the thumbs of both hands up. 'You found yourself a smasher there, sir, if ya don't mind me saying. *Very* nice!'

He put two fingers into his mouth, emitted a powerful wolf-whistle, and strolled away.

*

In the thirteen weeks since term began, time had fled past.

With the sudden death in a Suffolk hospital of her father, whose boast it had always been that he had scarcely suffered a day's illness in his life, Emily had become more vulnerable, clinging to Robert for reassurance and comfort, and looking ahead towards marriage for a new beginning, away from the Village, away from her aunt and uncle's household. And here now at her side was Robert: a salaried teacher, already two months into his probationary year, with a classroom of his own at last.

The caretaker had carried Whacker Pierce's mouldering French readers off to the boiler-room, and now the new text-books were ranged in the cupboard, with their unsullied green covers and their crackling pages smelling of printing ink.

Newly-learnt faces and names were defining themselves, coming into a sharper focus.

'Gubbo' Gilbertson B.Sc., the Headmaster, a middle-aged man with a Tyneside accent. Basil Kent, ex-wartime RAF admin, the silver-haired Deputy Head who presided over Science. Ken Cricklewood, P. E. and Games, a former army PT instructor. Francis Ruby — 'No, no, dear boy, *please*! I *never* answer to "Frank". It's "Francis" in full, if you *don't* mind' — Head of English; who was 'Dear Boy' or 'Lady Precious Stream' to the rest of the staff when he was out of earshot. Joe Martin, Art. Joe Sherman, who played the organ in his synagogue on Saturdays and the school piano for morning assembly: in charge of Music and History. 'Bully' Bulstrode, Head of Maths and Senior Master.

And alongside Mr Druce at the bottom of the pecking order, 'Ol' Gorilla' Probert: Geography.

Twenty-three years old, uncouth-mannered, wry-mouthed and with a pate as glabrous as a peeled egg, Probert's Geography lessons were an ongoing riot. And a comfort to R. Druce. Whenever things threatened to get out of hand in his own classroom, he could reassure himself that he could never be as crass and idiotic as Ol' Gorilla..

Foremost among the boys, Moggy McCloughlin: the class clown of 3B, of Catholic Irish stock, who had fastened upon Mr Druce and addressed him as an equal from the first. 'You're "Bob" to us, he told him, towards half-term. 'Bob. I mean, that ain't too bad fer a nickname, is it, eh? Not like Grilla, or ol' Whacker Pierce. Cor, I tell ya, everybody hated that old bugger's guts.'

'I think I'll forget you made that last remark, Moggy...'

Inked into the raw plywood of the top drawer of Pierce's desk — his own desk now — he had found the message: 'WACKER PEIRCE IS A ~~CUNT~~.' He had nipped across for a brushful of white paint from Joe Martin's art room and swiftly obliterated it. But it amazed him that Pierce had been content with making an, in the event utterly futile, attempt to scratch out the epithet, while leaving his own name visible to whoever's eyes might fall upon it. No, first and foremost blot your name out, surely?

Or, better still perhaps, replace it with the name of somebody you had no liking for, and leave the rest alone?

'Our lads are not academically-minded, Mister Er,' Gubbo had assured him after school on his first day. 'They are the future hewers of wood and drawers of water. Examinations are not for them. Keep that in mind and you won't go far wrong... French, now. A few simple phrases. Enough to buy a train-ticket, understand simple directions, order a meal perhaps. That's all you need to teach them. They won't thank you for a lot of frills and fallals.'

For the rest of that first term he had tried his hardest to recreate the magic of Walter Mason's teaching in a twice-weekly French-language class which, he discovered on his first morning, was a hopeless agglomeration of selected members of 1A, 2A, and 3A. The nineteen first-year boys were beginners, while the older boys were split between those who had undergone either one year or two years of Whacker Pierce's French. Trying to hit upon a common starting-point, without alienating the goodwill of everyone, was not within reach of the few skills he had.

What every boy at Lowther School needed far more urgently, it was obvious, was a better command of, and excitement in, his own native language. He began to experiment in the English classes he took..

'*I scrambled to my feet, to see the tail-lights of the car vanishing into the darkness...* Write a short story that begins with that sentence. Or ends with it. Or contains it somewhere in the middle.

'*Trembling, I held out my hand.* Do the same with that sentence.

'Or with this: *The icy grey water lapped over the stones...*

Or with this: *It wasn't until the screaming started, that I lost my nerve...*'

'Write the first page of your diary for the day when you woke up and discovered that you'd grown a halo during the night. Or a tail. Or both...'

What his pupils found themselves capable of in his English classes began to amaze both him and them. Alongside the short stories, the novels, the plays and the poetry they read and talked about in class, their free composition eased the way into other, more formal kinds of writing. Reports, summaries, letters of complaint, letters of condolence; play-scripts, film-scripts...

One afternoon, he suddenly woke up to the fact that he was *looking forward* to collecting up the English exercise-books. Not sighing at the thought of more laborious hours of marking, but anticipating the pleasure of sharing the ideas that each individual was struggling to put into words.

One Friday in late October, Francis Ruby informed the staff-room at lunch-time that he had applied for a post as an announcer in an Australian radio station and would be quitting at the end of the term.

At four o'clock R. Druce BA clambered up the staircase to Gubbo's room.

His pulse was beating faster than usual. With no tradition of or opportunity for homework, and no more than two lumped-together classes a week, he told Gubbo, French in his opinion could never be anything more than window-dressing; while for most of those who sat through it, it was a waste of time that would be better spent on English.

To his huge surprise, the Head did not demur. 'Very well. So you would not be averse to taking over Mr Ruby's post next term, would you?' he said, leaning back in his swivel-chair and sucking at his pipe. 'Because if that's the case I'll support your application. There's no additional allowance going with the post. But it would be an upward move, a stepping-stone to higher things. Do you take my meaning? You'll be a headmaster yourself one day...'

*

December 18th.

The moment he and Brendan called to announce their presence in Cornard late that morning, Emily's mother — *The Mother!* — had hustled him safely away from her front door and out of harm's way.

'Has nobody ever told you that the groom mustn't set eyes on his bride on their wedding-day *until* she walks up the aisle? It's unlucky… Be off with the pair of you. Emily will be there on time, don't worry.'

So while Joan scampered around upstairs, making sure that items old, new, blue, and borrowed all lay ready to hand, Brendan and he wandered along to St Andrews, and wandered around the churchyard, reading out the names on the gravestones, until the wedding guests — among them his own parents and The Aunt and The Mother, both couples smiling pursed-lipped smiles at one another — began to congregate in the church porch. From minute to minute for the past quarter of an hour Brendan's fingers had been sliding up and down into his jacket pocket, checking that the ring was still safely there. The sun was shining.

The organist and choir-master of St Andrews, who owned a music shop a mile away in Sudbury, began to play, pattering the keys of the organ in a Bach prelude, as groups of guests began to divide right and left. Brendan and the groom moved along the aisle amongst them, pausing to greet people and shake their hands, slowly edging their way towards the chancel steps.

The Reverend Thomas stepped into the church through the vestry door, settling his scarlet MA hood around his shoulders, and joined them at the chancel rail.

There was a long pause and a penetrating smell of alcohol. The Reverend Thomas had been wetting his whistle with an O, Be Joyful! or two — as he was wont to call the midday double sherries he downed in The Five Bells.

Fleetingly a vision of Nadia moved through Robert's mind. A dark-haired girl in a white dress pacing along a sunlit aisle somewhere in a future no longer his.

He turned his eyes towards the vacant choir-seats in the chancel, and the glittering altar window.

The South door creaked open, gravel squeaked on the path outside, and the harmonies slid in mid-phrase from Bach to Handel's Water Music, as Emily approached on The Uncle's arm. Feet shuffled as the congregation stood up and turned to watch. He stared resolutely forward until there came a touch on his left hand, and Emily was at his side.

'Dearly Beloved' — the Rector's tones were sonorous, orotund, in the sudden silence. 'Dearly Beloved, we are gathered together in the sight of God and in the face of this congregation to join together this Man and this Woman in holy Matrimony...'

So. This is it, then. All or nothing. In for a halfpenny, in for a guinea...

'Which is an honourable estate, instituted by God in the time of man's innocency...'

*

'It's still not too late to change your mind. Do you really know what you're doing?'

His mother's last words to him as he had left the house in Honey Hill that morning.

Already that moment felt as if it must have taken place a lifetime ago.

'I did think that at least you might have waited a year or two, gone on living in this house, pulling your weight, repaying something for all the money we've spent on your education. But no. No you...

'Marriage is not something to be taken on lightly, you realize that? It's for better or poorer... To love and to cherish till death you do part... Remember that.'

In the leather-bound prayer-book clutched in his mother's gloved hand that afternoon and lying now below *my* hand, the phrase is bracketed by a cross in each margin and an underline, scratched in blue-black ink. Apotropaic, perhaps. Her attempt, now that things were slipping out of her grasp, to forestall any counter prophecy.

*

'To have and to hold, from this day forward...

'With this ring I thee wed...

'O, well is thee, and happy shalt thou be. They wife shall be as the fruitful vine upon the walls of thine house; Thy children like the olive branches: round about thy table...'

At last the hymns and the prayers and the interspersed blessings wound to an end.

As the organ keys rattled and wheezed yet again, Emily and Robert edged away from the Rector's alcoholic haze. The Uncle was turning them round and prodding them into line.

And now they were stepping it out down the ringing aisle — man and wife, and wife and man…

'Hey! Not so *fast*,' Emily murmured. 'We're not in a race.'

Her right arm lay heavy on his left arm. His right hand moved itself across to lie on hers, as they marched out into the sharp December sunshine, 'and aren't we lucky with the weather?'

Out to the photographer and the aunties' snapping Kodaks. Out into the confetti fluttering into their ears and eyes, and the two-hundred-yard ride in a taxi, with Emily's bridesmaid perched, faute de mieux, on Robert's knees. Out to the spread in The Five Bells and the speeches and laughter and flying corks and the forced smiles on his parents' and The Aunt's and Uncle's lips.

To the quick-change act and the taxi ride to the station, and the trains to and across London. To a makeshift honeymoon in Rosebank Gardens with a hissing inadequate gas-fire in the sitting-room. To Emily shivering and naked as her talcum-powder was blown sideways on a draught that came up between the bedroom floor-boards; and George Rotkin and Mrs Frisk murmuring in an adjacent room. To the twice-daily brimming Thames at the end of the street. To crab apple trees, and the down platform, and every quarter of an hour the slamming of carriage doors, and people peering down towards their kitchen window. To Lowther County Secondary School for Boys, and Room Number Five, and fourteen pounds a week, and a wife to keep, and yet another nipped-out cigarette tucked into his top pocket before the start of each lesson, and bits of chalk and red ink stains in the lining of all his other pockets.

*

'Well, Dorothy,' said Robert Druce senior, as the long line of guests straggled through the lychgate and out along the lane, 'That boy has made his bed—'

He broke off to hurl a smile towards The Aunt and The Uncle, who were dawdling ahead and looking back, expecting the Druces to join them.

'No, Dorothy, kindly hear me out… It's all I'm going to say and then the subject is closed…

'That boy has made his bed… And now, God help him, he can lie on it.'

Wedding Day

EDITORIAL NOTES

ROBERT DRUCE

Anyone who grew up or lived in the areas of south west Essex during the period covered by *My Dad's a Policeman* may recognise the correct identity of the places that Robert describes. Former pupils of Staples Road Primary School, Loughton, or Buckhurst Hill County High School, Chigwell during the 1940s will easily recognise not only the schools but the identity of the key characters, despite the fact that all names have been changed.

It is probably no coincidence that the least-changed name of the teaching staff at "Monkswood" was that of Walter May ("Mason") who was Robert's French teacher. Walter May's inspired teaching methods were way ahead of his time, and he appreciated Robert's ability from the start. He became something of a father figure for Robert, whose tricky relationship with his own father is the central theme of *My Dad's a Policeman*.

Walter May and Robert Druce left Buckhurst Hill CHS at the same time. Walter became a Schools' Inspector, before continuing as Headmaster of Hornchurch Grammar School. Many years later, the pupil was reunited with his teacher and they then remained close friends until Robert's death.

By the end of *My Dad's a Policeman* Robert Druce had married Christine Bird ("Emily"). They had two children: Robert born 1958 and Katharine born 1963. The school where he began his teaching career was Barnes Secondary Modern. After a few years he became Head of English at Townmead School, West Drayton. While there, he pioneered the teaching of creative writing and published his first book, *The Eye of Innocence*, based on his work, in 1965.

In the same year, as a result of his book's success, he moved to Trent Park Training College as a lecturer. It was here, while attending a poetry conference, that he met Elizabeth Brook. During the following year, they began living together, and were subsequently married in 1976.

While at Trent Park Robert acquired a Diploma in Teaching English as a Foreign Language at University College, London when he realised that many of his students would have to face classes in which many children spoke very little English. This led him to giving workshops in Holland to Dutch teachers of English where he came to the attention of a senior inspector in the Dutch government who asked him to take a year out from Trent Park to give courses to Dutch teachers of English all over Holland. This was extended to a second year, and the huge increase in salary led Robert to look for a permanent job in Holland. In 1974 he began teaching in Delft at a Dutch Teachers Training College, subsequently moving to Leiden University where he taught until 1996. While he was at Leiden he gained a doctorate and was awarded a cum laude for his thesis comparing Enid Blyton with Ian Fleming. While he was teaching he continued to write poetry and fiction, and a children's book *Firefang* was published by Bell in 1972.

After Robert's retirement, he and Elizabeth moved to Suffolk. During retirement, Robert remained active as a guest speaker and lecturer until his sudden death in 2005 following a brain haemorrhage.

ROBERT DRUCE – BIBLIOGRAPHY

Structural English, A series of English text books, some of which were co-authored with Margaret Tucker, English Universities Press, 1964-69.

Firefang, a fiction book for children, Bell, 1972.

Go and Find Out, Learning Development Aids, 1979.

A Centre of Excellence (edited) essays presented to Seymour Betsky, Rodopi Press, 1987.

This Day Our Daily Fictions (Doctorate thesis), Rodopi Press, 1992.

An Irishman Abroad by Cuey-na-Gael (edited), Academic Press, Leiden 2000.

Collected Poems Two volumes published privately, 2008.

ACKNOWLEDGEMENT & POSTSCRIPT

The availability of *My Dad's a Policeman* has only been possible thanks to the encouragement and co-operation of Elizabeth Druce. Although she had not met Robert until after the period covered in the book, she was able to confirm the accuracy of his account.

My own first encounter with Robert was in 2000, when I had recently undertaken an eccentric mission of tracing all the former pupils and teachers from my school – Buckhurst Hill CHS ("Monkswood"). Robert and I were not contemporaries, but my project covered the whole period from its opening, two years before Robert joined, to its closure in 1989. On speaking with Robert, it was clear that he was part of a very talented cohort of wartime pupils, many of whom had become distinguished both in academic and other areas.

I was intrigued to hear that Robert was writing his autobiography, and especially when he told me he had recently finished the part covering his time at Buckhurst Hill CHS. He sent me the "Monkswood" chapters, and it was clear to me that Robert's story deserved to be published, not only because of its special interest for his contemporaries, but as a sharply observed account of life at a grammar school during the war.

A few months later, I had the pleasure of meeting Robert along with Walter May ("Mason"). The two had returned to Chigwell for a reunion at which Walter – then a sprightly 92 – met with many of his former pupils. I was pleased to hear from Robert that he had finished writing *My Dad's a Policeman* and he hoped to find a publisher.

Sadly, this didn't happen at the time. After Robert's sudden death in 2005, I remained in contact with Elizabeth, who continued to try various publishers without success. We are delighted that thanks to the digital publishing revolution we have now been able to make Robert's book available.

Walter May outlived Robert by eight years, and died in 2013 at the age of 103.

Graham Frankel